FUNDAMENTALS OF

Photographic Theory

FUNDAMENTALS OF

Photographic

Theory

By T. H. JAMES, Ph.D.
GEORGE C. HIGGINS, Ph.D.
Research Laboratories of Eastman Kodak Co.

MORGAN & MORGAN, INC., *Publishers*
Hastings-on-Hudson, New York
THE FOUNTAIN PRESS, LONDON

First Edition 1948
Second Edition
  First Printing 1960
  Second Printing 1968

Typography by
Morgan Press, Hastings-on-Hudson, N. Y.
Printed in U.S.A.

Preface to First Edition

THE SCIENCE OF PHOTOGRAPHY can be divided into several separate, though somewhat interdependent, branches, each of which can be assigned to a special field of chemistry or physics. Thus, the preparation of the light-sensitive layer is essentially a colloidal chemical operation. The action of light upon this sensitive layer is a photochemical process involving secondary physical and chemical processes. The method of transforming the light impression into a visible image is chemical in nature. Finally, the problem of evaluating the photographic image in terms of the light which initiated its formation and the light which enables it to be seen is essentially a problem of physics and psychophysics.

The purpose of the present book is to give a general account of the theory of the photographic process, based on the fundamental chemical and physical concepts. A basic knowledge of physics and physical chemistry is presupposed, but a specialist's knowledge in these fields is not required. The historical development of the theory of the photographic process and detailed references to original literature have been avoided for the most part. This procedure, we believe, will permit the general reader to follow the argument with greater economy of space and thought. The reader who desires greater detail on any branch of the subject will find ample material in the general references given at the end of each chapter.

Some omissions require explanation. Only the photographic process which involves the use of silver salts is considered here. This is by far the most important process. The sensitive materials which do not involve the use of silver salts are used only for special purposes, and a satisfactory treatment of the theory involved would require an expenditure of space out of all proportion to their relative importance. No attempt is made to consider the theory of lens design or of camera construction. These are separate subjects. Although they are of considerable importance to the practice of picture making, they do not belong to the science of the photographic process. Finally, the field of color

3

photography is not treated specifically. Much work remains to be done in this field before a satisfactory general theoretical treatment can be given. The omission of an explicit treatment of color photography, however, is less important than it might seem at first glance. Every major color process in use today involves primarily a black-and-white photographic process, and only secondarily a color factor. Latent image formation in color photography is the same as in color-sensitized black-and-white photography, and the primary act of development in both is the reduction of silver halide to silver.

Finally, it is a pleasure to acknowledge the assistance which we have received from our associates. The very existence of the book owes much to the encouragement and advice of Dr. C. E. K. Mees. Others who have read the original manuscript in part or in its entirety and have offered valuable suggestions include: R. Barrows, L. G. S. Brooker, B. H. Carroll, G. T. Eaton, M. L. Huggins, C. E. Ives, E. E. Jelley, L. A. Jones, G. Kornfeld, J. A. Leermakers, L. E. Muehler, C. N. Nelson, F. Perrin, H. D. Russell, J. L. Tupper, R. H. Wagner, J. H. Webb, and H. C. Yutzy.

T.H.J.
G.C.H.

Rochester, N. Y.
November, 1947

Preface to Second Edition

In the eleven years which have passed since the appearance of the first edition, rapid advances have been made in many fields of photographic theory. These advances have made it necessary to revise extensively the chapters on the photographic emulsion, the formation of latent image, the mechanism of development, the kinetics of development, and the structure of the developed image. Advances have also been made in the understanding of the theory of color photography. While this field is still not treated in detail, it is now possible to include a discussion of color sensitometry and a brief description of the chemistry of formation of the dye images.

We have retained the use of the simple hexagon as the symbol for the benzene ring, although this no longer conforms to standard American Chemical Society usage, since it reduced the number of changes which had to be made. We have also retained references to some useful books cited in the first edition which are now out of print. These books, however, are still available in libraries.

In the preparation of the second edition, we have had the assistance of R. L. Lamberts, D. L. MacAdam, R. E. Stauffer, K. F. Stultz, P. W. Vittum, W. West and F. C. Williams, in addition to several colleagues who are mentioned in the preface of the first edition.

We would especially like to acknowledge the assistance of F. H. Perrin, who has written much of the chapter on the structure of the developed image as well as assisted in the editing of the entire book, and also the assistance of F. C. Williams, who prepared the material on color sensitometry and on the interpretation of sensitometric data.

T.H.J.
G.C.H.

Rochester, N. Y.
October, 1959

Contents

1.

Outline of the Photographic Process.   Terminology

The steps normally involved in the making of a photograph are (1) exposure of the sensitive material in a camera or other suitable device, (2) development of the exposed material to give a *negative*, (3) fixing, (4) washing and drying, (5) exposure of a second sensitive material through the negative, and (6) development of this material to give the positive, which is then fixed, washed and dried as before.

The theory of these steps will be considered in some detail in subsequent chapters of this book. It will facilitate the presentation of the theory, however, if these steps are considered briefly at the outset and definitions are given of certain terms commonly used in the literature.

The Light-Sensitive Material (the Emulsion)

The normal sensitive layer consists of a very large number of tiny crystals (*grains*) of silver halide embedded in a layer of gelatin. Figure $1 \cdot 1$ (*a*) shows the appearance under the microscope of some of the grains of a typical photographic material.

The combination of grains and gelatin is often referred to as the *photographic emulsion,* or simply the *emulsion.* It is not a true emulsion, but the terminology is firmly fixed in the photographic literature, and no useful purpose can be served by trying to change it here. In this book, where it is clear that the sensitive photographic layer is being referred to, the simple term *emulsion* will be used.

The silver halide most commonly employed is the bromide, with or without the addition of small amounts of iodide. Some slow photographic emulsions, however, contain only silver chloride, and some contain a mixture of chloride and bromide.

The emulsion is coated on some suitable support before it is used to "take a picture." If a photographic film is desired, the

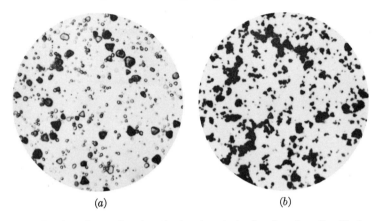

(a)   (b)

Fig. 1·1 Photomicrographs of undeveloped and developed grains. Magnification 1125×. (a) Undeveloped grains of a typical photographic emulsion. (b) The same grains after exposure and development. (Loveland.)

support is a sheet of cellulose ester, e.g., acetate. If photographic paper is wanted, the support is a sheet of suitably sized paper. If photographic plates are desired, the emulsion is coated on glass. Other supports may be used for special purposes.

The Latent Image

Any light that produces a photographic effect must be absorbed by the sensitive material. In ordinary practice the photographic effect is not revealed by any visible change in the appearance of the emulsion, unless the exposure to light has been excessive. The exposed emulsion, however, contains an invisible *latent image* of the light pattern which can be translated readily into a visible silver image by action of a *developing agent.*

Development

Development is possible because certain agents react with the exposed silver halide in preference to the unexposed, reducing the former to metallic silver in a substantially shorter time. Thus, the developing agent is simply a reducing agent which differentially attacks the exposed grains first. The developing agent is used in a solution containing certain other ingredients which facilitate or mediate the reaction. The complete solution often is referred to simply as the "developer."

When the developed image is examined under the microscope it is seen to consist of tiny particles of metallic silver, as shown in Fig. 1·1 (b). This figure represents the same portion of the emulsion as that shown in Fig. 1·1 (a), except that now the grains have been exposed and developed. For the most part, each silver particle corresponds to the development of a single silver halide grain, although it is apparent that in some places two or more grains are closely aggregated.

Fog

If the development process is continued for a sufficiently long time, all the silver halide, unexposed as well as exposed, will be converted to silver. Even during normal development, some unexposed grains may be reduced, some silver may be deposited rather uniformly over the emulsion, or both may occur. This unselective, and generally undesirable, action constitutes the formation of photographic *fog*, and the silver formed is often referred to as *fog silver*.

Fixing

After development, the unreduced silver halide is dissolved out in a *fixing bath*. The principal ingredient of this solution is a thiosulfate, usually sodium thiosulfate ("hypo") or ammonium thiosulfate.

The Negative and The Positive

Exposure and development of the usual photographic sensitive material yield a photographic *negative*, in which the light and shadow values of the photographed object are reversed. In order to obtain a *positive*, another sensitive material (usually having different characteristics from the first) is exposed through the negative, developed, fixed, washed and dried as before.

Density

The photographic effectiveness of light is measured by the image which can be developed. The developed image, in turn, can be evaluated in terms of its ability to block the passage of light. The most direct measure is either the *transmittance* or the *opacity*. The former is defined by the ratio I_t/I_o, where I_t is the intensity of the transmitted light and I_o that of the incident light. Thus, the transmittance gives the fraction of the incident light transmitted through the material. Opacity is simply the reciprocal of the transmittance, that is, I_o/I_t.

For most purposes, it is prefarable to use the common logarithm of the opacity as a means of evaluating the developed image. The logarithm of the opacity is termed the *optical density*, photographic density, or simply the *density* of the developed image. (For a more complete definition of density, see Chapter 10.) The use of density, which was introduced by the founders of photographic sensitometry, Hurter and Driffield, is dictated partly by the convenience of the logarithmic scale, but also by the relationship which exists under certain conditions between the density and the mass of developed silver per unit area. This relationship can be seen from the following considerations.

If a layer of developed silver particles in a transparent support is placed in front of a light source, it will reduce the intensity of the transmitted light to $1/m$ the value of the incident light. If a second, identical layer of silver particles is placed against the first, the intensity of the transmitted light falls to $(1/m)^2$ because the second layer blocks the passage of the same *fraction* of the light incident upon it as does the first layer. If n layers are used, the intensity falls to $(1/m)^n$.

If a developed photographic emulsion containing n grains of uniform size per unit volume is sliced into n layers in such a way that each layer contains only one grain, in effect n superposed layers will have to be dealt with. A single grain absorbs or prevents the passage of the fraction b of the incident light. The intensity of light transmitted by each layer, then, is given by $1 - b$ of the light incident upon that particular layer, and the intensity transmitted by all n layers is $(1 - b)^n$. Since b is very small, the quantity $(1 - b)^n$ can be replaced to a good approximation by the quantity e^{-nb}. The opacity, therefore, is equal to e^{nb}, and the density is given by

$$D = nb \cdot \log_{10} e = 0.434 nb$$

Thus, when the size of the individual silver particles is approximately uniform, the density is nearly proportional to the number of such particles per unit volume.

The Characteristic (H & D) Curve

When the intensity and the quality of the light to which the emulsion is exposed are kept constant, the photographic effect (developed density) increases with increasing time of exposure,

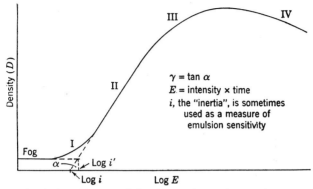

Fig. 1·2 The characteristic curve of the photographic emulsion. I, the toe region; II, the straight portion; III, the shoulder; IV, the region of solarization.

up to a certain limit. Conversely, if the time and quality are kept constant, the photographic effect increases with the intensity of the exposing light, again up to a limit. The relationship between the density and the amount of exposure is commonly represented by the *characteristic curve,* which is also known as the H & D curve because it was first employed by Hurter and Driffield. This curve is obtained by plotting the density against the common logarithm of the exposure, where exposure E is determined by the product It of the light intensity I and the time of action t. Figure 1·2 shows the typical form of the characteristic curve.

The characteristic curve may be divided, somewhat arbitrarily, into four regions: a toe (I), a straight portion (II), a shoulder (III), and a region of solarization (IV). The toe portion is sometimes termed the region of underexposure, although the upper part of it can be quite useful for photographic purposes. The straight portion is a region of linear increase of density with log E. This portion is quite extensive in some curves, but may be small or almost nonexistent in others. The shoulder is the region of overexposure, where an increase in exposure produces only a relatively slight increase in density. The curve bends away from the straight line and toward the exposure axis, eventually becoming parallel to it. Beyond the shoulder lies the region of solarization, where an increase in exposure actually results in a decrease in developed density.

The density obtained by a standardized development of a given photographic material, however, is not uniquely determined by the value of E; it usually depends to some extent upon the individual values of I and t. If E is obtained by high-intensity light acting for a short time, or by low-intensity light acting for a long time, the result usually will not be the same as that produced by light of moderate intensity acting for an intermediate time, even if the product It is identical in every case. This phenomenon is *reciprocity law failure*. Because of it, a characteristic curve obtained by plotting densities corresponding to constant light intensity and varying exposure time will not, in general, coincide with one obtained by plotting densities corresponding to varying light intensity and constant exposure time.

Gamma (γ)

In the region of the straight portion of the characteristic curve, where the change in density is proportional to the change in the logarithm of the exposure, the density is given by the relation

$$D = \gamma \left(\log E - \log i \right) \qquad (1 \cdot 1)$$

In this equation, $\log i$ is the point where the extrapolated straight line cuts the $\log E$ axis (see Fig. $1 \cdot 2$) and γ is the proportionality factor, that is, the slope of the straight line. Numerically, the value of γ is equal to the tangent of the angle α.

The value of $\log i$ is sometimes taken as a measure of the *sensitivity* of the photographic emulsion. If the fog is appreciable, suitable fog corrections are applied, or the $\log E$ value corresponding to a density on the straight line equal to the fog density is used instead of $\log i$ itself. This point is represented as $\log i'$ in Fig. $1 \cdot 2$. The actual sensitivity values in this system are expressed in terms of $1/i$ (or $1/i'$) or some multiple thereof, and the value of the sensitivity will increase numerically as i diminishes. In Chapter 11 a more elaborate and, for many purposes, more useful method of determining sensitivity will be discussed. Knowledge of the characteristic curve, however, is essential to that method as well as to the simpler one given here.

The characteristic curve depends upon both the nature of the photographic emulsion and the development process. Different emulsions may vary greatly in the form and position of their characteristic curves. The time and temperature of development, the composition of the developing solution, and the way in which

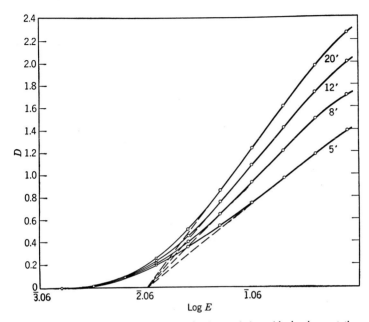

Fig. 1·3   A family of characteristic curves, showing variation with development time.

development is carried out likewise play important parts in determining the shape and position of the curve. Figure 1·3 shows a series of characteristic curves obtained by varying the time of development and keeping all the other factors constant. It will be noted that gamma increases with the time of development. For this reason, gamma is sometimes referred to as the "development factor."

2.

The Photographic Emulsion

The two principal ingredients of the photographic emulsion are gelatin and silver halide. Neither has a serious competitor for general use. Materials such as collodion and albumin have been used in place of gelatin (and indeed were its predecessors) but they are far less satisfactory for most purposes. Certain synthetic polymers can be used, but are for the most part still in the experimental stage. Some materials other than the silver halides are sensitive to light, but none has the wide range of usefulness possessed by the latter.

Gelatin

The medium in which the silver halide particles are embedded must satisfy a number of rather exacting requirements. The medium must keep the silver halide grains well dispersed to eliminate, in so far as possible, clumping of the grains and consequent granularity of the photographic image. It must be relatively stable to insure a reasonable degree of permanence to both the undeveloped and the processed emulsion. It must not impart undesirable photographic characteristics to the emulsion. It must be such that the processing solutions can penetrate it rapidly and without serious detriment to its strength or permanence after the processing operations are completed. Finally, large quantities of it must be available in fairly uniform quality. Gelatin satisfies these requirements quite well. In addition, certain properties of gelatin make it possible to prepare emulsions with it which have a greater sensitivity to light than emulsions prepared with any other dispersing medium.

Gelatin is not a sharply defined chemical individual. Its properties, particularly its photographic properties, depend upon its origin and upon its previous history. Vastly different results can be obtained by the use of gelatins which differ only very slightly in their chemical constitution. Photographic gelatin is generally made from selected clippings of calf hide, ear and cheek. Pigskin is used for some preparations, and important quantities are made from bone. The raw materials must be carefully selected, and they must be free from bacterial decomposition.

Gelatin belongs to the protein group of natural products. The molecules are made up of amino acid residues, joined end to end to form chains, the joint being made between the acidic group of one amino acid and the basic group of the neighboring one. This kind of joint is known as the *peptide bond,* and the chain is called a polypeptide chain. The gelatin chain is characterized by the repeating grouping

$$\begin{matrix} & R' & H \\ & | & | \\ -N & -C & -C- \\ & | & \| \\ & R & O \end{matrix}$$

as in the following typical segment, which contains three such groupings:

$$-N-\overset{\underset{\displaystyle CH_3}{|}}{\overset{\displaystyle H}{C}}-\overset{\underset{\displaystyle O}{\|}}{C}-N-\overset{\underset{\displaystyle H}{|}}{\overset{\displaystyle H}{C}}-\overset{\underset{\displaystyle O}{\|}}{C}-N-\overset{\overset{\displaystyle CH_2-CH_2-CH_2}{|}}{}\quad\overset{\underset{\displaystyle H}{|}}{C}-\overset{\underset{\displaystyle O}{\|}}{C}-$$

The chain length is large, but not constant even in a specific sample of gelatin. Thus, in one typical gelatin used in the manufacture of photographic emulsions, the average chain length lay in the region of 350 to 500 units, but fractions obtained therefrom appeared to have average chain lengths as low as 250 units and others as high as 800. Chain lengths of over 1000 to 1500 units have been reported for some gelatin preparations. The molecular weights are roughly 100 times the number of units making up the chain.

The gelatin molecules contain both $-NH_2$ and $-COOH$ groups on the ends and side chains. Thus gelatin, just like its constituent amino acids, possesses both acidic and basic properties; that is, it is amphoteric. When it is in solution or surrounded by an aqueous medium containing a high concentration of hydrogen ions, the amino groups add hydrogen ions to form $-NH_3^+$ groups, and the molecule as a whole acquires a positive charge. When the hydrogen ion concentration is sufficiently low, the $-COOH$ groups ionize to $-COO^-$, and the molecule as a whole acquires a negative charge. At some particular intermediate hydrogen ion concentration, the gelatin molecules will have no net charge. This concentration defines the *isoelectric point* of the gelatin. The electrical behavior of the gelatin with respect to changes in pH (pH is the common logarithm of the reciprocal of the hydrogen ion concentration, that is, $1/\log_{10}[H^+]$ or simply $-\log_{10}[H^+]$) may be symbolized roughly by the process

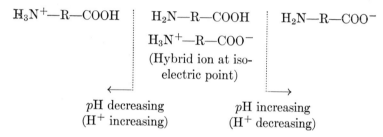

$$H_3N^+\!\!-\!R\!\!-\!COOH \qquad H_2N\!\!-\!R\!\!-\!COOH \qquad H_2N\!\!-\!R\!\!-\!COO^-$$

$$H_3N^+\!\!-\!R\!\!-\!COO^-$$
(Hybrid ion at isoelectric point)

$\longleftarrow$ $\longrightarrow$

pH decreasing pH increasing
(H^+ increasing)   (H^+ decreasing)

Many of the physical properties of gelatin, such as solubility, osmotic pressure, and degree of swelling vary with the pH and have their minimum values at the isoelectric point. The isoelectric points of most gelatins used in photographic work lie in the pH range of 4.7 to 5.2, but some gelatins, prepared by the acid hydrolysis of collagen, have isolectric points at a pH of 8.0 or above.

A sufficiently concentrated solution of gelatin will set into a rigid jelly upon standing at ordinary room temperature or slightly below. Precise figures on the concentration, temperature and time of setting can be given only for specific gelatins, as the quantities vary somewhat with the origin and history of the gelatin and with the pH and composition of the solution. The strength and rigidity of the jelly depend upon concentration, temperature and other factors.

"Dry" gelatin, stored at room temperature and in an atmosphere which is not perfectly dry, contains some water in equilibrium with the air. The greater the relative humidity, the greater is the amount of water. When the gelatin is placed in cold water, it takes up additional water and may swell to several times its original bulk. The amount of liquid taken up depends upon the pH and the salt content of the water. Swelling is a minimum at the isoelectric point in the absence of salt or in the presence of small amounts thereof. Neutral salt depresses the swelling on both sides of the isoelectric point, but may actually produce some increase in swelling at the isoelectric point.

The swollen gelatin is soft, flexible and easily scratched or torn. If it is placed in a cold solution containing molecules of fairly small size, such as those of the developing agents, the dissolved molecules easily penetrate the swollen gelatin. This is an important property, since the developing agent must penetrate to the silver halide grains before development can occur. At about 40° C or above, the gelatin itself will pass into aqueous solution. However, by suitable hardening, gelatin layers can be obtained which still retain porosity to the developing agent and the salts of the developing bath, but dissolve in water only at considerably higher temperatures.

By suitable treatment, a gelatin layer can be "hardened" to increase its softening and "melting" temperature and to decrease its tendency to "swell" in the presence of water. Such treatment is of value in the manufacture of photographic emulsions, as the hardening helps to protect the finished product against softening or sticking at high temperatures and humidities. Hardening agents also are usually added to the fixing bath (see Chapter 8) as a safeguard against damage of the wet film during the fixing, washing and drying operations.

Gelatin layers can be hardened by the action of certain inorganic agents, particularly salts of chromium and aluminum. The mechanism of this type of hardening will be considered in Chapter 8. Certain organic agents, particularly formaldehyde, are also of value.

Formaldehyde reacts with the amino group of an amino acid, tying up that group and permitting direct titration of the carboxyl group. The reaction follows the general pattern

$$R-NH_2 + HCHO \rightarrow R-N{=}CH_2 + H_2O$$

and

$$\begin{matrix} R-NH_2 \\ \\ R-NH_2 \end{matrix} + HCHO \rightarrow \begin{matrix} R-NH \\ \diagdown \\ \diagup \\ R-NH \end{matrix} CH_2 + H_2O$$

A reaction which followed the second equation could markedly harden the gelatin. One molecule of formaldehyde, by reacting with a free amino group of each of two polypeptide chains, may "weld" these chains together by forming a methylene crosslinkage between them. In successive reactions, a three-dimensional network of polypeptide chains held together by crosslinkages may be built up. Although this may be an oversimplified picture of what actually happens in the hardening of gelatin by formaldehyde, it undoubtedly represents an important aspect of the hardening process.

The Silver Halide

The silver halide is the light-sensitive material of the photographic emulsion. It is present in the form of fine crystals (grains), and it usually makes up 30 to 40 per cent of the total weight of the emulsion. In emulsions of low sensitivity, such as those used in making photographic papers, the silver salt may be the chloride, a solid solution of chloride and bromide, or practically pure bromide. The sensitivity generally increases in the order given. Chlorobromide emulsions are used also in making very slow plates, such as lantern slides. The silver halide crystals in all emulsions of high sensitivity, as well as in some of the less sensitive ones, are essentially silver bromide containing small amounts (seldom exceeding 5 mole per cent) of iodide. Pure silver iodide emulsions are of no commercial importance and of much less scientific interest than those composed of chloride or bromide.

Silver chloride and bromide crystals are made of positively charged silver ions and the corresponding negatively charged halide ions, arranged in a symmetrical structure. No one halide ion is the sole property of any one silver ion. Each ion is surrounded in space by six ions of the other kind.

X-ray analysis has shown that silver bromide and silver chloride have cubic structures of the same type as sodium chloride. The structure is illustrated in Fig. 2·1. The distance between an ion and its nearest neighbor is 2.88×10^{-8} cm for silver bromide and 2.77×10^{-8} cm for silver chloride. Pure silver iodide crystallizes in either of two structures, both of which are different from that of silver bromide, but the small amounts of iodide used in making the more sensitive silver bromide emulsions dissolve in the bromide without changing its crystal arrangement. The only observed change is a small increase in the average spacing of the ions.

The observed crystal *faces* of the photographic grains are generally octahedral* even though the lattice structure is cubic. Emulsions containing grains that present cubic faces have been prepared, but are not common. The relationship between the octahedral and cubic faces is illustrated in Fig. 2·2. The three sides of the cube show a checkerboard-like array of alternate silver and bromide ions. These make up normal cubic faces. If a corner of

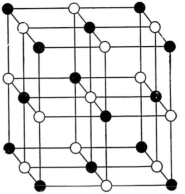

Fig. 2·1   Structure of the silver bromide and silver chloride crystals.

the cube is cut off as indicated, a face is obtained which is made up entirely of silver ions. This is an octahedral face (shaded area). Just beneath it and parallel to it lies another octahedral face composed of bromide ions only, then another of silver ions only, and so on. In this direction, the crystal is formed by adding alternate *layers* of silver and bromide ions.

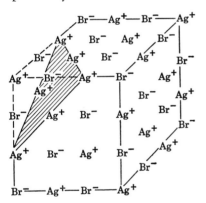

Fig. 2·2   Octahedral and cubic faces of a silver bromide crystal.

During the formation of the crystal, the relative rates of growth normal to the possible faces determine whether the crystal will present octahedral or cubic (or some other) faces. If the crystal grows by adding ion layers much more rapidly to the octahedral faces than to the cubic, the crystal as a whole will develop *cubic* faces. If the reverse is true,

---

*This terminology originates from the fact that, if the crystal presented only octahedral faces of *equal* area, the outward crystal shape would be that of a regular octahedron. The crystal shapes actually observed in the photographic emulsion can be derived from a regular octahedron by a differential growth or extension of certain faces.

the crystal will develop *octahedral* faces. Under certain conditions, both types of faces may develop. The relative growth is sometimes determined by the presence of impurities in the solution from which the crystal separates. The presence or absence of an excess of one of the crystal-forming ions in the solution also can determine the relative rates of growth of the crystal faces. Cubic faces are produced when silver nitrate and potassium bromide solutions are mixed in such a way that there is little excess of either silver or bromide ions in the solution. Octahedral faces are formed when the normal excess of bromide is present.

The tiny silver halide crystals, which are the "grains" of the photographic emulsion, may vary considerably in outward appearance. Some emulsion grains are flat tablets, either triangular or hexagonal in outline. These tablets are oriented predominantly with their flat planes at angles of less than 45° to the plane of the support on which the emulsion is coated and dried. Thus, evaluation of data obtained for one emulsion coated on glass showed that 90.5 per cent of the grains had inclinations between zero and 45°, whereas only 9.5 per cent had inclinations of greater than 45°. Some emulsions contain long, needle-shaped crystals in addition to the triangular and hexagonal ones; other emulsions contain grains of almost spherical shape, although high magnification usually reveals well-defined crystal faces.

Fig. 2·3   Electron micrograph of grains of a negative-type silver iodobromide emulsion. The grains have been "shadowed" at an angle such that the thickness of the grain is one-third the length of the shadow.
(J. Hamilton.)

The size of the grains in the photographic emulsions varies through a wide range, from several microns in diameter to below the limits of visibility under the optical microscope. It is not difficult to grow triangular grains which are as large as 20μ on a side, although the largest grains in practical emulsions seldom exceed about 5μ. At the opposite extreme, the grains of the Lippmann emulsion are so small that they are not visible through the optical microscope, but are revealed only by the electron microscope. Some of them are only 10 to 15 mμ in diameter, and the majority lie between 20 and 40 mμ. Ordinary commercial emulsions cover a fairly wide range of grain sizes between these two extremes. Grains of a typical negative type emulsion are shown in Fig. 2·3.

It is important to consider the grains as individuals in a photographic emulsion because *the grains act as individuals in the photographic process.* Each grain is a unit for latent image formation; each is a unit for development. In the normal exposure region, the number of developable grains increases with increasing exposure.

Reference to Fig. 1·1 shows that a single emulsion may exhibit a rather wide range of grain sizes. This variation in size is of considerable practical importance, and much study has been accorded it. The variation is usually represented in terms of a size-frequency curve which records data obtained by an actual

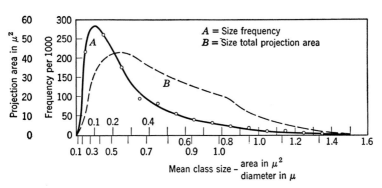

Fig. 2·4   Size-frequency distribution of grains in a typical photographic emulsion.

microscopic examination of the grain population. A sample of the emulsion is coated on a microscope slide and the *projection area* (often termed projective area) of each grain within a suitable area of the slide is determined. (The projection area of the grain gives the effective area which the grain presents as a target to a beam of parallel light impinging upon it.) The grains are then divided into size classes, each of approximately constant projection area, and the number of grains in each class is plotted against the area. Curve *A* of Fig. $2 \cdot 4$ shows a typical result. Some special emulsions have size-frequency curves of the symmetrical Gaussian form, but the badly skewed form shown in the illustration is much more common.

For purposes of correlation with the photographic characteristics of an emulsion, it is more convenient to use the total projection area of all the grains of each size group instead of simply the size distribution. The integral projection area is a measure of the relative importance of each size in contributing to the total area which the silver halide presents to the impinging light. In Fig. $2 \cdot 4$, curve *B* represents the total area as a function of size. The ordinate values used to construct this curve are obtained simply by multiplying each ordinate value of curve *A* by its corresponding abscissa value ($Y = xy$).

If the total projection area of *all the classes* is divided by the total number of grains, a value for the average area, $\bar{a}$, is obtained. This value is given in Table $2 \cdot 1$ for a number of commercial emulsion, together with the total number of grains per cubic centimeter of emulsion.

TABLE $2 \cdot 1$

Average Grain Sizes and Numbers for Certain Representative Commercial Emulsions

	$\bar{a}$ in μ^2	Number
Motion-picture positive	0.31	117.85×10^9
Fine-grain roll film	0.49	52.35
Portrait film	0.61	25.66
High-speed roll film	0.93	22.61
X-ray film	2.30	6.32

The larger grains in a given emulsion absorb more light during a given uniform exposure and are, on the average, more sensitive than the smaller ones; that is, they become developable at a lower exposure. On this basis alone, it may be expected that an emulsion containing a wide range of grain sizes will contain grains of a corresponding range of sensitivities. Such an emulsion should have a much greater range of light response (*lati-*

tude) than an emulsion containing only a small range of grain sizes. This is generally so in practice. Size, however, is by no means the only factor governing sensitivity. There can be no doubt that grains of equal size taken from emulsions of different preparation can vary considerably in inherent sensitivity. Important factors leading to such differences will be considered later in this chapter. It is not even certain that grains of equal size taken from a single preparation have identical inherent sensitivities. Toy[1] found, for example, that geometrically identical grains taken from an ordinary emulsion had a distribution of sensitivity similar to that of the emulsion as a whole, except that the range was narrower. This, however, does not necessarily imply a variation in inherent sensitivity. In Chapter 3 it will be shown that, because of the quantum structure of light and the statistical variations in the number of quanta which strikes each grain or a particular area of a grain during a photographic exposure, it would be possible to obtain this result even when the inherent sensitivities of the grain are equal.

Preparation of the Emulsion

A great deal of secrecy surrounds the actual practice of commercial emulsion making. The following discussion, therefore, will be confined to general principles and to some of the methods employed and results obtained in the preparation of relatively simple emulsions.

The preparation of the silver halide emulsion involves a series of steps, generally including all or most of the following:

1. The silver halide is precipitated in a dilute gelatin solution.

2. The precipitate is allowed to *ripen*. During this period, the silver halide grains attain approximately their ultimate size and form. In practice, a certain amount of overlapping between precipitation and ripening is almost inevitable. The extent of the overlapping will depend primarily upon the conditions of precipitation.

3. When ripening has reached the desired stage, enough additional gelatin is introduced into the solution to allow the latter to set to a firm gel upon cooling and standing. This is the gelation stage.

4. The washing operation follows the gelation stage. The set emulsion is shredded into small pieces, which are then washed to free the emulsion from soluble salts.

5. Subsequently, the washed emulsion is melted, fresh gelatin is usually added, and the emulsion is kept for some time at a carefully controlled temperature. This is the important *after-ripening period*. Various ingredients may be added before the after-ripening or just before step 6.

6. The emulsion is finally coated on the support.

Two broad types of emulsions have been distinguished in the literature. The first is termed the *boiled* or *neutral-type* and the second, the *ammoniacal* or *ammonia-type emulsion*. The preparation of a simple neutral-type emulsion is illustrated by the the following example.[2]

Two solutions are prepared which have the composition:

Bromide Solution			
KBr	165 grams		
KI	5 grams	Silver Solution	
Gelatin	65 grams	AgNO$_3$	200 grams
Water	1700 ml	Water	2000 ml
Temperature	70° C	Temperature	72° C

The bromide solution is stirred mechanically while the silver nitrate solution is added through a calibrated nozzle. The emulsion is allowed to ripen for 20 minutes at 70°C; then it is cooled quickly to 45°C. Two hundred fifty grams of gelatin is added, and the whole stirred for 20 minutes at 45°C in order to dissolve this gelatin. The mixture is then allowed to gel by standing overnight in a cold room, after which it is shredded, washed, and then remelted at 42°C. The total weight is then made up to 6.3 kg by the addition of water and 100 grams of gelatin. The emulsion is allowed to after-ripen for 30 minutes at a temperature of 60°C and is then coated on the support.

The preparation of the ammonia-type emulsion differs from from that of the neutral-type in that an ammoniacal silver solution is used instead of a plain silver nitrate solution, and the temperatures of precipitation and ripening are generally lower. The following formula and preparation illustrates a simple ammonia-type emulsion.

Bromide Solution		Silver Solution	
KBr	200 grams	AgNO$_3$	250 grams
KI	5 grams	Water	750 ml
Gelatin	125 grams		
Water	1750 ml		

Prior to the precipitation of the silver halide, ammonia is added to the silver nitrate until the precipitate first formed (silver oxide) just redissolves. This requires more than 2 moles of ammonia for each mole of silver nitrate, and the precipitate dissolves by way of formation of the soluble complex $Ag(NH_3)_2{}^+$. The resulting ammoniacal silver solution is added to the bromide solution at 50°C. The emulsion is maintained at approximately this temperature for 30 minutes. Then 250 grams of gelatin in 1250 ml water at 50°C is added. The emulsion is digested for a second period of 15 minutes, and then the container is placed in ice water to allow the emulsion to set. Suitable washing and finishing are carried out as described previously.

The Precipitation Stage

When a solution of silver nitrate is added to a solution of some readily soluble halide, such as potassium bromide, the very slightly soluble silver halide is formed and separates out. The reaction is a simple double decomposition, exemplified by the equation

$$AgNO_3 + KBr \rightarrow AgBr + KNO_3 \qquad (2 \cdot 1)$$

If the initial solutions are sufficiently dilute and one of the reactants is in slight excess, the silver halide can separate out in the colloidal form even though no gelatin is present. Such particles are extremely small and may remain in suspension for a considerable period of time. The particles are electrically charged as a result of having adsorbed some of the excess ion at the particle surface. For example, if the potassium bromide is in excess, the silver bromide surface has adsorbed bromide ions and the particles are negatively charged. This charge is an important factor in keeping the particles suspended in the solution when protective colloids are absent.

In the preparation of photographic emulsions, it is necessary to use relatively concentrated solutions of silver nitrate and either alkali or ammonium halide. A protective colloid must then be used to prevent the silver halide particles from coalescing into a curdy mass. One of the functions, but by no means the sole function, of the gelatin in the preparation of the emulsion is to supply such protection. The gelatin forms an adsorbed layer which serves as a virtual cushion around each particle and prevents or greatly inhibits coalescence. The gelatin, however, does not prevent adsorption of the halide ions.

The method of mixing the component solutions is important. If the silver nitrate solution is simply dumped into a rapidly stirred bromide solution, the resulting mixture at first is highly supersaturated with respect to silver bromide. Almost immediately, a very large number of solid silver bromide nuclei are formed. These grow quickly as more silver bromide crystallizes out upon them, and the process goes forward until the separation of the solid is complete. If, at the other extreme, the silver nitrate solution is added very slowly, silver bromide nuclei are formed by the first few drops to enter the bromide solution, but they are fewer in number. As more silver nitrate is added, most of the silver bromide formed from it crystallizes out on the nuclei already present, rather than forming new nuclei. The net result is an emulsion containing a smaller number of grains but of much larger average grain size.

Table 2·2 illustrates the effect of time of precipitation upon the average area $\bar{a}$, average thickness $\bar{t}$, average number of grains per milliliter $\bar{n}$, inertia speed, and gamma for a neutral-type emulsion prepared by Trivelli and Smith. The time of precipitation was varied by changing the size of the nozzle. A plot of the time against the average grain size gives a reasonably straight line. The inertia speed increases with increasing average area, and gamma decreases. In this type of emulsion preparation, Trivelli and Smith found that photographic speed often increased as the first power or as a fractional power of the average grain area.

TABLE 2·2

RELATION OF GRAIN SIZE, NUMBER, SPEED, AND GAMMA TO TIME OF PRECIPITATION

Time of Precipitation	Average Number per Milliliter $\bar{n}$	Average Area $\bar{a}, \mu^2$	Average Thickness $\bar{t}, \mu$	Speed	Gamma
0′31″	6.85×10^{11}	0.14	0.062	12	2.50
4′22″	2.09	0.28	0.096	52	2.08
10′12″	0.63	0.50	0.183	150	1.50
19′30″	0.28	0.82	0.248	250	1.36
42′40″	0.17	1.47	0.333	450	0.94
54′50″	0.09	2.35	. . . .	630	0.83
85′10″	0.04	2.56	0.589	910	0.65

Hautot[3] found that the average size of the grains in a series of ammonia-type emulsion preparations generally increased with increasing time of precipitation, but a simple proportionality did not hold. The relation between speed, gamma, and grain size likewise was more complicated.

It will be noted (page 26) that only a portion of the total gelatin of the finished emulsion is present during the mixing operation. In general, the presence of larger quantities of gelatin during the precipitation results in smaller grain size. In the preparation of some emulsions of very fine grain, gelatin is added to both the silver and the halide solutions before mixing. The grain size also depends upon the concentrations of the silver nitrate and the potassium bromide.

All high-speed emulsions contain some iodide. This is present, usually as potassium iodide, during the precipitation stage. The amount of iodide generally does not exceed 5 mole per cent of the total halide, but this small quantity produces a marked increase in the emulsion speed. The relation of speed to iodide content is not simple, in so far as the available data reveal, but the speed passes through a maximum at a concentration of only a few per cent, and further increases in iodide content lead to a loss of speed.

The iodide in a finished emulsion is distributed throughout nearly all the grains. Sheppard and Trivelli, in an extensive investigation, failed to find pure silver iodide crystals in an iodobromide emulsion. Renwick, Sease, and Baldsiefen prepared emulsions in which the iodide was added in the form of coarse silver iodide particles; they obtained results which were practically identical with those obtained by adding the same amount of iodide in the form of the soluble potassium salt. However, Renwick and Sease made the observation that the larger grains of an emulsion which they examined contained a higher percentage of iodide than the smaller grains. The distribution ranged from 4.3 to 1.8 per cent, the average for the entire emulsion being 3.2 per cent.

Berry and Marino[4] have shown that, when the silver nitrate solution was added to a solution containing a mixture of bromide and iodide (or bromide and chloride), the less soluble component precipitated first. Thus, iodide precipitated first in the iodide-bromide mixtures. During the later stages of the precipitation, a large amount of solution and redistribution occurred, although equilibrium was not attained within the times normally used in the preparation of a photographic emulsion. In some preparations, localized concentrations of iodide up to 45 mole per cent remained in some grains.

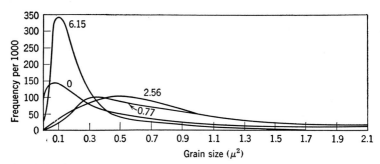

Fig. 2·5 Influence of iodide upon the size-frequency distribution of the grains in a simple photographic emulsion. The figures on the curves give the iodide content in mole per cent. (Trivelli and Smith.)

Iodide exerts an influence on the size and shape of the grains, as the size-frequency curves in Fig. 2·5 show. The emulsions were prepared according to the first method (neutral) given on page 26, except that varying amounts of potassium iodide were present during the precipitation. The emulsions of the series contained (1) no iodide, (2) 0.77 mole per cent, (3) 2.56 per cent, and (4) 6.15 per cent. These amounts of iodide produced a change in the outward form of the crystals. The pure silver bromide grains had the form of flat tablets. With increasing iodide concentration, the average thickness became greater, and the average projection area became smaller. The changes, however, did not show simple relations to the iodide concentrations, and exceptions were observed.

The Ripening Stage (Physical Ripening)

In the physical ripening stage of emulsion making, the grains attain approximately their final size and form. After the initial precipitation is complete, an increase in the size of some crystals can take place only at the expense of other crystals, which then tend to disappear. The phenomenon is well-known to the analytical chemist. Precipitates of calcium oxalate and barium sulfate, for example, are commonly allowed to ripen before they are filtered.

The increase in particle size can take place in two principal ways. One is a coalescence of two or more individuals, which clump together and may undergo local recrystallization to form a more or less well-unified single crystal. The second way involves the so-called Ostwald ripening; it appears to be the more important of the two in the preparation of the photographic emulsion under most conditions.

In Ostwald ripening, the larger grains grow at the expense of the smaller ones because of a difference in solubility. The basis for this difference is found in energy considerations. If a large crystal is reduced to a powder, energy will be spent in tearing apart the original structure. This energy is stored at the broken surface where the ions are only partly surrounded by compensating partners. The small particles will have a greater surface energy per unit mass than the larger ones. Suppose, now, that the powdered substance is placed in contact with a liquid which can dissolve it, even though slightly, and the liquid is in contact with large crystals of the substance. The small particles will dissolve and deposit out on the large particles because the process involves a decrease in the surface energy.

Physical ripening by coalescence apparently occurs to an important extent under some conditions. Malinowski,[5] in a study of the physical ripening of ammonia-type emulsions, found that high concentrations of ammonium hydroxide, low concentrations of iodide, and a potassium bromide excess of 10 - 20 per cent led to a grain growth in which an initial low rate of growth was followed by a much more rapid stage and finally by another slow stage ("S"-shaped growth curve). Microscopic observations of the growing grains led him to conclude that growth in the initial and final slow stages occurred by Ostwald ripening and that coalescence dominated during the period of rapid growth.

The rate of physical ripening depends upon the concentration and the nature of the gelatin present. Commercial gelatin can show evidence of both a ripening-accelerating and a ripening-restraining action. The restraint may predominate in one gelatin concentration range and the acceleration in another. Impurities or compounds formed by a breakdown of the gelatin molecule, often removable by washing the gelatin with water, can have a marked restraining action. These restrainers are compounds, such as cysteine, which are strongly adsorbed by the silver halide surface. They need be present only in small concentrations. However, not all strongly adsorbed substances retard physical ripening. The thioureas are strongly adsorbed, and Oyama[6] has shown that these agents can promote physical ripening under proper conditions. They also markedly increase the rate of solution of silver bromide. The gelatin molecule itself may promote physical ripening. Thus, Jones[7] has shown that well-washed gelatins promote grain growth and that the effect depends upon pH. The growth-promoting action decreases with decreasing pH, and ceases when the pH is about two units below the isoelectric point, both for a gelatin of isoelectric 5 and one of 9.

Mild silver halide solvents, such as excess bromide ion and ammonia, increase the rate of physical ripening. The former is the principal solvent in the preparation of neutral-type emulsions and the latter in the preparation of the ammonia-type emulsions. Both the solubility of the silver halide and the rate of solution are increased. An increase in temperature causes an increase in the rate of ripening, which is the reason for the high temperatures used in the early stages of emulsion making.

The idea that excess bromide ions can increase the solubility of silver bromide may seem a violation of the solubility product principle, but it is not. The concentration of silver ions in solution actually does decrease with increasing bromide ion concentration, as required by the solubility product principle. The total solubility of the silver bromide, however, shows a more complicated behavior. At very low bromide ion concentrations the total solubility of silver bromide decreases with increasing

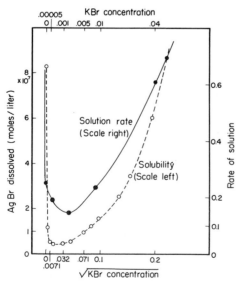

Fig. 2·6 Dependence of equilibrium solubility of silver bromide (broken curve) and rate of solution (solid curve) on the concentration of potassium bromide at 20°C.

bromide ion concentration, but a minimum solubility is reached at about 0.0002 M Br$^-$. The solubility increases at higher bromide ion concentrations, becomes equal to that in pure water when the bromide ion concentration reaches about 0.05 M at 25°C, and continues to increase with further increases in bromide ion concentration. The basis for this behavior lies in the formation of soluble complex ions, such as AgBr$_2$$^-$ and AgBr$_3$$^=$. At low bromide concentrations, the complexes are not formed to a significant degree, and the solubility decreases because of the solubility product effect. At higher concentrations, the formation of complex ions becomes sufficient to offset the effect of depressing the silver ion concentrations. In practical emulsion making, the usual excess of bromide generally lies well within the range where the complexes become important in accelerating the ripening process. Figure 2·6 shows the effect of an increase in bromide ion concentration on both the equilibrium solubility (broken curve) and the rate of solution (solid curve) of silver bromide.

Ammonia increases the solubility of silver halide because it forms a soluble complex, Ag(NH$_3$)$_2$$^+$, with silver ions. Even low concentrations of ammonia will markedly increase the rate of solution of silver halide[8] and, as was stated earlier, there is evidence that high concentrations of ammonia may promote ripening by coagulation.

From the available data, it appears that excess bromide in all concentrations produces a decrease in the solubility of silver bromide in ammoniacal solution. The solubility in the presence of ammonia is still greater than in its absence, however, and the ammonia causes a net acceleration of the ripening process.

A change not connected with an increase in size also may occur during the ripening process. Pure precipitates of silver halide, thrown down in the absence of gelatin, pass through a period of rather rapid "aging" during which the amount of free surface decreases rapidly and the crystals become more and more perfect in structure. This particular process does not involve Ostwald ripening, since it bears little relation to the solubility of the salt in the surrounding solution. The decrease in free surface probably is accomplished by a movement of ions along and through an essentially solid surface. It is not known, however, to what extent such a process operates during the ripening of a photographic emulsion.

Physical ripening occurs to some extent during the precipitation stage. The amount of overlapping of the two stages depends to a great extent on the conditions of precipitation (e.g., the presence of excess halide or ammonia) and on the duration of the precipitation stage. The amount of ripening during precipitation can be minimized by a procedure in which the silver solution and the halide solution are added simultaneously to a dilute gelatin solution, and the rates of addition are controlled so that a constant slight excess of halide, corresponding to minimum solubility of the silver halide, is maintained throughout the precipitation stage.

Washing

At the conclusion of the ripening period, the emulsion contains soluble alkali or ammonium nitrate, excess soluble halide, and, in the ammonia process, excess ammonia. If the emulsion is coated on an impervious support, such as cellulose acetate or glass, the alkali nitrate will tend to crystallize out when the emulsion is dried and may adversely affect its physical properties. Ammonia remaining in the emulsion will cause excessive fog. A large excess of soluble halide will decrease considerably the sensitivity of the finished emulsion. In practice, therefore, emulsions which are to be coated on impervious supports are generally washed to completely remove ammonia (if present) and to eliminate or greatly reduce nitrates and soluble halides. The emulsions coated on paper supports, however, are often coated without washing, since they usually do not contain ammonia, and the salts present penetrate the paper and do not crystallize out on the emulsion surface.

In preparation for the washing operation, the gelled emulsion is shredded into noodles. These noodles are washed for several hours in a suitable apparatus. The progress of washing can be followed by analytical tests, and the washing itself is usually carried to an empirically determined end point. It is possible to wash an emulsion until the silver ion is actually in excess of the bromide, because silver ion combines with gelatin to form what is loosely termed silver gelatinate. At the equivalence point of pure silver bromide, where the silver ion concentration is approximately 10^{-6}, 1 gram of gelatin is in equilibrium with approximately 1 mg of silver ion in a neutral solution. A gelatin-silver bromide emulsion of average composition can be washed until about 0.4 per cent of the total silver is in combination with gelatin instead of with bromide.

In practice, washing usually is continued only until the excess bromide has been reduced to about the amount desired for the after-ripening and finishing. If washing is carried beyond this point for special reasons, more bromide is added at the conclusion of the washing. The halide should be in some excess in the finished emulsion.

Procedures have been reported in the literature in which the washing stage is avoided by adding an agent which causes the gelatin-silver halide emulsion to coagulate. The supernatant liquid can then be removed and the coagulum redispersed in pure water or in gelatin solution.

After-Ripening (Chemical Sensitizing)

After the completion of the washing stage, the emulsion is melted for the after-ripening stage. The temperature is maintained at a constant value, e.g., around 50°C, for an empirically determined time, which may amount to an hour or so. Little or no change occurs in the size of the grains or in their general form during this period, since the ripening accelerators, such

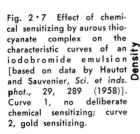

Fig. 2·7 Effect of chemical sensitizing by aurous thiocyanate complex on the characteristic curves of an iodobromide emulsion [based on data by Hautot and Sauvenier, Sci. et inds. phot., 29, 289 (1958)]. Curve 1, no deliberate chemical sensitizing; curve 2, gold sensitizing.

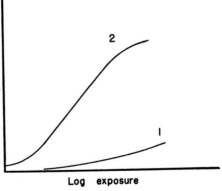

as excess bromide ion and ammonia, have been removed in the washing process. The important change photographically is an increase in sensitivity and contrast, brought about by a chemical sensitizing reaction. Figure 2·7 illustrates the change in the characteristic curve of an ammonia-type iodobromide emulsion produced by one kind of chemical sensitizing.

Chemical sensitizing can be produced by a reaction of the gelatin or impurities in it with the silver halide. Gelatins vary greatly in their behavior as sensitizers. Some gelatins act very slowly, others act rapidly. This special photographic behavior of the various gelatins depends upon the presence, often in very small concentrations, of compounds which promote or interfere with the sensitizing reaction or reactions. An "inactive" or "inert" gelatin, comparatively though probably never completely free from such agents, can be obtained by suitable treatment of ordinary gelatin, e.g., by treatment with silver bromide itself, which is subsequently removed, or with peracetic acid.

At the start of the after-ripening stage, a gelatin rich in natural sensitizer may be added to the emulsion, or sensitizers of known composition may be added. The sensitizer present in active gelatin was first identified as allyl thiourea or a related compound in a classic piece of work by Sheppard[9] and his associates in 1925. More recent work[10] suggests that thiosulfate is the more probable sensitizer in commercial gelatins, and that aldehydes and reducing sugars present in the gelatin can also act as sensitizers. The known sensitizers can be grouped under several class headings.[11] These include (1) compounds which react with silver halide to form silver sulfide (sulfur sensitizers), (2) compounds which reduce silver ions to silver (reduction or silver sensitizers), and (3) salts of gold and certain other noble metals.

The amount of sensitizer necessary for optimum results is often very small. One part of allyl thiourea added to a million parts of an emulsion prepared with low-activity gelatin can produce a detectable change in sensitivity, and as little as one part in 50,000 can produce optimum sensitivity. Much larger concentrations of allyl thiourea produce excessive fog formation.

The mechanism of the reaction of thiourea and its derivatives with silver bromide has been studied in some detail. The thioureas are strongly adsorbed by silver bromide, and the reaction that is significant for sensitizing takes place on the grain surface. Under suitable conditions, silver sulfide is formed as indicated by the equation:

$$S{=}C\Big\langle{}^{NH_2}_{NHC_3H_5} + 2Ag^+ \rightarrow Ag_2S + 2H^+ + N{\equiv}C{-}NHC_3H_5$$

Both the photographic sensitivity and the rate of the reaction which forms silver sulfide increase with increasing temperature, increasing pH, and decreasing excess halide ion concentration. This parallel behavior between sensitivity and reaction rate strongly suggests that the increase in sensitivity is associated with silver sulfide formation on the grain surface. Silver sulfide catalyzes the reaction between silver ions and thiourea, but the catalysis may not be significant for the reaction of the very small amounts of thiourea involved in chemical sensitizing. Thiosulfate ion, which is likewise a sulfur sensitizer, is also strongly adsorbed by the silver halide surface and will react under favorable conditions to form silver sulfide on the grain surface.

Certain reducing agents, such as stannous chloride and hydrazine, act as sensitizers. These agents react with silver ions to form silver atoms, and the latter appear to be responsible for the increased sensitivity produced by the reducing agents. As already mentioned, gelatin itself may contain reducing agents which act as sensitizers. Chibisoff[12] contends that silver, rather than silver sulfide, is responsible for the increase in sensitivity obtained by after-ripening in the presence of sulfur sensitizers, such as thiourea and thiosulfate. However, several investigators[11, 13] have shown that the sensitizing produced by the sulfur sensitizers is more resistant to the action of mild oxidizing agents, such as ferricyanide, and there appears to be a real difference in the actions of the sulfur sensitizers and the reduction sensitizers.

A third type of sensitizing is produced by the action of certain gold compounds and gold-ion complexes. The aurous thiocyanate complex is effective, and it can increase the sensitivity of an emulsion well beyond that obtainable with sulfur or reduction sensitizers. This type of sensitizing has been attributed to the formation of gold atoms on the grain surface.

Direct evidence that silver, silver sulfide, and gold can act as sensitizers for latent-image formation is supplied by some experiments which Mitchell[14] and his co-workers carried out with silver bromide crystals prepared by cooling purified, molten silver bromide between glass plates. These crystals could be markedly sensitized for latent image formation by condensing silver, gold, or a suitable sulfide vapor onto the surface of the silver bromide in the absence of gelatin. Excessive amounts of any of the three sensitizers caused fog. Possible reasons why silver sulfide, silver, and gold increase photographic sensitivity will be considered in the next chapter.

Final Additions before Coating

The changes in swelling that the gelatin will undergo during development, fixing and washing result in considerable mechanical stress on the gelatin. The ability of gelatin to resist stress can be increased by the addition of certain hardening agents before the emulsion is coated. Chrome alum, in a proportion of about 1 gram per 100 grams of gelatin, can be used for this purpose, and other hardening agents, formaldehyde for example, are available. Excessive hardening, however, can lead to retarded development and loss in sensitivity.

The excess bromide ion and hydrogen ion concentrations are important to the properties of the finished emulsion. In addition to the irreversible effects on chemical sensitizing, discussed in the preceding section, each has a certain reversible effect upon the sensitivity of the finished product. Increase in excess bromide results in a decrease in sensitivity, other things being equal. The sensitivity of the emulsion may likewise be altered by changing the hydrogen ion concentration, provided that it is changed before the final coating. Thus, Rawling[15] found that the sensitivity of an experimental emulsion was two to five times as great at pH 8.5 as at pH 5.0.

The spectral sensitivity of the photographic emulsion can be greatly extended by the addition of suitable dyes called optical sensitizers (see Chapter 14). When these are added, as in the preparation of orthochromatic and panchromatic materials,* the addition is usually made toward the end of the emulsion-manufacturing process. The amount of dye used is extremely small. The dye must be adsorbed to the silver bromide surface before it can sensitize, and the maximum effect is usually reached before the entire surface of the grains has been covered.

The list of known sensitizing dyes is large, and the sensitization can be adjusted to suit the particular requirements within a rather wide range. In addition to the familiar orthochromatic

---

*Orthochromatic materials are sensitized in the green; therefore the spectral sensitivity range covers green, blue and violet, and extends for a short distance into the ultraviolet. Panchromatic materials, on the other hand, are sensitized to all visible colors from 400 to 650 mμ. The spectral sensitivity of silver bromide emulsions which have not been optically sensitized is negligible at wavelengths greater than about 490 mμ.

and panchromatic materials, some commercial emulsions are specially sensitized in a particular region, according to the use to which they are put. It is possible, for example, to sensitize emulsions far into the infrared—to about 1300 mμ.

Other special additions, such as of preservatives and antifoggants, are frequently made just before coating. The patent literature on the subject is quite large, but the additions actually made to commercial emulsions usually are not specifically designated.

Coating

The finished emulsion is coated upon some suitable supporting material. The support in ordinary photographic film is a cellulose ester, such as the acetate. Glass is the support for photographic plates and paper for the photographic papers. Other materials, such as wood and metal, can be coated with the emulsion for special purposes.

The composition of the finished photographic material varies considerably according to the purpose for which it is intended. Definite figures on silver halide content, gelatin, emulsion thickness, and so on can be given only for specific emulsions. Typical emulsions for negative film contain about 60 parts by weight of dry gelatin to 40 parts of silver halide. The coating thickness is about 0.02 mm, with approximately 1.5 mg of silver halide per square centimeter. The finished film contains some moisture (about 10 per cent of the total weight of gelatin), excess halide, and small amounts of various impurities and additions, as discussed previously. Positive emulsions are usually thinner and contain a somewhat smaller percentage of silver halide.

Notes on Some Special Emulsions

X-ray emulsions are bromide or iodobromide emulsions. Numerous possible substitutes, such as silver tungstate, have been tested but silver halide has proved superior. In order to obtain as effective absorption as possible, these emulsions are coated considerably thicker than normal, and coatings are frequently made on both sides of the supporting film.

High-contrast emulsions are obtained by rapid mixing of the component silver and bromide solutions, followed by a minimum of ripening. An example of such an emulsion, which brings out one extreme in emulsifying conditions, is patterned after a formula originally published by Eder. The silver nitrate is merely wetted with water, then dissolved in ammonia. This very concentrated solution is literally "flopped" into the bromide solution. An instantaneous precipitation of tiny grains of relatively uniform size results. The bulk gelatin is added immediately, no ripening time being allowed. In general, rapid mixing, low excess bromide or other silver halide solvent, and a very short ripening time (or none at all) are used in the preparation of the high-contrast emulsions. Gelatin may also be used in both the silver and the bromide solutions.

The emulsions used in coating photographic papers are of the slow, relatively fine-grain type. They may contain silver chloride alone, a solid solution of chloride and bromide, or almost pure silver bromide. In general, speed increases in the order given. The details of preparation of these emulsions are largely matters of practical consideration and will not be entered into here. The same theoretical considerations apply to these emulsions as to the higher-speed negative materials.

The so-called print-out emulsions represent a rather different type. The sensitive material in these emulsions is silver chloride or some organic silver salt, such as the citrate, tartrate, or oxalate, or more commonly a mixture of silver chloride and some organic salt. Unlike the normal emulsions, the silver ion in print-out emulsions is usually in excess. These emulsions are not developed, the image silver being formed directly by exposure to intense light.

While silver bromide grains are sensitive to radiation far in the ultraviolet region, ordinary emulsions show a marked drop in sensitivity from 250 to 180 mμ. This loss of sensitivity is a result of absorption of the radiation by the gelatin, which thus effectively prevents the radiation from reaching the grains themselves. Special emulsions of very low gelatin content can be prepared, however, which show sensitivity to 55 mμ and even below. This type of preparation was suggested by Schumann, whose name is generally associated with one type of plate. A thin coating of emulsion is used, and the grains receive very little protection by the gelatin from abrasion handling marks. The thin emulsion layer can be coated on a gelatin sub-layer to improve adhesion to the base. Electron micrographs of such coatings show the grains projecting out from the binding in a way suggestive of a cobblestone wall.

Another type of low-gelatin emulsion is used in the recording of cosmic rays, nuclear particles and electrons. The silver halide content of such emulsions may exceed 80 per cent. The emulsions are coated at much greater thickness (often several hundred microns) than is usual for negative materials, or they may be used in the form of pellicules without a base support.

REFERENCES

General

Mees, *The Theory of the Photographic Process*, revised edition, Macmillan, New York, 1954, Chapters, 1, 2, 3.

Baker, *Photographic Emulsion Technique*, American Photographic Publ. Co., Boston, 1941.

Carroll, "Preparation of Photographic Emulsions," *J. Chem. Education*, **8**, 2341-67 (1931).

Glafkides, *Chimie photographique*, 2nd edition, Paul Montel, Paris, 1957, Chapters 17, 18, 19, 20, 21.

Specific

1. Toy, *Phot. J.*, **61**, 417 (1921).
2. Trivelli and Smith, *Phot. J.*, **80**, 285 (1940).
3. Hautot, *Bull. soc. roy. sci. Liège*, **16**, 204 (1947).
4. Berry and Marino, *Photo. Sci. and Tech.* (2), **2**, 149 (1955); **4**, 22 (1957).
5. Malinowski, *Z. wiss. Phot.*, **51**, 186, 200 (1956).
6. Oyama, *Proc. Roy. Phot. Soc. Centenary Intern. Confer. on the Science and Applications of Photography*, London, Sept. 19-25, 1953, publ. by Roy. Phot. Soc., 1955, p. 37.
7. Jones, *Z. wiss. Phot.*, **50**, 138 (1955).
8. James and Vanselow, *Phot. Sci. and Tech.* (2), **2**, 135 (1955)
9. Sheppard, *Phot. J.*, **65**, 380 (1925).
10. Wood, *Sci. et inds. phot.*, **23**, 209 (1952); *J. Phot. Sci.* **2**, 154 (1954). Russell, *J. Phot. Sci.*, **4**, 94 (1956).
11. Lowe, Jones, and Roberts, "Some Chemical Factors in Emulsion Sensitivity," in *Fundamental Mechanisms of Photographic Sensitivity*, edited by J.W. Mitchell, Butterworths Sci. Pubs., London, 1951, pp. 112-125.
12. Chibisoff, *Z. wiss. Phot.*, **51**, 59 (1956).
13. Wood, *J. Phot. Sci.*, **6**, 33 (1958).
14. Evans, Hedges, and Mitchell, *J. Phot. Sci.*, **3**, 73 (1955).
15. Rawling and Glassett, *Phot. J.*, **66**, 495 (1926).

3.

Formation of the Latent Image

The latent image, strictly speaking, is known only by its activity, not by its substance. It has been detected with certainty only by development. Accordingly, arguments concerning its nature and mechanism of formation must be based, for the present at least, on indirect evidence.

The theory of the latent image can be divided into two essentially separate branches. The first deals with the statistical relation between the developable density and the amount of exposure. This branch is essentially the theory of the origin of the characteristic curve. The second deals with the actual mechanism of latent image formation in the individual silver halide grains.

Origin of the Characteristic Curve

The characteristic curve is obtained by plotting the developed density against the logarithm of the exposure (Chapter 1). The variation in density along the curve is caused primarily by a variation in the *number of grains* developed per unit area. At any particular exposure below that represented by the maximum point on the curve, only a fraction of the total number of grains will develop. This fraction increases with the amount of exposure.

Numerous attempts have been made to formulate quantitatively the relation between exposure and the number of developed grains. Some of these attempts, which have been purely empirical, have little significance and will not be treated here. The more important theoretical formulations are based upon one or the other of two substantially different viewpoints. In the first,[1] it is assumed that the grains of equal projection area in any given emulsion are all of approximately the same inherent sensitivity, or that the grains can be regarded as belonging to a very small number of equal-sensitivity classes, usually not exceeding two or three. In the second, it is assumed that the individual grains vary widely in sensitivity, and therefore the number of incident quanta required to make a grain developable differs considerably from grain to grain.

If the grains are all of approximately the same inherent sensitivity, the change in number of developable grains with change in exposure can be explained only by the random distribution in the incidence or absorption of light quanta hitting the emulsion. The number of times a grain is hit during a given exposure varies from grain to grain according to the laws of probability. Conversely, the number of grains hit by a fixed number of quanta (say 1, 2, or 3) is controlled by probability.

Suppose that the grains under consideration are of equal size, that N is the number of grains in a given area, and that the grains are arranged in a single layer, that is, none of the grains is shielding any other from the light. The layer is now exposed uniformly to light. Although the exposure is uniform from the macroscopic viewpoint, the quanta actually strike the emulsion in a random distribution with respect to areas as small as those presented by photographic grains. If the total number of quanta striking the grains is s, the probability that any one grain will be struck by *at least one* quantum will be $1 - e^{-s/N}$. This is also the *fractional* number of grains struck by at least one quantum. If one quantum is sufficient to make a grain developable, the total number of developable grains will be given by the equation

$$k = N\left(1 - e^{-s/N}\right) \tag{3·1}$$

If one quantum is not sufficient but two are, k can be calculated by multiplying the term $e^{-s/N}$ in equation 3·1 by the factor $1 + (s/N)$. If three are required, the exponential term should be multiplied by the factor $\{1 + (s/N) + (1/2!)\,(s/N)^2\}$, and so on.

Various elaborations of the preceding formulation have been made to allow for the failure of the grains to utilize effectively (for latent image formation) all the quanta striking them, and to take into account the fact that the grains in a normal photographic emulsion lie in multilayers instead of a single layer. The characteristic curve can be represented rather well by such formulations. A significant feature of them is that they invariably make a small number of quanta, usually one to three, sufficient to make a grain developable.

The second method[2] of formulating the relation between the amount of exposure and the number of developable grains assumes that the inherent sensitivities of the individual grains vary widely. The distribution of sensitivities is treated as a statistical problem. With the aid of certain assumptions concerning the probable distribution of sensitivity, Webb has succeeded in "deriving" the characteristic curves of several commercial emulsions on this basis. In his treatment, the number of incident quanta required per grain ranges from a very few for the most sensitive grains to several hundred for the least sensitive ones. The random distribution of quantum hits (or absorption) still must be considered when the number of quanta per grain is small, but may be ignored when it is large. The function giving the distribution of individual sensitivities is determined empirically from the photographic data.

The transfer from number of developed grains per unit area to optical density is sometimes made merely by multiplication by a suitable factor; that is, it is assumed that $D = A(k/N)$, where A is a constant. This procedure must not be followed indiscriminately, however. In some cases, the relation holds to a good approximation over a large section of the characteristic curve; in others the error is considerable even over a much smaller segment. It is doubtful that the relation ever holds over the entire course of the curve. The validity or lack of validity over a more restricted portion depends upon both the nature of the emulsion and the development process. Development can be particularly influential when the process is incomplete. This subject will be treated further in Chapter 7.

Absorption of Light by Silver Halides

Only light or radiation which is absorbed can be effective in latent image formation. When the emulsion does not contain optical sensitizers, the absorption must be by the silver halide crystal itself to be effective. The major portion of this absorption by silver bromide and iodobromide is confined to the blue, violet, and ultraviolet regions of the spectrum. Some absorption may extend into the red region, but this is very weak relative to that at the short-wave end of the visible spectrum and is apparently caused by impurities in the silver halide. The present discussion will be confined to the action of light or ultraviolet radiation absorbed in the region of "inherent sensitivity" by the silver halide itself. Details on the spectral distribution of absorption will be given in Chapter 14.

Nature of the Latent Image

A heavy exposure of silver bromide or silver chloride to photographically active light produces free silver and halogen. There is no evidence that any intermediate chemical substance, such as the sub-halide suggested at one time, is formed by the action of the light. The general reaction can be represented by the equations

$$Br^- + h\nu \rightarrow Br + \epsilon \qquad (3.2)$$

and

$$Ag^+ + \epsilon \rightarrow Ag \qquad (3.3)$$

where $h\nu$ is a quantum of radiation and ϵ is an electron.

Because analytical methods are not sufficiently refined to detect silver or halogen in grains which have been given only a normal photographic exposure, direct identification of the latent image with one of the photolytic products has not been achieved. However, several factors point to silver as the latent image material.

For one thing, the chemical reactions of the latent image and of silver are approximately the same. Thus, the latent image is destroyed by strong oxidizing agents, such as chromic acid, potassium persulfate, and free halogen. These agents readily oxidize silver. The parallel between the destruction of the latent image and the oxidation of free silver is not quite complete quantitatively, but the differences are such as might be expected if the latent image were intimately associated with the silver halide and hence partially protected by the latter.

Furthermore, the silver halide can be dissolved out of an exposed emulsion without destroying the latent image. The latter can still be developed by a special treatment (physical development) which will be discussed in Chapter 5. Silver nuclei, prepared by the condensation of silver vapor on glass, can be developed in the same way.

Again, in the region where exposure is great enough to produce analytically determinable amounts of silver, a direct proportion has been established [3] between the silver liberated at

20°C and the number of quanta absorbed, provided effective methods are used to remove the halogen liberated. When the data are extrapolated to lower exposures, the straight line passes through the origin. From this it may be deduced that silver is formed in the latent image region. To be sure, the argument is based on an extrapolation, but there are no experimental facts that suggest that the extrapolation is not valid. All in all, the experimental evidence strongly supports the belief that the latent image material is essentially silver.

The photolytic formation of silver is accompanied by the formation of free halogen. If the halogen is not removed, it can recombine with the silver in a "dark" reaction. In experiments on the relation between silver formed and light absorbed, such as those just mentioned, recombination is prevented by the use of a halogen acceptor which reacts with the halogen. In the presence of such an acceptor, one silver atom is formed for every quantum of light absorbed; in its absence, the quantum yield falls well below unity.

Latent Image Nuclei and Development Centers

The photolytic silver produced by a heavy exposure appears in the form of discrete particles[4], which are shown quite clearly by electron microscope photographs. Figure 3·1 reproduces an electron micrograph of nuclei formed by the action of ultraviolet light upon a silver bromide grain. Except for the indicated size of the particles, this actual photograph ears a striking resemblance to the theoretical picture of the latent image nuclei

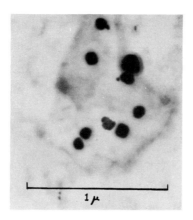

1 μ

Fig. 3 · 1   Electron micrograph of photolytic silver particles formed by action of ultraviolet light on a silver bromide grain. (Hall and Schoen).

which Svedberg, Sheppard and others had previously constructed from considerations of photographic phenomena.

Apart from the electron micrographs, our knowledge of the discrete nature of the latent image is dependent upon development studies. Development of exposed grains starts at discrete points on the grain surface. These *development centers* presumably coincide with the latent image centers which can be reached by the developer.

Svedberg counted the development centers on a large number of partially developed grains and found that the centers were distributed in accord with Poisson's law of chance. This law states that the probability $P(n)$ for the occurrence of n centers in a silver bromide grain is

$$P(n) = \frac{\bar{n}^n \cdot e^{-\bar{n}}}{n!} \qquad (3 \cdot 4)$$

where $\bar{n}$ is the *average* number of centers per grain, taken over all grains.

Concentration Speck Hypothesis

Early work on sensitization by silver sulfide suggested that the sulfide was present in the form of discrete particles, and that some connection existed between the silver sulfide nuclei and the latent image nuclei. However, the effective light is not absorbed by the sulfide. The *spectral* distribution of the photographic sensitivity of the emulsion is not significantly changed when the sulfide is destroyed by vigorous treatment with chromic acid. The spectral sensitivity is that of the silver bromide, not of the silver sulfide. Moreover, the sulfide nuclei do not affect the number of quanta absorbed.

From the preceding and other considerations, Sheppard, Trivelli, and Loveland [5] concluded that the function of the silver sulfide nuclei was to bring about a change in the distribution of the silver atoms formed by the light action. Specifically, they suggested that the sulfide nuclei serve as concentration centers for the photolytic silver. The light can be absorbed over the entire area of the grain, or at least over a considerable part of the entire area, but the silver atoms are formed only at discrete points adjacent to the pre-existing nuclei. The grain becomes developable when some particular nucleus has acquired a sufficient number of silver atoms.

The concentration-center role of the sensitivity specks has been retained in the more recent hypotheses of latent image formation. The application of quantum mechanics has produced a more specific mechanism for the concentration of silver atoms at the specks, although the structure and even the nature of the sensitivity specks or "sensitivity centers" is in doubt. It is by no means certain that actual nuclei composed of groups of molecules or atoms of a particular compound or element act as the sensitivity centers. Other possibilities will be discussed later in this chapter.

Physical Imperfections in Silver Halide Crystals

Physical imperfections in the silver halide crystals have figured prominently in recent speculations on the cause of photographic sensitivity and the formation of the latent image. It has been suggested that a latent image could not form in perfect silver halide crystals, and experimental evidence tends to support this suggestion. The physical imperfections considered are of two kinds: lattice-site irregularities or point defects, and irregularities which extend over a great distance, such as dislocations.

Point defects may arise from thermal vibrations which cause some of the ions to be displaced from their regular positions, or they may occur when a foreign ion of different size or valence is incorporated in the crystal.

The two kinds of point defects which may be in thermal equilibrium in the silver halides are known as Schottky defects and Frenkel defects. A *Schottky defect* occurs when a pair of oppositely charged ions is missing from the normal lattice positions inside the crystal. The vacancies which represent the missing ions can move separately in the crystal. Although this type of defect has figured in some theories of latent image formation, evidence from various sources strongly indicates that the number of Schottky defects in a silver bromide crystal at room temperature is negligible.

The *Frenkel defect* consists of an ion which has moved out of its normal lattice position into an interstitial situation, as illustrated schematically in Fig. 3·2A. In the silver halide crystals at room temperature, only cationic (silver ion) Frenkel defects are possible, since the size of the halide ion and the energy necessary to move it out of its normal lattice position are too great to permit an anionic defect. The energy required to form an interstitial silver ion, leaving a silver ion vacancy, is 1.27 ev.

for pure silver bromide according to an estimate of Ebert and Teltow. This energy is low enough so that a small concentration of Frenkel defects is produced at room temperature. At high temperatures a considerable dark conductivity exists in silver bromide owing to a high concentration of Frenkel defects, which may move easily in an applied electric field. Point defects arising from impurity ions may also lead to dark conductivity, and such defects are of higher concentration at room temperature than Frenkel defects. A typical impurity defect would result from the replacement of two singly-charged silver ions by one divalent ion such as cadium, thus introducing one vacant site which can diffuse through the crystal.

In crystals having such small dimensions as typical emulsion grains, a movement of ions along the surface may occur to a significant extent in an applied electric field or during latent image formation.

A *dislocation* is a line imperfection which can extend for a relatively long distance through the crystal. A dislocation which originates in the interior of the crystal will continue until it reaches the surface, or meets itself to form a closed loop, or runs into other dislocations. Two types of dislocations are illustrated in Fig. 3 · 2. Fig. 3 · 2B illustrates a *screw dislocation*. This type

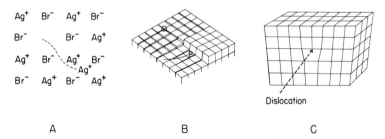

A	B	C

Fig. 3 · 2   A, Frenkel defect; B, screw dislocation; C, edge dislocation.

derives its name from the fact that if the point P is moved in a clock-wise direction, as indicated, over the lattice plane around O as an axis and at a constant distance from O, the point will describe a helix suggestive of a screw thread. An *edge dislocation* is formed by an extra plane or pair of planes of atoms or ions extending only part way through the crystal, as indicated in the drawing in Fig. 3 · 2C.

The importance of structual imperfections in latent-image formation was suggested by Steigmann and others at a time when the nature of the imperfections was not known. Later, Haynes and Shockley showed that photolytic silver in sheets of silver chloride formed preferentially along slip bands produced by bending the sheets, and Hedges and Mitchell showed that photolytic silver formed at dislocation arrays in polygonized crystals of silver bromide. The importance of dislocations in the formation of a latent image inside the emulsion grains (*internal latent image; see Chapter 4*) was indicated by Berry's observation[6] that an emulsion made up of grains which contained no detectable edge dislocations had very low sensitivity for the formation of an internal latent image. Mitchell[7] suggests that an internal latent image is formed by the separation of silver atoms along edge-dislocation lines, but not along screw-dislocation lines. However, he suggests that the areas around the points at which dislocations of both types meet the surface have enhanced chemical reactivity which can play a part in chemical sensitization, e.g., the chemical sensitizers may react selectively at such areas. The increase in sensitivity caused by the presence of small percentages of iodide ions in the silver bromide grains may be connected, in part, with an increase in the number of dislocations caused by an uneven distribution of the iodide in the grains.

Another type of imperfection which may be important to surface latent image formation depends upon the presence of an incomplete layer of ions on the surface. The last ion in the incomplete row of such a layer is said to occupy a *kink site.* The kink site is illustrated in Fig. 3·3. Kink sites can be oc-

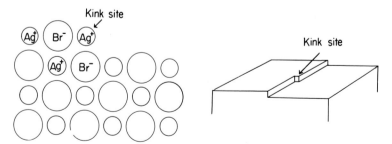

Fig. 3 · 3   Left, side view of a kink site in a (001) silver bromide plane; right, top view of a kink site on a crystal surface.

cupied by either silver or halide ions. Their possible role in latent image formation will be discussed later in this chapter. A closely related imperfection located inside the grain is termed a

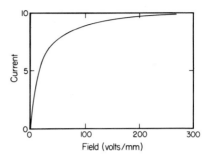

Fig. 3·4 Current-voltage curve for photoconductance in silver bromide under constant illumination.

jog site. These sites occur along the edge formed by a partial plane of atoms in an edge dislocation. Like the kink site, a jog site can be occupied by either a silver or a halide ion.

Photoconductivity and Its Relation to Latent Image Formation

The electrical conductivity of silver bromide or silver chloride, as measured by the current carried when a potential is applied across a crystal of the material, is very low when the crystal is kept in the dark. At room temperature it is of the order of 10^{-8} ohm^{-1} cm^{-1} for silver bromide. The conductivity is increased when the crystal is exposed to blue or ultraviolet light. The increase in conductivity induced by light is termed *photoconductivity.* Under constant illumination, the photocurrent increases at first as the applied potential is increased and then approaches a maximum. The effect, for a relatively pure crystal, is illustrated by Fig. 3·4.

A certain parallel exists between photoconductivity and photographic sensitivity. The long wavelength thresholds of the two are the same within the rather wide limits of experimental error. Both increase with decreasing wavelength until maxima are reached. The photoconductivity maximum measured in large crystals of a given halide occurs at longer wavelengths than the maximum in photographic sensitivity of the same halide in an emulsion, but the available evidence indicates that the photoconductivity maximum shifts to shorter wavelengths for thinner crystals. The agreement between the photoconductivity of very thin crystals and the photographic sensitivity of single-layer emulsions is satisfactory in so far as indicated by the rather limited experimental data, and measurements[8] of photoconductivity made on actual photographic emulsions confirm the parallel trends of the two phenomena. Accordingly, it may be anticipated that knowledge of the mechanism of photoconductance is directly applicable to the formulation of the mechanism of latent image formation.

The photocurrent is carried by electrons moving through the crystal, and it is found that the maximum conductance is directly proportional to the light intensity except at very high intensities. Thus, an increase in the number of quanta absorbed per unit time produces a corresponding increase in the number of photoelectrons, which carry the current.

The contribution made by each electron to the total current depends not only upon the charge of the electron, which is constant, but also upon the fractional distance which it travels between the electrodes. Above a certain applied potential the electrons are pulled all the way from their point of origin to the positive electrode. At lower potentials some of the electrons apparently are caught in some manner before they reach the electrode, and therefore a smaller current flows through the crystal.

The results of photoconductivity studies are best interpreted in terms of the quantum mechanics model of crystal structure. This treatment brings out clearly the similarity between photoconductance and normal *metallic* conductance. In a metallic crystal, the electric current is carried by the movement of electrons through the crystal. These electrons occupy an energy band, termed the *conductance band*,* which is only partially filled with electrons. If the metal atoms have an uneven number of valence electrons, these are not enough to fill completely the uppermost occupied energy band. Such electrons can move with considerable freedom through the crystal. On the other hand, if the number of valence electrons is even and hence sufficient to fill the upper band, a second band overlaps the uppermost filled band, and electrons from the filled band can move into and through the second band with considerable freedom.

In a crystal of silver bromide, unlike a metallic crystal, the conductance band normally is completely empty and is separated from the highest filled band by a relatively large energy gap. In

---

*This energy band also is commonly called the *conduction* band. See Appendix and references cited at the end of this chapter for further discussion of the theory.

this case, an electron cannot acquire from thermal sources alone the energy required for it to pass into the empty conductance band. The electron can obtain the energy, however, from the absorption of a light quantum of suitable wavelength. A photoelectron, thus liberated from a bromide ion, can pass through the crystal with a freedom comparable to that of a conductance electron in a metal crystal.

The energy bands in silver bromide are represented schematically in Fig. 3 · 5. The full band is separated from the empty conductance band by an energy gap of approximately 2.5 ev. The figure includes another energy level which corresponds to an empty or incompletely filled band of a hypothetical impurity or to a region of dislocation in the silver bromide. An electron from the normal conductance band would lose energy on passing into this lower band, and would require energy to get back into the normal conductance band. Accordingly, the electron would be "trapped" by the region of lower energy, and the duration of its stay in the trap would depend on the amount of energy necessary to put it back in the conductance band of the silver bromide.

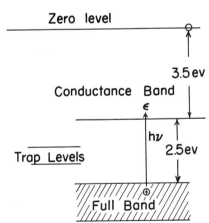

Fig. 3 · 5 Schematic representation of the energy bands in silver bromide.

Webb[9] applied the preceding theory directly to the problem of latent image formation and proposed the following mechanism. The absorption of a quantum of light by the silver halide grain is followed by the transfer of an electron to the conductance band. The photoelectron can move freely through the crystal for relatively large distances, so long as it does not enter a region of impurity or fault in the crystal. It becomes trapped, however, when it encounters a sensitivity speck of silver sulfide or silver. Thus, an electron can be trapped in an entirely different part of the crystal from that where the quantum of light was absorbed. The latent image, in this hypothesis, is identified with electrons trapped at the sensitivity specks.

If the formation of the latent image involves a movement of electrons for some distance through the crystal, as required of this theory, it should be possible by means of an electric field to influence the location of the latent image centers on a single grain. The electrons should move preferentially in a direction opposite to that of the applied field, i.e., they should move toward the positive electrode. A striking effect of this kind has been demonstrated[10] by Hamilton, Hamm, and Brady on some large silver bromide photographic grains. Exposures were made to pulsed light, and a pulsed electric field could be applied at the same time. The latent image centers were detected by giving the grains a brief development, which enlarged them, and then examining the grains under the electron microscope. Fig. 3·6 shows typical results. No field was applied to the grains at the left, and the distribution of centers is random; at the right, where a field had been applied, there is an obvious shift of centers in the direction opposite to that of the field. This result is in complete accord with the prediction made on the basis of Webb's mechanism, or of any mechanism which assumes that the trapping of photoelectrons is essential to the formation of the latent image.

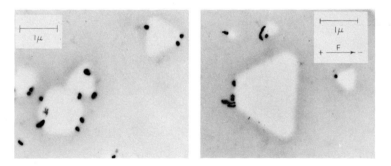

Fig. 3·6   Shift of latent image centers by electric field. Left, no field; right, field of 10,000 v/cm applied in direction indicated. (J. Hamilton.)

A number of photographic effects can be explained by Webb's mechanism, and all the virtues claimed for the concentration speck hypothesis can be transferred directly to it. However, gaps between experiment and theory remain. Some of these were removed by an addition which Gurney and Mott made to the theory.

The Gurney-Mott Hypothesis

The Gurney-Mott hypothesis[11] divides latent image formation into two parts: (1) a primary, electronic process associated with photoconductance, and (2) a secondary, ionic process involving the migration of interstitial silver ions. The primary process is essentially the same as that postulated in Webb's treatment. The photoelectrons, moving through the crystal with thermal energy, are trapped by the sensitivity specks. The electrostatic potential thus created brings the secondary process into play. Interstitial silver ions are attracted to the negatively charged specks and migrate toward them. At the specks, the ions are neutralized by the electrons, forming silver atoms. Thus, silver nuclei are built up at the sensitivity specks by the alternate process of trapping electrons and neutralizing them with interstitial silver ions.

Experiments at low temperatures offer an excellent means of testing the Gurney-Mott hypothesis. At liquid air temperature, for example, the migration of interstitial ions is negligible. Thus, the ionic process becomes distinctly separated from the electronic, and this separation should be readily evident in the photographic effect. Several tests of this point have been made. The following[12] is an example.

The characteristic curves A and B shown in the upper left-hand quadrant of Fig. 3·7 represent continuous exposures made at room temperature and at liquid air temperature, respectively. The curves in the other three quadrants represent two series of interrupted exposures, both made at liquid air temperatures. In the A series, the emulsion was warmed up to room temperature during the dark periods intervening between exposures and then returned to liquid air temperature. In the B series, the emulsion was maintained at the low temperature during the dark periods. A comparison of the several B curves shows that no effect is produced by interruption of the exposures made at liquid air temperature, provided that temperature is maintained during the dark periods. The A curves, on the other hand, show that the warming-up periods greatly increase the photographic effect.

Moreover, the effect is enhanced by an increase in the number of warming-up periods, and as the number increases the density approaches that obtained by giving the emulsion the same total exposure at $20°$ C.

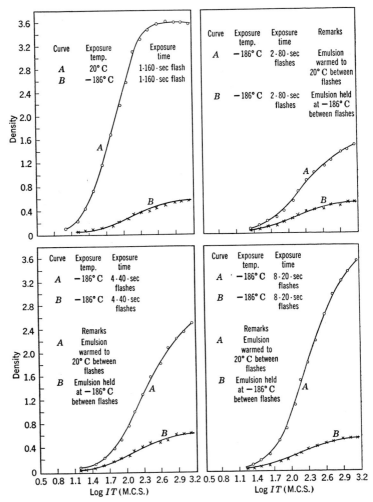

Fig. 3·7 Curves illustrating effect of interrupted exposures at liquid air temperature with warm-up periods between exposures. (Webb.)

According to the Gurney-Mott hypothesis, the electrons should be formed and trapped at liquid air temperatures almost as readily as at room temperature. However, when one electron is trapped but not neutralized at a given speck, the approach of a second is hindered by the electrostatic repulsion. If an interstitial silver ion can move to the speck and neutralize it before a second electron approaches, the latter will be captured. Otherwise, the second electron will probably go elsewhere, either to another trap or to a bromine atom. Thus, the rate at which a speck will collect silver depends upon the frequency with which both electrons and ions approach the speck. At liquid air temperature, the charged specks can be neutralized only at an extremely low rate; hence exposure at this temperature is very inefficient. Intermediate warming-up periods, on the other hand, permit the silver ions to move rapidly and to neutralize the charged specks, which can then trap additional electrons during the next exposure. Thus, the greater the number of warming-up periods, the faster the specks can build up by the addition of silver atoms. The experimental facts are just what would be expected on the basis of the Gurney-Mott picture. The low temperature sensitivity indicated by Curve B of Figure 3 · 7 probably results largely from the warming up required before the emulsion can be developed.

Modifications of the Gurney-Mott Hypothesis

A. *Nature of the Electron Traps.* The proposal by Gurney and Mott that latent image formation involves both an electronic stage and an ionic stage has been widely accepted. There is no general agreement on the detailed mechanism, however, and several modifications have been proposed.

The electron trap in the Gurney-Mott mechanism is the silver sulfide sensitivity speck or silver nucleus. Experiments carried out on crystals of silver bromide prepared from the melt have, for the most part, failed to supply evidence that silver sulfide or silver nuclei can act as effective traps for conduction electrons. However, West[13] has shown in his experiments on the photoconductance of *photographic grains* that sulfur sensitizing produces a significant decrease in the photoconductance. This result could be explained by a trapping action of the silver sulfide for the conduction electrons.

Matejec[14] has suggested that the sensitivity specks in the photographic grain are positively charged by adsorbed silver ions, e.g., a speck could be $(Au_nAg_m)^{+m}$ or $(Ag_2S)_nAg_m^{+m}$. Such charged specks could attract the conduction electrons, which would become trapped and neutralize the adsorbed silver ions. This suggested mechanism, in effect, reverses the order of the steps in the Gurney-Mott mechanism, i.e., silver ions become attached to the specks first, and then electrons are trapped, rather than vice versa.

Electron trapping by silver sulfide or silver cannot be involved in latent image formation in chemically unsensitized emulsions which have been treated with bromine to destroy such impurities, and it is unlikely that silver sulfide is present in a significant amount on the inside of grains which have been sulfur sensitized. Yet latent image formation occurs readily on the inside of grains which have not been chemically sensitized or which have been sulfur sensitized, and surface latent image forms to some extent on chemically unsensitized grains.

Berry and Griffith[15] suggested that dislocations in silver bromide crystals act as electron traps in the formation of the internal image, and this suggestion has received considerable support. The absence of impurity nuclei offers no real obstacle in latent image formation. Dislocations may even be the trapping centers in chemically sensitized as well as in unsensitized grains.

B. Fate of the Halogen. The Gurney-Mott mechanism does not give an adequate account of what happens to the halogen atoms that are formed whenever electrons are transferred from the halide ions to the conductance band during an exposure. Some of these halogen atoms may recombine with electrons or may attack photolytically formed silver atoms and reform halide ions and silver ions. Some of the photolytically formed silver atoms must survive, however, or a permanent photographic effect could not be obtained. There are several ways in which the halogen atoms could be prevented from reacting with the silver atoms.

If the halogen atom remained immobilized where it was formed, it could not attack a silver atom at a distance, but it could trap and combine with an electron. The nucleus of a halogen atom formed inside the crystal would not be mobile itself, but movement of another type can occur which would produce the same effect as a movement of the nucleus. The halogen atom is surrounded by silver ions, and the region has an excess positive charge. The atom and its region of positive charge is termed a *positive hole*. An electron can jump from a neighboring halide to the halogen atom. In effect, the ion and atom change places, and the region of excess positive charge moves to the site of the new halogen atom. By a succession of electron jumps of this kind, the positive hole can move through the crystal until a halogen atom is formed at the surface of the crystal or until the halogen atom in some way becomes "trapped." One of the objections raised to the Gurney-Mott mechanism was that a negatively charged sensitivity speck might be expected to attract a positive hole as readily as an interstitial silver ion. If the positive hole moved to the sensitivity speck, it would simply recombine with the electron and nullify the effect of the absorption of the light quantum responsible for the photoelectron. This difficulty in the Gurney-Mott mechanism is avoided by the mechanism suggested by Matejec, mentioned previously, and by a mechanism suggested by Mitchell which will be considered in Section D.

A halogen atom on the silver halide surface may react chemically with some substance other than photolytic silver, or the halogen atom may first form a halogen molecule with another atom, and the molecule may react with a "halogen acceptor," which is a substance that combines with the halogen or reduces it to a halide ion. Gelatin, water, sensitizing dyes, and the products of chemical sensitization, i.e., silver, silver sulfide, or gold, have been suggested as halogen acceptors in a normal photographic emulsion.

Bromine and chlorine react with silver, silver sulfide, and even gold. However, no conclusive evidence has been presented to show that the sensitizing is due in any large measure to the halogen acceptor action, and it has been demonstrated that, under certain conditions, a halogen acceptor powerful enough to protect silver sulfide from attack by photolytically formed bromine will not sensitize a silver bromide emulsion to a significant degree.[16]

C. Other Actions of Sensitizing Centers. A pre-existing nucleus of silver sulfide, silver, or gold may act in another way to increase photographic sensitivity, i.e., it may stabilize the photolytically formed silver. Some results of studies of reciprocity failure (see Chapter 4) indicate strongly that a single silver atom formed in a grain by exposure to light is very unstable and may dissociate into a silver ion and an electron within a small fraction of a second. If the silver atom forms a pair with another silver atom, or is adsorbed by a silver (or gold or silver sulfide) nucleus, its stability is markedly increased. Moreover, it should take fewer photolytically formed silver atoms to produce a development center if they are associated with pre-existing silver or gold nuclei, and probably the same would be true for silver sulfide nuclei. Gold sensitizing and gold latensification (see Chapter 7) decrease the induction period of development of an exposed grain, and this effect could be explained on the basis of the formation of a larger center.

D. *Mitchell's Mechanism*. Still another explanation of sensitization by silver sulfide has been suggested by Mitchell.[7] He assumes that the positive holes are trapped before conduction electrons can be trapped. The holes are trapped by surface halide ions which occupy kink sites, or by adsorbed molecules of silver sulfide, or by other sensitizing impurities. A bromide ion at a kink site, for example, can trap a bromine positive hole to form the Br_2^- ion, and this is stabilized by the passage of an adjacent silver ion into an interstitial position. If the positive hole diffuses to a silver sulfide molecule, an electron can pass from the sulfide ion to the positive hole, leaving S^-, and one of the silver ions of the molecule passes into an interstitial position. The absorption of energy by the silver halide, in this mechanism, is thus assumed to make interstitial silver ions as well as electrons available for latent image formation. On the basis of measurements made on large crystals, Mitchell concludes that the concentration of interstitial silver ions which are in *thermal equilibrium* with the silver halide is much too small to be of significance in latent image formation.

Mitchell assumes that silver ions situated at surface kink sites and at jogs along edge-dislocation lines cannot in themselves trap a conduction electron at room temperature. If an interstitial silver ion is nearby, however, the electron can be drawn into the space between the interstitial silver ion and the one at the jog or kink site. It draws them together and forms a silver atom. The result is a silver atom adsorbed to a silver ion at a kink site or jog. This forms Ag_2^+, which is termed a *latent pre-image speck*. It is rather unstable, however, and will dissociate into an interstitial silver ion and a conduction electron in a second or less if it is not further stabilized during that time. It can, however, combine with another conduction electron if another interstitial silver ion arrives within the period of its stability, and the result is a pair of silver atoms that are comparatively stable. This pair of silver atoms adsorbed at a site adjacent to a jog or kink-site silver ion is called by Mitchell the *latent sub-image speck*.

A latent sub-image speck is transformed into a stable latent image speck by combining with a third interstitial silver ion and conduction electron. Mitchell postulates that a group of three silver atoms can adsorb a silver ion and thus become positively charged. This group forms a developable latent image nucleus. The positive charge can also attract and neutralize another conduction electron, forming a silver atom, after which another silver ion can become adsorbed, restoring the positive charge. The cycle can thus be repeated, and the size of the silver speck can be readily enlarged. The positive charge on the latent image speck, in addition to its action in attracting electrons, can also serve to protect the silver speck from attack by positive holes, since the latter would be repelled by the like charge.

Appendix to Chapter 3

Electron Conductance from the Viewpoint of the Band Structure of Crystals

It will be useful first to consider the structure of silver. The individual silver atom is composed of a positively charged nucleus and a group of external electrons. Each electron in the normal isolated atom occupies a discrete energy level and is characterized by a set of quantum numbers. One can think of the atom as having been constructed stepwise, as if electrons were added one by one to fill each energy level, the process starting with the lowest and continuing until the excess positive charge of the nucleus was neutralized. According to the Pauli exclusion principle, each energy level can be occupied by only two electrons, which are mutually equivalent in every way except that they are of opposite "spin." The silver atom, however, contains an odd number of electrons, and so the last occupied level contains only one electron. This outer electron is the valence electron. When it is lost, a silver ion is formed.

When silver atoms are arranged in an orderly fashion to form a crystal of silver metal, the situation is modified. Each atom is now influenced by the energy field of its neighbors. The electrons in the lower levels are not materially affected, and for the present they may be considered still to be simply members of closed atomic shells. The valence electrons, however, are markedly influenced, and are best considered to belong to the crystal as a whole. The energy levels of these electrons are crowded closely together into a quasi-continuous *band*, or zone, of the crystal.

The energy band which the valence electrons occupy in a metal is only partly filled, and it is called the conductance band because the electrons which conduct an electric current through the metal move in it. There are as many levels in the band as there are atoms of metal in the system. Each level can be occupied by two electrons of opposite spin. In order that an electron can move through the crystal and thus carry an electric current, it must be able to find an unoccupied level in the conductance band. If the normal atom of the metal has only one valence electron, such as silver, the electron can move freely because the conductance band is only half filled. If the atom has two valence electrons, the band is nominally full, but this filled band may overlap the lower states of an unoccupied band. In that event, an electron can move easily into the unoccupied band and hence move through the crystal. This is why divalent metals, such as magnesium and calcium, can easily conduct an electric current. On the other hand, if the band that is completely filled with electrons is separated from an unoccupied band by a large energy gap, the substance is an insulator rather than a conductor. Silver bromide is in this category. The highest occupied band is completely filled with electrons belonging to the bromide ions; the lower edge of the unoccupied band is separated from the upper edge of this valence band by about 58 kilocalories per mole, and at room temperature the electrons in the valence band cannot acquire enough energy from thermal fluctuations to bridge this gap. The upper band remains empty.

Excitation of a bromide ion by a light quantum of the necessary energy will drive an electron from the valence band to the empty band, and this electron can now move through the crystal in the same way as an electron moves through a metal crystal. It is therefore appropriate to call the unoccupied level in the silver halides the conductance band.

REFERENCES

General

Mees, *The Theory of the Photographic Process,* revised edition, Macmillan, New York, 1954, Chapters 4, 5.

Mott and Gurney, *Electronic Processes in Ionic Crystals,* The Clarendon Press, Oxford, 1940.

Webb, "Theory of Photographic Latent Image Formation," *J. Applied Phys.,* **11,** 18–34 (1940).

Berg, "The Physical Chemistry of Latent Image Formation," in *Annual Reports on the Progress of Chemistry* for 1942, Chemical Society, London, 1943.

James and Kornfeld, "Reduction of Silver Halides and the Mechanism of Photographic Development," *Chem. Revs.*, 30, 1–32 (1942).

Mitchell, "Photographic Sensitivity," in *Reports on Progress in Physics*, Vol. 20, The Physical Society, London, 1957, pp. 433-515.

Quantum Mechanics of Crystals

Seitz, *Modern Theory of Solids*, McGraw-Hill, New York, 1940.

Mott and Gurney, *Electronic Processes in Ionic Crystals*, second edition, The Clarendon Press, Oxford, 1948.

Seitz, *The Physics of Metals*, McGraw-Hill, New York, 1943, Chapter 17 (non-mathematical).

Specific

1. Silberstein and Trivelli, *J. Optical Soc. Am.*, 28, 441 (1938); **35**, 93 (1945).
2. Webb, *ibid.*, **29**, 314 (1939).
3. Meidinger, *Physik. Z.*, **44**, 1 (1943).
4. Hall and Schoen, *J. Optical Soc. Am.*, **31**, 281 (1941).
5. Sheppard, Trivelli, and Loveland, *J. Franklin Inst.*, **200**, 51 (1925); Sheppard, *Phot. J.*, **65**, 380 (1925).
6. Berry, *J. Applied Phys.*, **27**, 636 (1956).
7. Mitchell, *J. Phot. Sci.* **5**, 49 (1957); **6**, 57 (1958).
8. West and Carroll, *J. Chem. Phys.*, **15**, 529 (1947).
9. Webb, *J. Optical Soc. Am.*, **26**, 367 (1936).
10. Hamilton, Hamm, and Brady, *J. Applied Phys.*, **27**, 874 (1956).
11. Gurney and Mott, *Proc. Roy. Soc. London*, **A164**, 151 (1938).
12. Webb and Evans, *J. Optical Soc. Am.*, **28**, 249 (1938).
13. West, "Correlations between Photographic and Photoconductive Sensitivity of Silver Halides," in *Fundamental Mechanisms of Photographic Sensitivity*, Butterworth, London, 1951, p. 99.
14. Matejec, *Z. Phys.*, **148**, 454 (1957).
15. Berry and Griffith, *Acta Cryst.*, **3**, 219 (1950).
16. Sutherns and Loening, *J. Phot. Sci.*, **4**, 154 (1956).

4.

Reciprocity Law Failure and Other Exposure Effects

The electron traps that are capable of participation in the formation of a latent image may be distributed throughout the entire grain. Usually, the most effective traps are located at the grain surface, but those situated in the interior of the grain may, and often do, play a part in determining the photographic effect of a given exposure.

Distribution of the Latent Image

The existence of a latent image in the interior of exposed grains was indicated by the work of Kogelmann in 1894. It is easily demonstrated. Developing solutions that do not contain silver halide solvents act as normal developers toward grains that contain latent image nuclei on the surface. If, however, the external image is destroyed by proper treatment of the grain with an oxidizing agent such as ferricyanide, the grain will not develop in the solvent-free solution, or at best it will develop only upon prolonged treatment in that solution. The internal latent image centers do not promote development because the developing solution does not have access to them. If, now, the grains are treated with a mild silver halide solvent, some of these centers will be uncovered. The grains in which internal latent image is thus made accessible to the developing solution will then develop normally.

Surface latent image and *internal latent image* are defined, strictly, in terms of their reaction towards certain developer compositions. A surface latent image is one that can be developed by a developer which has a minimum of solvent action on the silver halide. (Water, always present, has a very slight solvent action which cannot be eliminated entirely.) Such a developing solution is often called a *surface developer* or, more properly, a *surface latent-image developer*. Internal latent image can be developed by an active developer solution which contains a suitable solvent for silver halide, such as sodium thiosulfate. Such a solution is termed an *internal developer*. If the surface latent image is destroyed by a suitable mild oxidizing agent, such as ferricyanide, the internal latent image can be developed by an internal developer without complication from surface latent image. Some oxidizing agents, however, destroy internal as well as surface latent image.

A quantitative method for determining the distribution of the latent image between surface and interior is still lacking. Semi-quantitative determinations [1,2] show that the distribution may vary with both the conditions of exposure and the nature of the emulsion. The development centers produced by very low exposures of low or moderate intensity are found almost entirely on the surface of the grain in some chemically sensitized bromide emulsions. More and more centers form in the interior as the exposure increases. A predominant formation of internal centers can be obtained with a very intense exposure of short duration, or even with a normal exposure of certain specially prepared emulsions. Some well-known photographic phenomena, such as reciprocity law failure and the Clayden effect (see subsequent sections of this chapter), involve changes in the distribution of the latent image.

Reciprocity Law Failure

The reciprocity law of Bunsen and Roscoe states that the amount of a photochemical reaction is dependent simply upon the actual light energy absorbed and not upon the rate of absorption. According to this law, the total amount of reaction for light of a given wavelength is specified by the product of the light intensity I and the time of irradiation t. This law applies to any *primary* photochemical process. It likewise is valid for the *formation* of *photoelectrons* in the silver halide grains during a photographic exposure. However, *it does not hold* for the photographic effect, which is measured by the developed density.

Schwarzschild suggested that the photographic effect is determined by the product It^p instead of simply It, where p is a constant having a value of approximately 0.8. However, Schwarzschild's relation holds over only a limited range in practice. Some data are fitted over a rather wide range by a simple catenary equation, but no formula of really general validity is known.

The failure of the reciprocity law is usually represented graphically as follows: The total exposure It required to produce a fixed density is determined for various values of I and t. Log It is then plotted against log I. If the reciprocity law held, this plot would give a horizontal straight line. The actual curve often is characterized by a minimum which corresponds to an optimum intensity. This is the intensity level at which the smallest amount of light energy is required to produce a given photographic effect. The curve rises at intensity values above and below the optimum. Figure 4·1 shows several experimental curves. The parallel straight lines at a 45° angle to the coordinates are lines of constant exposure time. These are drawn merely to aid in the interpretation of the reciprocity failure plots.

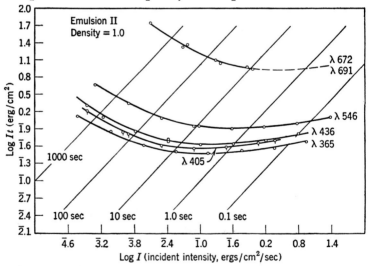

Fig. 4·1 Conventional reciprocity law failure plots for various wavelengths of exposing light. (Webb.)

The reciprocity failure varies greatly with the nature of the emulsion. However, there appears to be no general rule by which the failure can be related to other attributes of the emulsion,

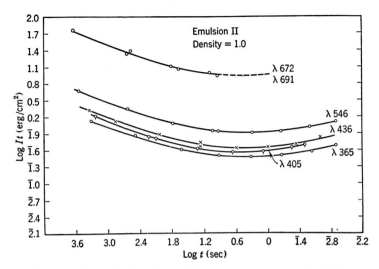

Fig. 4·2   Reciprocity law failure plots on a log *t* — log *It* basis. (Webb.)

such as speed, grain size, or color sensitivity. The maximum efficiency usually occurs at an intensity value that produces a medium density (for example, 1.0) in 0.1 to 10 seconds.

The variation of reciprocity failure with the wavelengths of the exposing light follows a rather simple pattern. If the reciprocity failure curves for different wavelengths are plotted as in Fig. 4·1, they have the same general shape but are displaced parallel to each other along the 45° constant-time lines. The displacement can be represented more simply by plotting log *It* against log *t* (instead of against log *I*) whereupon the curves become displaced vertically from one another (Fig. 4·2). Thus, the relative amounts of exposure required to produce a given density at two different wavelengths remain constant with changing time of exposure. In this sense, the spectral sensitivity of an emulsion is independent of the time of exposure.

The reciprocity failure shows a marked variation with the temperature of exposure.[3] A series of curves representing temperatures of 50° to −186°C is reproduced in Fig. 4·3. At high intensities, the log *It* value for a given log *I* is greater the lower the temperature. At low intensities, the log *It* value at first decreases, passes through a minimum, then increases with decreasing temperature. This means that the photographic sensitivity

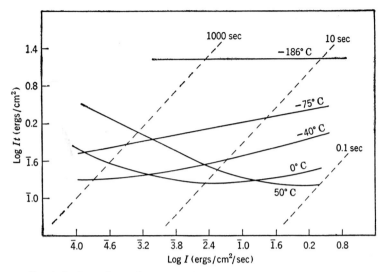

Fig. 4·3 Dependence of reciprocity law failure upon temperature. (Webb)

of the emulsion to low-intensity light increases at first with decreasing temperature and continues to increase until temperatures well below zero degrees centigrade are reached. Use has
been made of this fact in astronomical work, where it is often
necessary to make lengthy exposures to low-intensity light
sources, by maintaining the temperature of the photographic material well below the prevailing room temperature.

At a sufficiently low temperature, the reciprocity curve becomes parallel to the log I axis: that is, reciprocity failure disappears (*cf.* curve for −186°C). The level of sensitivity at this
temperature, however, is generally much below that at room
temperature.

The difference in the temperature dependence of low-intensity and high-intensity reciprocity failure suggests that the basic
causes of the two phenomena are different. The effects of low
and high-intensity exposure show differences in other ways.
The latent image formed by low-intensity light starts to develop
sooner in a developer which shows an induction period (see
Chapter 7) than does a latent image formed by high-intensity
light when the exposure levels are adjusted to give the same
image density on prolonged development (Cabannes-Hoffman

effect). Electron micrographs made of grains in the early stages of development show that the grains which have received a high-intensity exposure contain more development centers than the grains which have received a low-intensity exposure. The ratio of internal latent image to surface latent image is much larger for high than for low-intensity exposure. Indeed, the internal latent image shows no high-intensity reciprocity failure.

High-intensity failure for surface image formation can be eliminated in certain materials, such as motion picture positive film, by treatment of the film after exposure with an aurous thiocyanate solution (latensification by gold; see Chapter 7). Images formed by low-intensity exposure are affected to a much smaller degree, and low-intensity failure is not eliminated by this treatment.

Mizuki and Fujisawa[4] found that a mild treatment of a sulfur-sensitized emulsion in a silver halide solvent before exposure affects its sensitivity to high-intensity and low-intensity exposures differently. Etching treatments with several solvents such as thiosulfate and thiocyanate could be applied to a degree which had substantially no effect on the sensitivity to low-intensity light, but markedly decreased the sensitivity to high-intensity light. It is possible that the role of chemical sensitization is different for exposures to low and to high intensities.

It has been suggested that high-intensity failure is a consequence of the sluggishness of the ionic process in latent image formation. According to the Gurney-Mott mechanism, a trapped electron must be neutralized by the movement of an interstitial silver ion to that spot before a second electron can be trapped there; otherwise, the second electron is repelled and may be trapped elsewhere. Therefore, if electrons arrive at a particular sensitivity center faster than the ions can migrate to that center, some electrons are repulsed, and the center does not build up with maximum efficiency. The same general reasoning applies on the basis of Mitchell's mechanism. The second electron will not be trapped unless a silver ion has had time to move into the area to assist in the trapping. An increase in temperature will increase the rate of arrival of the interstitial silver ions and hence will increase the photographic sensitivity to high-intensity exposures.

At very low temperatures, the ionic mobility becomes insignificant. The electronic process alone takes place during the exposure period, and the secondary ionic process occurs only after the emulsion has been warmed up for development. Under these conditions, there should be no effect of intensity level over a wide range, because the rate of charging the sensitivity specks would be immaterial. This prediction of the Gurney-Mott hypothesis was confirmed by subsequent experiment.

The low-intensity failure is diminished by a decrease in temperature (Fig. 4·3). This fact led to the suggestion that the low-intensity failure arises from a thermal disintegration of the pre-latent image speck, probably the initial silver atom formed at a given sensitivity center. This disintegration would simply involve the thermal ejection of an electron from the silver atom. This electron could subsequently form another silver atom, but it might also recombine with a positive hole and thus nullify the photographic effect of the light quantum which originally liberated the electron into the conductance band.

Temperature dependence studies by Webb suggest that the energy required for the disintegration is roughly 0.77 ev. for a surface atom. The probability that a given atom obtains this energy from thermal fluctuations increases with increasing time. Hence the probability that the disintegration will occur before a second silver atom is formed at that spot increases with decreasing intensity of exposure. The probability of disintegration will also increase with increasing temperature. If, however, photoelectrons are liberated at such a rate that a second silver atom is formed at a given center before the first disintegrates, a pair of silver atoms is formed which is much more stable than the single atom. An increase in intensity of the exposing light, therefore, increases the photographic efficiency of the exposure.

The preceding interpretation of low-intensity reciprocity failure is supported by experiments in which exposures of two widely different intensities were made consecutively on the same emulsion. In an experiment by Webb and Evans,[5] the one intensity used corresponded approximately to the value for greatest photographic efficiency, the other to ¹⁄₁₀₀₀ of that value. The low-intensity exposure by itself was quite inefficient in producing a latent image, but its efficiency was greatly increased when it was preceded by an exposure made at the optimum intensity. When the latter exposure was long enough, the subsequent low-intensity exposure became just as efficient as the optimum. In other words, the reciprocity failure disappeared.

The experiments just described can be explained on the basis that the preliminary exposure at optimum intensity produces a developable latent image in some of the grains and a latent sub-image which is not developable in others. This sub-image might consist simply of specks large enough to be reasonably stable, but not large enough to constitute development centers. Such centers, however, can be efficiently built up to development centers by a subsequent low-intensity exposure.

If the spontaneously developable fog grains were ignored, the grains of an exposed emulsion might be classified as follows:

$$\text{All grains} \begin{cases} \text{developable grains} & \begin{cases} \text{full-image grains} \\ \text{sub-image grains} \end{cases} \\ \text{undevelopable grains} & \begin{cases} \text{grains unaffected by exposure} \end{cases} \end{cases}$$

The result of the primary exposure to light of optimum intensity in the experiment just described can be illustrated schematically[6]

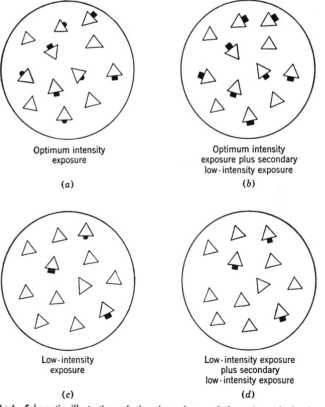

Optimum intensity
exposure

(a)

Optimum intensity
exposure plus secondary
low-intensity exposure

(b)

Low-intensity
exposure

(c)

Low-intensity exposure
plus secondary
low-intensity exposure

(d)

Fig. 4·4 Schematic illustration of the dependence of formation of developable latent image and latent sub-image upon the intensity of the exposing light and the manner of exposure. (After Burton and Berg.)

as in Fig. 4·4 (a) in which the grains are represented as triangles, full-image (developable) specks as black squares on the
grains, and sub-image specks as black semicircles. Four* of the
twelve grains represented have full-image specks and are developable. Four more have sub-image specks and are not developable, but can be made developable by a subsequent low-
intensity exposure which will efficiently convert the sub-image
specks into full specks, Fig. 4 · 4 (b). On the other hand, a primary exposure of equal energy but low intensity produces the
situation illustrated in Fig. 4 · 4 (c). Only two grains have full-
image specks, and only one has a sub-image speck. Most of the
exposure has been wasted. A secondary exposure to low-intensity light will be much less efficient here than in the preceding
example, since only one-fourth as many stable sub-image specks
exist which can be converted into full-image specks, Fig. 4·4
(d).

The secondary low-intensity exposure technique has a practical application in latent image intensification. If an under-
exposed picture is taken at moderate intensity, a second uniform exposure to light of low intensity will often materially improve the picture obtained on subsequent development. The low-
intensity exposure builds up at least part of the sub-image to a
developable latent image. If the secondary exposure is not continued too long, little fog is produced on the parts of the emulsion unaffected by the original exposure, since the reciprocity
failure of the low-intensity exposure is at its full value in those
areas. There is, of course, a limit to the amount of secondary
exposure that will lead to beneficial results, and this limit depends upon the emulsion.

An alternative explanation of low-intensity reciprocity failure attributes it, at least in part, to rebromination. This explanation can account qualitatively for the temperature dependence
and for the dependence of the extent of the reciprocity failure
upon the procedure followed in making the photographic emulsion. A final choice between the two explanations has not been
made.

Intermittency Effect

An exposure given in a number of discrete installments may
lead to the same developable density as a continuous exposure

---

*These figures are, of course, arbitrary, and are intended merely to illus-
trate the general idea rather than to give quantitative data.

involving equal total energy. More often, however, the intermittent exposure gives a density that is greater or less than that obtained by the continuous exposure. This *intermittency effect* is closely associated with the reciprocity law failure[7] of the emulsion. Its magnitude for a given emulsion depends primarily upon the intensity levels of exposure and the rate of interruption.

The effect of an intermittent exposure lies between the effects of equal-energy continuous exposures, one of intensity equal to that of the light used in the intermittent exposure, the other of intensity equal to the average over both light and dark periods. For example, if an intermittent exposure is given to light of intensity I and the light and dark periods are of equal duration, the density obtained after a total time t (over both light and dark periods) will lie between the density produced by a continuous exposure of intensity I and duration $\frac{1}{2}t$ and the density produced by a continuous exposure of intensity $\frac{1}{2}I$ and duration t. It may, of course, equal the density produced by one of these extremes.

A continuous exposure and an intermittent exposure of the same *average* intensity become equal in their effects when the frequency of flash exceeds a certain critical value which varies with the intensity level. This equivalence of the two exposures above the critical frequency has been explained on the basis of the quantum hits upon the photographic grains. The normal "continuous" exposure of a grain is really an intermittent exposure from the quantum-hit viewpoint. When the frequency of flash in the intermittency effect experiments becomes great enough, the time-distribution of hits upon each grain becomes essentially the same as for a continuous exposure of the same average intensity. The two exposures then become practically identical in so far as their reciprocity failures are concerned. An abnormally high frequency of flash is not required, since the rate of incidence of quanta on a single photographic grain is moderate even in an exposure of relatively high intensity.

The Clayden Effect

If a photographic emulsion is given first a very short exposure to light of very high intensity and then a second exposure to light of moderate intensity, the two do not add in a simple fashion. The very high-intensity exposure effectively desensitizes the emulsion toward the second exposure. If the first exposure has affected only a part of the emulsion and the second exposure is uniform over all of the emulsion, the image of the first often appears reversed when the film is developed; that is, a positive instead of a negative is formed. This phenomenon is known as the *Clayden effect.* It has been observed frequently in the photography of lightning flashes, where it gives rise to the so-called "black lightning."

The Clayden effect is easily explained on the basis of the Gurney-Mott picture. In the initial high-intensity exposure, electrons are liberated much more rapidly than they can be neutralized at the surface traps. Accordingly, most of the electrons go to the interior of the grain and form internal latent image or sub-image nuclei. These internal image nuclei act as effective electron traps and compete with the surface sensitivity centers for the electrons liberated during the secondary exposure. The competitive action of the internal centers may become so successful that less total surface image is formed by the two exposures together than would have been formed by the moderate-intensity exposure alone. The secondary exposure in this way leads to a greater developable density in the regions which have not been touched by the primary exposure.

Solarization

For many photographic materials, the curve representing developable density as a function of exposure passes through a maximum. If the exposure is increased beyond that which produces the maximum density, a decrease in developable density will occur (Fig. $1 \cdot 2$). This effect is known as *solarization.* From the standpoint of the individual grains, solarization means that the increased exposure is actually destroying the developable state which had been induced in some of the grains by the earlier part of the exposure.

Different emulsions vary greatly in the extent to which they exhibit solarization. The solarization curves of some emulsions even pass through a minimum, and a second stage is reached where increase in exposure again produces an increase in density. Many commercial emulsions exhibit enough solarization to be of some practical significance, but really large effects are obtained only with special emulsions. In certain silver iodide emulsions, solarization becomes evident when only about 20 per cent of the grains have been made developable.

Experiment has shown that the amount of solarization is markedly dependent upon the character of the development.

Solarization is most readily obtained when the developing solution contains no solvent for silver bromide, and, conversely, strong solvents such as thiosulfate remove solarization completely. The mild solvent action of sodium sulfite, which is a normal constituent of most practical developers, is sufficient to remove much of the solarization *provided development is prolonged.* With short times of development, solarization can still be obtained even in the presence of considerable amounts of sulfite.

Solarization is decreased, and sometimes eliminated, when halogen acceptors are present during exposure. This fact strongly suggests that solarization is in some way connected with a rehalogenation of the latent image. In the conventional silver bromide emulsion, for example, it is probable that, as long as the exposure is small, the bromine formed is adequately removed by reacting with the gelatin at the grain surface, and rebromination does not occur to any significant extent. When the exposure is large, however, the amount of bromine is too great to be effectively removed by the gelatin in the surface layer, and some of the bromine attacks the latent image. When a latent image nucleus becomes coated over by a surface layer of silver bromide, its effectiveness in promoting development is seriously impaired or completely destroyed; the silver nucleus remaining beneath this coating may still be large, but the developer no longer has ready access to it. In pure silver iodide emulsions, the gelatin does not adequately prevent reiodination even at low exposures, and auxiliary iodine acceptors must be added before the maximum photographic effect can be obtained even in the normal exposure range.

The rehalogenation hypothesis of solarization accounts for the previously mentioned dependence upon the developer. In the absence of a silver halide solvent, the latent image centers are insulated from the developer by the silver bromide sheath, and no development occurs. In the presence of a mild solvent, contact occurs only after the solvent has had time to dissolve off the protecting layer of silver bromide, and this process may take considerably more than the normal development time. A stronger solvent, such as sodium thiosulfate, rapidly removes the silver bromide layer and allows the unbrominated parts of the latent image nuclei to function once more as development centers. The thiosulfate also can uncover internal latent image centers which have not been affected by the bromine. There is no solarization of the internal latent image.

As already mentioned, the solarization curve sometimes passes through a minimum, and a second stage is reached where increase in exposure produces an increase in density. The result of experiments on latent image distribution have suggested an explanation for this second reversal. Debot[8] obtained a definite second reversal on normal development of the emulsions he used in his investigation. However, the density obtained by development of the surface image alone continued to decrease with increasing exposure in the solarization region, whereas the density obtained by development of the internal image (after destruction of the surface image) continued to increase with increasing exposure in this region and thus showed no solarization. Addition of the two curves (representing surface and internal image densities) produced a curve which showed initial solarization followed by a second reversal at the higher exposures. The shape of this composite curve corresponded closely to that of the curve representing normal development of the exposed emulsion.

Solarization shows a significant dependence upon temperature. Figure 4·5 gives a set of curves[9] obtained over a temperature range of 20° to −196°C. The first effect as the temperature decreases is a drop of the maximum density value. After the temperature drops below −73°C, this maximum shifts toward the higher exposure values. Below −100°C, the curve continues to shift and begins to rise again, thereby showing a decrease in solarization. At −196°C, no solarization at all occurs.

The initial increase in solarization with decrease in temperature may be explained on the basis of a progressive loss in the efficiency of gelatin as a halogen acceptor. Such a loss in efficiency would occur if the rate of reaction of halogen with gelatin decreased more rapidly than the rate of reaction with silver. Experiments with other halogen acceptors tend to confirm this explanation.

The absence of solarization at −196°C evidently requires another explanation. The maximum density at this temperature is even greater than at 20°C; and practically all the grains are developable. The exposure required to produce the maximum density, however, is about a hundredfold greater than that required at 20°C. As already indicated, silver probably is not formed at all at the low temperature. Some electrons are simply trapped at the surface specks, charging them to maximum capacity, and electrons subsequently liberated go to shallow traps

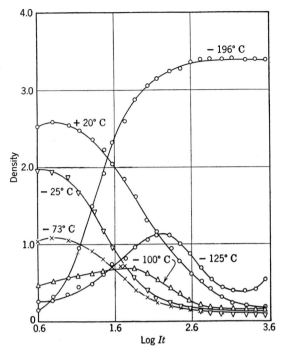

Fig. 4·5 Dependence of solarization upon temperature of exposure. (Webb and Evans.)

in the interior of the grain. The bromine meanwhile has more time to combine with the gelatin or to diffuse away. When the emulsion is warmed, the silver ion migration can come into play, and silver ions neutralize the charge of the sensitivity specks. The electrons in the shallow internal traps are released by thermal energy and contribute to the further building up of the nuclei on the surface into development centers. Alternatively, it might be supposed that bromination is simply too slow to be effective at −196°C and that the bromine diffuses away from the grain surface without reacting with either silver or gelatin.

Several other explanations of solarization have been given in the literature, but none is in sufficient agreement with experimental results to warrant consideration here.

Herschel Effect

If an emulsion which has not been dye-sensitized to red or infrared is exposed to blue light, a latent image will be formed in the normal way. If the emulsion is subsequently exposed to a red or infrared radiation before it is developed, some of the effect of the original exposure will be erased. Thus, the long wavelength radiation is capable of destroying to some extent the latent image formed by the blue light. This phenomenon is known as the *Herschel effect*. It is not subject to reciprocity law failure so far as is known.

The Herschel effect can be produced by radiation over a rather wide range of wavelengths. The wavelength at which the maximum effect occurs depends upon the photographic material used, and different workers have obtained different results. The most effective region of the spectrum for silver bromide emulsions generally lies at wavelengths longer than 700 mμ, but it can vary with conditions. Thus, Gorokhovskiĭ and Shestakov[10] found that the position of the maximum shifted toward shorter wavelengths as the excess bromide ion concentration in the emulsion increased. For a pBr (i.e., the common logarithm of the reciprocal of the bromide ion concentration) of 2.22, the maximum was at 810 mμ; for pBr 1.30, it was at 775 mμ; and for pBr 1.07, it was at 610 mμ. The maximum effect for silver chloride emulsions is obtained at shorter wavelengths than for silver bromide emulsions. The experimental results are often complicated by the fact that many emulsions show some sensitivity for latent image *formation* even at these long wavelengths, and latent image formation may proceed simultaneously with latent image destruction during an exposure to the long-wave radiation.

The incident energy required to produce the Herschel effect is much larger than that required to form a latent image by blue light. According to Webb, about 10^6 times more quanta of the most effective infrared radiation are required to destroy the latent image than are required to form it by blue light. This very low efficiency is easily understood if the quanta which are effective in destroying the latent image must be absorbed by the latent image material itself. The area which can act as a receiver for light quanta which *form* the latent image consists of the entire grain surface. The area which can act as a receiver when only the latent image can absorb the radiation is far smaller. Nevertheless, the actual efficiency of the Herschel effect in terms of quanta *absorbed* may be rather high.

The Herschel effect can be treated as a photoelectric effect. The absorption of a quantum of radiation by latent image silver results in the ejection of an electron into the surrounding silver halide. This leaves at the speck an unneutralized silver ion that subsequently moves away, leaving the size of the silver speck diminished by one silver atom. The process may be repeated until the speck becomes too small to act as a development center.

In support of the preceding explanation, Webb and Evans have shown that no Herschel effect is obtained when the primary (blue light) exposure is made at room temperature and the secondary (long wavelength) exposure is made at −186°C. At the latter temperature, the silver ions cannot move away from the latent image centers. If, however, the primary exposure is made at −186°C, so that the latent image consists only of trapped electrons, the secondary exposure to long wavelength radiation produces a Herschel effect at the low temperature. The trapped electrons apparently are set free by the secondary exposure and do not participate in, or are less effective in, the subsequent formation of silver at the sensitivity specks after the emulsion has been warmed up.

Experiments by Debot[11] not only add further support to the preceding explanation of the Herschel effect, but also add some detail of mechanism. Debot showed that, if a photographic emulsion exposed to actinic light is treated with a bleaching bath which destroys the surface latent image, subsequent exposure of this emulsion to red or infrared light can result in the formation of a new surface latent image. The exposure to the long wavelength light has resulted in a transfer of latent image material from the interior of the grains to the surface.

In general, it appears from Debot's experiments that an exposure to long wavelength light after pre-exposure to actinic light can produce four different results. Surface latent image silver can be transferred either to other surface specks or to specks in the interior of the grains; internal image silver can be transferred either to other internal specks or to the surface of the grains. All four processes may occur simultaneously during the secondary exposure of a normal emulsion, and the transferred latent image silver may attach itself to existing "subspecks," thus building them up to the size necessary for development, or the silver may be deposited where it will not contribute to developability. In each process the mechanism of the transfer involves these steps: (1) ejection of an electron from a silver speck as a result of absorption of a red light quantum,

(2) the trapping of the electron at some other point in the crystal, (3) "evaporation" of the excess silver ion from the initial speck, and (4) neutralization of that silver ion or some other interstitial silver ion by the electron at the new site.

A reversal which is similar in form to the Herschel effect can often be obtained if the photographic material is bathed in a solution of a suitable desensitizing dye (see Chapter 14) between the blue-light exposure and the exposure to radiation of longer wavelength. It is possible that two distinct "sensitized" reversals exist. A desensitizing dye may act primarily as an electron acceptor, preventing the return to latent image or subimage specks of electrons that are ejected by absorption of the long-wave radiation. The mechanism of a reversal sensitized in this way would be essentially that already proposed for the Herschel effect. In at least some cases of dye-sensitized reversal, however, a correlation appears to exist between the region of spectral absorption of the adsorbed dye and the region of the sensitized reversal. Hautot and Sauvenier[12] found that this reversal did not occur if nitrite or acetone semicarbazone, both effective halogen acceptors, were present in addition to the desensitizing dye. They attribute the reversal to halogen liberated by a dye-sensitized photolysis of the halide, the halogen acting to destroy surface latent image to produce the reversal.

A comparison of the Herschel effect and the dye-sensitized reversal is given in Fig. 4·6. Curves 4 and 5 represent the normal Herschel effect. It was obtained by exposing the emulsion first

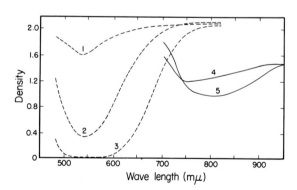

Fig. 4·6 Spectral distribution curves for the Herschel effect. Broken lines, effect in the presence of a densensitizing dye, for three long-wave exposures; solid lines, effect for the same emulsion in the absence of the dye for two long-wave exposures. Based on data by Webb.

to blue light that would produce a density of 1.4 and then exposing the emulsion to radiation of longer wavelength for two different lengths of time. Curves 1, 2, and 3 represent the result obtained when a blue-light exposure that would produce a density of 2.0 was applied initially, followed by treatment of the emulsion in a solution of desensitizing dye and then exposure to radiation of longer wavelength.

Extragranular Factors in Photographic Sensitivity

At least three factors external to the grain influence photographic sensitivity: (1) the pH of the gelatin, (2) the silver (or halide) ion concentration, and (3) the water content. As already mentioned (Chapter 2), the first two have irreversible effects upon the after-ripening which takes place during the manufacture of the emulsion. However, these factors also have reversible effects upon the sensitivity of the finished emulsion. The sensitivity decreases with increasing halide ion concentration (decreasing silver ion concentration), other things being equal. At constant halide ion concentration and water content, the sensitivity increases with increasing pH when the pH is adjusted and buffered before the final coating of the emulsion. Finally, when either the halide ion concentration or the pH is held constant and the water content is increased, the sensitivity at first increases; then it passes through a maximum (in the region of 12 to 16 per cent for the emulsion used by Sheppard and Graham[13]) and subsequently decreases.

Latent Image Production by X-rays

A latent image can be obtained by exposure of an ordinary photographic emulsion to x-rays. Certain differences are observed between light exposure and x-ray exposure phenomena, but these can be attributed to the much greater energy available in the x-ray quantum. Whereas a light quantum can produce only a single silver atom in the photolysis of silver halide, an x-ray quantum can produce hundreds to thousands of silver atoms. The latter photolysis is brought about by the action of secondary electrons liberated in the path of the initially liberated, highly energetic primary electron.

Despite the great number of silver atoms formed by the absorption of an x-ray quantum, considerably more would be produced if the energy were used to its greatest efficiency. The actual efficiency amounts to only 10 per cent or less. Günther and Tittel[14] found that this efficiency was nearly independent of the wavelength of the x-radiation over the range 0.024 to 0.154 mμ, and that therefore the number of silver atoms formed was inversely proportional to the wavelength. The actual number of atoms obtained per quantum absorbed varied from 930 to 148.

Except for very soft radiation, the absorption of one x-ray quantum is sufficient to make a grain developable, and there is evidence that, at least under some conditions, two or more adjacent grains can be made developable by the action of a single x-ray quantum. Since one quantum is sufficient to make a grain developable, there is no basis for a reciprocity law failure or an intermittency effect, and indeed none is observed in direct x-ray exposures. Solarization, however, can be obtained under proper conditions.

Only a very small fraction of the x-radiation falling upon a normal photographic emulsion is actually absorbed. Accordingly, intensifying screens often are used to increase the efficiency of the exposure. These screens contain a material, such as calcium tungstate, which emits fluorescent, photographically active light upon exposure to x-rays. The major portion of the latent image is then formed by action of the fluorescent light; therefore the photographic material becomes subject to the usual reciprocity law failure and intermittency effect.

REFERENCES

General

Mees, *The Theory of the Photographic Process*, revised edition, Macmillan New York, 1954, Chapters 6, 7.

Berg, "The Physical Chemistry of Latent Image Formation," in *Annual Reports on the Progress of Chemistry for 1942.*, Chemical Society, London, 1943.

Webb, "Theory of the Photographic Latent Image Formation," *J. Applied Phys.* 11, 18–34 (1940).

Mitchell, "Photographic Sensitivity," in *Reports on Progress in Physics*, Vol. 20, The Physical Society, London, 1957, pp. 443-515.

Specific

1. Berg, Marriage, and Stevens, *J. Optical Soc. Am.*, 31, 385 (1941); Kornfeld, *ibid.*, p. 598.
2. James, Vanselow, and Quirk, *PSA Journal* (*Phot. Sci. Tech.*), 19B, 170 (1953).
3. Webb and Evans, *J. Optical Soc. Am.*, 28, 249 (1938); Berg and Mendelssohn, *Proc. Roy. Soc. London*, A168, 168 (1938).
4. Mizuki and Fujisawa, in *Photographic Sensitivity*, Vol. 2, Tokyo Symposium, Maruzen Co., Tokyo, 1958, p. 163.
5. Webb and Evans, *J. Optical Soc. Am.*, 28, 431 (1938).
6. *Cf.* Burton and Berg. *Phot. J.*, 86B, 2 (1946).

7. Webb, *J. Optical Soc. Am.*, **23**, 157 (1933).
8. Debot, *Bull. soc. roy. sci. Liège*, **10**, 90 (1941).
9. Webb and Evans, *J. Optical Soc. Am.*, **30**, 445 (1940).
10. Gorokhovskiĭ and Shestakov, *J. Phys. Chem. U.S.S.R.*, **11**, 356 (1938).
11. *Cf.* Hautot and Sauvenier, *Sci. et inds. phot.*, **20**, 286 (1949), for a detailed investigation of this effect.
12. *Ibid.*, **29**, 401 (1958).
13. Sheppard and Graham, *J. Franklin Inst.* **230**, 619 (1940).
14. Günther and Tittel, *Z. Elektrochem.*, **39**, 646 (1933).

5.

The Mechanism of Development

Development is usually carried out by bringing the exposed photographic material into contact with a solution which contains a developing agent but no silver salt. The silver which forms the developed image comes from a reduction of the individual silver halide grains. This process is often termed *chemical* or *direct development*. These terms also are used in a more restricted sense, which we will consider in the section on mechanism.

In another process, seldom used in practice, the silver halide is dissolved out of the exposed material before development, and development is carried out in a solution which contains a soluble silver salt as well as a developing agent. This process is termed *physical development* or, more explicitly, *post-fixation physical development*. Here the silver which forms the visible image comes entirely from the developer. In a variation of this process, termed *pre-fixation physical development,* the exposed material is introduced without prior fixation into a developer that contains a soluble silver salt. In this process, at least part of the silver which makes up the developed image comes from the developer solution. The silver halide may or may not be reduced, depending on the activity of the developer.

Development as an Oxidation-Reduction Reaction

The chemical reaction involved in development is an oxidation-reduction reaction between silver ion and developer. The silver ion is reduced to silver, and the developer ion or molecule is oxidized in the process. The reaction can be stated very simply for some developing agents, e.g., vanadous salts and hydroxylamine:

$$Ag^+ + V^{++} \rightarrow Ag + V^{+++} \qquad (5 \cdot 1)$$

$$Ag^+ + NH_2O^- \rightarrow Ag + \tfrac{1}{2}N_2 + H_2O \qquad (5 \cdot 2)$$

The reaction of other developing agents, although often more complicated, is fundamentally the same. The basic reaction in development is the reduction of silver ions to silver.

Direct Development of the Silver Halide Grain

In direct development, the reduction of the exposed grain starts at one or more discrete points on the grain surface, corresponding to the latent image nuclei, and proceeds from these points until eventually the entire grain is reduced. In general, reduction will not spread from one developing grain to another grain which does not contain a development center, unless the latter grain is in direct physical contact with the former or unless such contact is established during development of the former. When reduction of adjacent grains is instigated by development of a single exposed grain, it results in the formation of a clump of silver particles. The extent of clump formation depends to some extent upon the composition of the developer. Instigation of the reduction of normally undevelopable grains situated at some distance from a developing grain also has been observed, but only for developing solutions of unusual composition. For example, "infectious" development of this type can be obtained with a highly alkaline hydroquinone solution containing hydrazine.[1]

The shape of the developed grain depends upon the composition of the developing solution and the nature of the original silver halide grain. For example, a pure bromide emulsion developed in a hydroquinone solution which contains $0.025\,M$ reducing agent, $0.5M$ sodium carbonate, $0.02M$ sodium sulfite, and $0.02M$ potassium bromide yields silver grains which, under the optical microscope, appear to have the same shape as the original silver bromide. If the sulfite is increased from $0.02M$ to $0.6M$, or if the emulsion contains a small amount of iodide, perceptible distortion of the the grain shape occurs during development. Development in some very active solutions is accompanied by marked distortion, and the silver particles formed bear little resemblance in shape to the original silver halide grains.

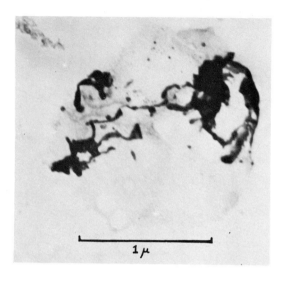

Fig. 5·1 Electron micrograph of partially developed silver bromide crystal, taken after the undeveloped portion had been dissolved out. (Hall and Schoen.)

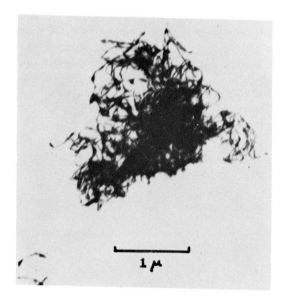

Fig. 5·2 Electron micrograph showing filamentary structure of completely developed grain. (Hall and Schoen.)

More detailed information on the structure of the developed silver grain has been supplied by the electron microscope. Figure 5·1 shows an electron micrograph of a partially developed silver bromide grain. (The unreduced silver bromide was dissolved out before the micrograph was made.) Development evidently was proceeding in an irregular fashion, and some of the silver is in the form of long, thin filaments. These filaments, however, are not simply the product of incomplete development. Figure 5·2 shows an electron micrograph of a completely developed grain. The silver occupies roughly the confines of the original grain, but evidence of filamentary structure remains. In some places, thin filaments project well beyond the probable boundaries of the original grain. Such filament formation is the normal occurrence in direct development. It will be considered in more detail subsequently.

Development as a Rate Process

The distinction which the developer makes between a sufficiently exposed grain (this term will be considered more explicitly later) and an unexposed or insufficiently exposed grain is primarily a matter of the time of reduction. Differences can appear in the physical character of the reduced silver according to whether it is obtained from exposed or unexposed grains, but the time factor is still the primary one. The *sufficiently exposed grain is reduced to metallic silver in a considerably shorter time.* This statement is subject to some qualification, since ordinary emulsions contain a small percentage of fog grains which will be rapidly reduced by the developer even without prior exposure. The statement is true for the great majority of grains, however. It is self-evident that the latent image material is in some way responsible for the distinction which the developer makes between exposed and unexposed grains. The primary task in formulating a theory of development is to discover why the latent image material accelerates the reduction process.

The classical Ostwald-Abegg hypothesis assumed that the latent image silver specks served merely as nuclei upon which silver formed in solution by the reduction of dissolved silver halide could condense. This hypothesis is not supported by the evidence and has been generally abandoned. It is highly probable that the *true action of the latent image silver is to accelerate or catalyze the actual reduction of silver ions.*

The following description of the development of an individual grain is in good accord with experimental evidence. The latent image silver nucleus or nuclei are in intimate contact with the silver halide which, it will be remembered, is an ionic crystal composed of silver ions and halide ions. The latent image silver acts as the initial accelerator or catalyst for the reaction between the developing agent and silver ions from the silver halide. The reduction of silver ions is accompanied by the formation of new silver around the latent image centers, and this silver in turn accelerates the reduction of more silver ions. Thus, the process of reduction of the individual grain continues as an auto-accelerated reaction.

The preceding considerations leave unanswered the question, how can silver accelerate the reduction of silver ions? The simplest approach to a solution of this problem is a consideration of the reaction between the developing agent and silver ions in solution—a reaction markedly catalyzed by colloidal silver. It can be considered as a simple prototype of the development reaction.

The Energy of Activation Necessary for Chemical Reaction

In the absence of the catalyst, direct collision of the reaction partners is a necessary condition for reaction, although not a sufficient one. Calculations show that most of the collisions between silver ions and the developing agent do not actually result in reactions in the system which we are considering; only a small fraction of them is fruitful. This situation is not unique for the reduction of silver ions by a developing agent; it is common to all except extremely fast chemical reactions. Evidently some special situation must exist for those collisions which do result in reaction.

Arrhenius explained this situation in terms of a critical energy requirement. He had observed that the rate of simple reactions could be represented by an equation of the type

$$\text{Rate} = AZe^{-E/RT} \qquad (5\cdot3)$$

where E is an energy term, R is the gas constant, T is the absolute temperature, A is a constant, and Z, the collision frequency, varies as $\sqrt{T}$. It is significant that the fraction $e^{-E/RT}$ is proportional to the number of molecules possessing energy at least E in excess of the average energy of all the molecules. The Arrhenius equation, therefore, implies that the number of molecules reacting in a unit time is proportional to the number which possesses a suitable energy excess, or is in a suitably activated condition. Accordingly, E is termed the activation energy of the reaction. The activation energy should not be confused with the heat of reaction or with the free energy of the reaction. These are quite different concepts and usually have quite different numerical values.

At constant temperature the rate of a reaction can be changed by a change in either the factor Z or the activation energy E. Since the latter appears in the exponential part of equation $5\cdot3$, the reaction rate is very sensitive to the value of E. Any device that will bring about a decrease in E without causing a compensating decrease in Z will accelerate the reaction. One way in which a catalyst can accelerate a reaction is to bring about such a decrease in E.

The Mechanism of the Silver-Catalyzed Reduction of Silver Ions in Solution

Two basic mechanisms have been suggested to explain how silver nuclei can accelerate the reduction of silver ions by a developing agent. In the first it is assumed that the developing agent simply donates electrons to the silver nuclei. The nuclei then act essentially as tiny electrodes at which the silver ions become reduced. The reduction thus includes two essential steps: first, the transfer of electrons to the silver; second, the neutralization of the silver ions by the electrons. The steps can be symbolized by

$$R \to \epsilon + \text{oxidized } R \text{ (at the ``electrode'')} \qquad (5\cdot4)$$

and

$$Ag^+ + \epsilon \to Ag$$

where R is the developing agent. The activation energy of these two processes may be considerably smaller than that of the single direct transfer of an electron to a silver ion, such as would be necessary for reaction in the absence of the catalyst. Moreover, the transfer of an electron to the silver could occur at any point on the silver surface, and the reduction of the silver ion could occur at that or any other point on the surface. Thus, the catalyst might increase the rate of reaction by decreasing the activation energy, by eliminating the necessity of direct collision between silver ion and developing agent, or by performing both operations simultaneously.

Following this scheme, Bagdasar'yan[2] has calculated the kinetics of the reduction of silver ions in solution on the assumption that the transfer of electrons from developing agent to silver (equation 5·4) is the rate-controlling step. According to this calculation, the reaction rate should vary as some fractional power of the silver ion concentration and as the first power of the developing agent concentration. Experimental results[3] on the reduction of silver ions by hydroquinone agree completely with these requirements. The reaction of silver ions with hydroxylamine likewise shows a fractional power dependence upon the silver ion concentration. On the other hand, this dependence is not observed in the p-phenylenediamine reaction, where the rate varies with a fractional power of the reducing agent concentration instead. A similar dependence of rate upon a fractional power of the developing agent concentration is obtained in the hydroxylamine reaction. However, these discrepancies might result from oversimplification in the formulation of the electrode reaction rather than from a fundamental error in the basic concepts.

The second mechanism which has been proposed is based on the assumption that silver ions or developing agent or both are adsorbed by the silver nuclei, and that this adsorption results in a decrease in the activation energy necessary for the reduction of the silver ions. The silver catalyst, by adsorbing and deforming one or both reactants, causes the reaction to proceed over a path where less activation energy is required than if the two reactants simply collided in solution.

The observed dependence of the reaction rate upon a fractional power of the silver ion concentration is accounted for in the following way. If reaction does not occur until after the silver ions are adsorbed, the reaction rate is determined by the concentration in the adsorbed state, not by the concentration in solution. Over a limited but sometimes rather wide range, the concentration of a substance in the adsorbed state (C_a) can often be related to the concentration in solution (C_s) by means of the empirical equation

$$C_a = k'C_s{}^n \qquad (5\cdot5)$$

where n is a fraction. This equation is known as the Freundlich isotherm. If it is applied to the data on the reaction between silver ions and hydroquinone in a slightly alkaline solution, the dependence of the rate upon the silver ion concentration can be expressed as

$$\text{Rate} = k \cdot C_a = k'' \cdot C_s{}^n \qquad (5 \cdot 6)$$

There is direct evidence that silver ions are adsorbed by silver.

The dependence of rate upon a fractional power of the concentration of the developing agent can be explained in an analogous way. Reaction depends upon the adsorption of the developing agent, and the concentration of adsorbed agent varies as a fractional power or as the first power of the concentration in solution. If the rate varies as the first power of the developing-agent concentration, as it does for hydroquinone, adsorption of the developing agent need not occur, although weak adsorption would not be excluded.

The difference between the two mechanisms appears to lie more in the formal statement of the mechanisms than in the physical concepts which they imply.[4] A silver ion adsorbed by a silver surface would, in effect, become a part of that surface and of the system of silver ions plus mobile electrons which make up the metal. The system as a whole would be deficient in electrons because of the adsorbed silver ions, and would be positively charged. The developer would supply the electrons to make up the deficiency and would, in effect, reduce the adsorbed silver ions. The electron transfer could occur on simple contact of the developer molecules or ions with the silver when the developer is not adsorbed. However, calculations based on the temperature dependence of the reaction indicate that a considerable energy of activation is required, and hence the electron transfer would occur in only a small fraction of the collisions between the developer and the surface. When the developing agent is adsorbed prior to reaction, the electron transfer would occur between the adsorbed molecule and the metal. The rate-determining step for the reduction of silver ions in either event could be the transfer of electrons from the developer to the silver metal, as suggested by Bagdasar'yan.

The system: colloidal silver — soluble silver salt — developing agent, should represent an accurate model of the process of *physical* development of the latent image. There is no reason to suppose that the mechanism of the physical development of a photographic layer is any different from the mechanism of the "physical development" of the collodial silver particles discussed in the preceding paragraphs.

The Mechanism of Direct Development

As already stated, development of the exposed silver halide grain starts at discrete spots on the grain surface and spreads from there. The same general explanation might be given for this direct development as that just outlined for physical development. Silver ions at the silver-silver halide interface may become detached from the silver halide lattice and adsorbed by the silver nucleus. Various model experiments have shown that development is possible in a system in which a metal acts essentially as an electron-conducting bridge between the silver halide and the developer, and development may actually occur by this process under some conditions. However, this simple mechanism does not offer a ready explanation of important aspects of the kinetics of development under many practical conditions.

Adsorption of the developing agent *by the silver halide*[4] or at the silver-silver halide interface appears to be of major importance in determining the rate of development by most agents. The importance of adsorption is indicated by the effect of certain dyes, like 3,3'-diethyl-9-methylthiacarbocyanine, that are strongly adsorbed in a monolayer by the silver halide. The dyes do not poison the catalytic activity of the silver towards reduction of silver ions by hydroxylamine, since they are substantially without effect on physical development by this agent, but they prevent adsorption of hydroxylamine by silver halide and they also inhibit the direct development of silver halide by hydroxylamine. On the other hand, these dyes promote the adsorption of hydroquinone by silver halide and also accelerate direct development by hydroquinone.

Hydroquinone shows some striking differences between its behavior as a direct developer and its behavior as a physical developer. The rate of direct development shows but little dependence on the area of the silver surface (as distinct from the area of the silver-silver halide interface), whereas the rate of physical development is proportional to the silver surface. Apparently hydroquinone molecules or ions which come in contact with the silver surface at a distance from the interface contribute relatively little to the direct-development process. The dependence of the rates of direct and physical development upon the concentration of the hydroquinone likewise is different. The rate of physical development varies as the first power of the concentration, whereas the rate of direct development under simple conditions varies approximately as the square root. The latter result could be explained on the basis of adsorption of the developer by the silver halide.

Adsorption of the developing agent by the silver halide probably involves the formation of a complex or a salt by the silver ion and the agent. A developer molecule that contains an amino group can form a complex with silver ions through this group, and one that contains a hydroxyl group can form a salt between the silver ion and the ionized hydroxyl group. In both types of adsorption, silver ions are displaced from their normal lattice positions and some halide ions may pass into solution. Then, the adsorption complex or salt has only to undergo an electronic rearrangement to break up into a silver atom and oxidized developer.

The activation energy of the reduction of unexposed silver halide by a developing agent is higher than that of the reduction of exposed silver halide. This suggests that the energy of activation required for the decomposition of the adsorption complex is lower at the silver-silver halide interface than on a pure silver halide surface. The decrease in activation energy brought about by the distortion of the complex at the interface would increase the rate of decomposition of the complex and hence the rate of reduction of the silver halide grain. A material of suitable electronic properties, such as metallic gold or silver sulfide, could cause the distortion of the complex and hence a lowering of the activation energy.

The activation energy of the direct development reaction varies with the developing agent. Thus, energies of 22 - 23 kcal/mole have been obtained for p-amino-N-diethylaniline in comparison with 5 - 8 kcal/mole for hydroquinone under the same conditions. The activation energies for fog formation were several kilocalories per mole higher than those for image development, but both of these values vary with the composition of the developer solution.

Solution-Physical Development

The terms "chemical development" and "direct development" are often restricted to the process which results in the reduction of silver ions at the interface between the silver and silver halide. This process appears to be the major way in which development occurs under most practical conditions, but it is not the only way. When the developer contains a solvent of silver halide, a species of physical development can take place, even while chemical development is taking place simultaneously.

When silver halide dissolves in the developer, the silver ions can be subsequently reduced by physical development at the latent-image centers or on the growing silver surfaces. This process has been termed *solution-physical development* because it involves first the solution of silver halide and subsequently physical development. The feasibility of such a process under practical development conditions can be demonstrated by a simple model, which also gives information on the rate of the process. The material for the model consists of an ordinary photographic emulsion to which colloidal silver is added before coating. When the coated film is immersed in a developer without being exposed to light, silver from the silver halide grains physically develops out onto the colloidal silver nuclei.

Under most practical developing conditions, some solution-physical development occurs in addition to the direct reduction of the grains at the silver-silver halide interface. The rates of the two processes depend upon different factors, however, and the relative extent to which solution-physical development takes place varies markedly from developer to developer. Under most practical conditions, the rate of solution-physical development is determined by the rate at which the silver halide dissolves,[5] since this is the slow step in the process. Factors which affect the rate of solution of silver halide will therefore affect the rate of solution-physical development even though they may not affect the specific rate of reduction of silver ions at the silver surface (i.e., the rate per unit concentration of silver ions).

During the course of development of a particular grain, the reaction can progress at the interface between silver and silver halide, and at the same time, silver ions derived from the solution of other parts of the grain can physically develop out on the silver formed by the interface reaction. The relative rates of the two processes will change as development progresses, since the relative amounts of interface and of silver halide surface change. It is also possible that silver ions derived from the solution of neighboring grains will physically develop onto the silver formed in a particular grain, and this process can occur to a considerable extent in the regions of low exposure level when the

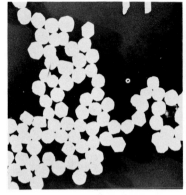 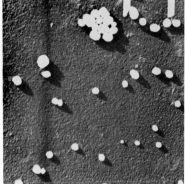

Fig. 5·3 Electron micrograph of silver produced by post-fixation physical development. Parallel bars at top indicate 1 micron. Length of shadow is three times particle thickness.

Fig. 5·4 Electron micrograph of silver produced by solution-physical development. Parallel bars at top indicate 1 micron. Length of shadow is three times particle thickness.

developer has a relatively high solvent action on the silver halide.

The Mechanism of Filament Formation

The silver formed by direct development in a solution where the solvent action on the silver halide is at a minimum has a characteristic filamentary structure (Fig. 5·2), whereas the silver formed by post-fixation physical development (Fig. 5·3) or under conditions where solution-physical development predominates (Fig. 5·4) does not.[6] Filamentary silver has also been obtained by pre-fixation physical development with a solution which was too weak to cause direct development and which contained no silver halide solvent other than water. The filaments produced under these conditions were substantially thicker than those commonly obtained in direct development.

According to one theory, the filaments are formed by an extrusion process in which interstitial silver ions are reduced at the inner surface between the latent image specks and the silver halide. The accumulation of silver at this inner surface forces out the silver which lies above. There is no experimental evidence to support an extrusion mechanism, however, and it is more probable that filament formation represents a crystal-growth phenomenon.[7] Filamentary silver can be formed by the deposition of silver atoms from the vapor phase on suitable

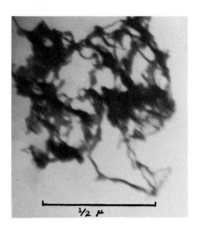

½ μ

Fig. 5·5 Electron micrograph of partially developed grain, showing triangular enlargements of some filaments.

nuclei. These filaments are the result of crystal growth in a favored direction, and a similar explanation has been proposed for the formation of filaments during development. This explanation is supported by the observation that the filaments often show angular enlargements of flat, triangular shape in the plane of the ribbon (Fig. 5·5).

The orientation of the latent image nuclei may be of major importance in determining the nature of the crystal growth in development. Adsorption of gelatin or impurities in the gelatin, or even of developing agent to certain crystal faces, likewise may play a part in determining the ultimate size and shape of the individual silver crystals. The relative amount of solution-physical development can also influence the form of the filaments. This is shown by experiments in which partially developed grains with well-defined filaments were transferred to another solution which developed predominantly by the solution-physical mechanism. The filaments became thicker than they would have if development had been continued in the original solution.

The Initiation of Development

Considerable time may elapse between the introduction of the exposed photographic material into the developer and the appearance of detectable development in a particular grain. This time does not represent a period during which nothing is happening, but rather one during which reduction is taking place relatively slowly and the development center or centers are being increased to a detectable size. Reliable quantative data on the reaction or reactions which occur during this early stage of development of a grain are difficult to obtain, because the reaction cannot be followed directly in a particular grain. Information has been obtained in two ways: microscopic observation of the time required to form a just detectable developing silver speck, and visual or analytical determination of the appearance of a just detectable amount of silver in a developing photographic emulsion.

The microscope observations are generally made on grains which are placed on a microscope slide and immersed in a drop of developer. However, the rate of development of a grain appears to be considerably greater when it is suspended in a liquid than when it is embedded in a set gelatin layer like the normal photographic film coating.

The second method of observation depends upon finding conditions such that a large number of grains in the coated layer starts to develop in about the same way, so that a relatively small degree of development of each grain represents enough silver to be detected analytically. This method has the advantage of using normal photographic coatings.

The overall activation energy of the reaction or reactions which take place during the initial stage of development is larger than that of continued development, in so far as the data for the few developing agents studied indicate. There are several possible reasons for this. The catalytic properties of the latent image centers are probably not identical with those of larger silver particles and may cause a smaller decrease in the activation energy of the reduction of silver ions. The early stages of the reduction may also occur by a different mechanism from that which applies to the later stages, or the relative extent to which two different mechanisms occur simultaneously may change as development proceeds. For example, the relative contribution of interface development and solution-physical development to the total reaction may change as development proceeds. Finally, the *charge effect* may influence the overall activation energy when the developing agent is active in the ionized form, and the importance of this effect decreases as the size of the developing silver specks increases. The charge effect has an important bearing on the rate of development by ionized developers.

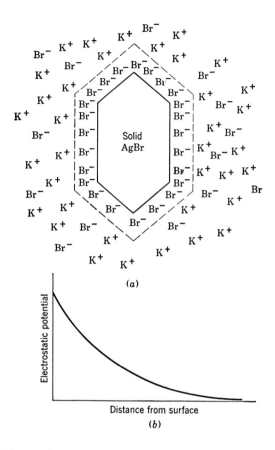

Fig. 5·6 Schematic illustration of electric double layer surrounding a silver bromide crystal. The curve illustrates the potential drop as a function of distance from the solid surface.

The Charge Effect

The charge effect[8] depends upon the fact that normal photographic emulsions contain an excess of halide ions and that some of these excess ions are adsorbed by the surface of the grain. The number of adsorbed excess ions is much smaller than the number needed to form a monolayer on the surface, but it is sufficient to give the surface a net negative charge. This charge tends to increase the concentration of positive ions in the surrounding medium in the immediate vicinity of the surface and tends to repel negative ions. The situation is illustrated schematically in Fig. 5·6 for a silver bromide particle in the absence of gelatin. The bromide ions are held rather rigidly at the surface, and the grain is surrounded by an ionic atmosphere in which positive ions predominate near the surface. The electrostatic charge at the surface sets up a potential gradient in the region surrounding the crystal, as illustrated in the lower part of the figure. In the actual photographic emulsion, the presence of gelatin undoubtedly causes some modification in the structure of the surface layer, but there is no reason to suppose that the gelatin prevents the adsorption of halide ions.

If development is to take place at the interface between the silver halide and the latent image center, the reducing agent must penetrate to the surface at or very near the latent-image center. Some developing agents, such as hydroquinone and p-aminophenol, are active primarily in the form of negatively charged ions, and the penetration of such ions to the silver halide surface is opposed by the negative charge on that surface. Only a fraction of the ions would have enough energy to overcome the forces of repulsion and come close enough to the surface to allow adsorption forces to come into play. The potential for silver bromide particles in the absence of gelatin, but in the presence of the excess of bromide ions that would be normal for a photographic emulsion, is about 40 to 60 millivolts. A potential of this magnitude would markedly decrease the effective concentration of developer ions in the vicinity of the surface, and would likewise decrease the concentration of adsorbed developer ions. The greater the surface charge and the larger the charge of the developer ion, the greater would be the effect of the charge upon the adsorption of the developer ions, and thus the greater would be the effect upon the rate of development.

At the very start of development, the surface charge in the vicinity of the latent image centers would not differ much from that at other portions of the silver halide surface. The latent image centers may cause a localized depression in the surface charge, but any such depression would not be large. As the size of the silver nucleus increases during development, however, the surface charge in this localized area decreases, since the halide ions are not adsorbed by the silver surface. As the charge decreases, the fraction of developer ions with enough energy to reach the surface increases, and the concentration of adsorbed ions in the vicinity of the growing silver area increases accordingly. Hence, the rate of development increases.

The charge effect could increase the calculated overall activation energy of development without changing the actual activation energy of the reaction of adsorbed developer at the silver-silver halide interface. The fraction of the developer ions which would have enough energy to overcome the forces of repulsion originating in the surface charge would increase with increasing temperature, and hence the effective concentration of developing agent in the vicinity of the surface would increase. The rate of development would increase as a consequence of the increased concentration. Since the activation energy is calculated from the measured increase in rate caused by an increase in temperature, the change in concentration would lead to an *apparent* increase in the activation energy. On the other hand, a decrease in the surface charge would lessen the relative increase in concentration and would, accordingly, cause a decrease in the apparent activation energy.

The charge effect is responsible for several kinetic phenomena in development by ionized agents. These will be considered in Chapter 7. The charge effect does not influence the behavior of agents which act in the non-ionized form.

Effective Size of the Latent Image Specks

Various attempts have been made to determine the number of silver atoms necessary to create a development center and the number of quanta necessary to make a grain developable. The two quantities are not necessarily identical. The number of light quanta absorbed in making a grain developable imposes an upper limit on the number of silver atoms that is necessary to form a development center. The actual atoms formed by the quanta, however, may be distributed among several centers.

It is known that some of the most sensitive grains are made developable by a very few quanta. Evidence from several independent sources indicates that less than ten quanta absorbed per grain are sufficient to form a latent image in some emulsions, and hence are sufficient to make some grains developable.

There is no reason to assume that a fixed-size threshold exists at which all nuclei acquire the power of initiating development. Orientation and position in the silver halide crystal may be of greater importance than mere size. Difficulty is even encountered in trying to establish a threshold of developability. Reduction of a grain must progress to the point where a measurable or microscopically visible amount of silver is formed before development of that grain can be detected. The time elapsing between the start of development and the point at which development can be detected is not the same for all grains, and it may vary over a wide range under some conditions. Hence, a grain which does not appear to be developable within a certain time of development may develop if given a longer time; the experimental time of development thus enters into the specification of a developable grain and a development center. If a well-defined border existed between development and the reduction of unexposed grains (fog formation), the problem could be met simply by specifying the grains which are reduced within the maximum development time. But the border is poorly defined, and development gradually merges into fog formation over a considerable range.

Mechanism of Fog Formation

All the reduced silver which cannot be ascribed to development of a latent image is lumped together under the label of fog. Several causes of fog can operate simultaneously, and it is often very difficult to distinguish them experimentally. The cause of fog can lie either in the emulsion or in the developer or in both. Some emulsions show much greater fog than others, and some developers produce much greater fog (relative to image formation) than others.

Emulsion fog arises primarily from the catalytic action of nuclei of silver sulfide, of metallic silver, or of gold which have been formed during the manufacture of the emulsion. These nuclei have grown beyond the stage of mere sensitivity centers and act in much the same manner as the latent image in promoting the reduction of the silver halide grain. It may be expected that any emulsion of high sensitivity will contain some grains which are thus spontaneously developable.

A direct attack by the developing agent upon silver ions in solution, or upon unnucleated silver halide surface, also can give rise to fog. This reaction in itself should produce little silver during the course of normal development, but it can form nuclei of high activity under the proper conditions. Subsequent catalytic reduction of the grains nucleated in this way, or of silver ions in the solution, can result in the formation of a significant amount of fog silver.

A type of fog which has been termed "solvent fog" or "dichroic fog" may be obtained if the developer contains a good silver halide solvent. The silver ions dissolved by this solvent are then reduced by the developing agent on nuclei that are not part of the grain itself. The initial reduction may be an uncatalyzed one which eventually forms the silver nuclei in the gelatin. These nuclei then act as centers for physical development. On the other hand, the nuclei may be already present in the gelatin, having been formed during the manufacture of the emulsion or in some subsequent reaction between silver ions and reducing agents present in the gelatin. The fog thus formed is composed of very finely divided silver and generally shows marked dichroism. A developer of high activity which contains an active silver halide solvent is most likely to produce this type of fog. Ammonia, thiocyanate, and bromide in high concentrations are common solvents which promote dichroic fog formation. This type of fog also can be obtained when an emulsion soaked with an active developer is transferred directly to a hypo fixing bath, particularly if that bath is not acidified.

Several secondary causes of fog may be met in practice. The presence of certain impurities in an improperly prepared developing solution can lead to fog formation. Sulfide ion is particularly troublesome in this respect. It forms silver sulfide nuclei which serve as catalytic centers for the reduction of the grains. Oxidation by air of some developing agents in the presence of the developing film gives rise to aerial fog. This type probably is caused by the action of a peroxide radical which is formed during the oxidation. The peroxide radical forms silver nuclei by reaction with the silver bromide, and these nuclei induce development of the grains containing them. Traces of copper salts in the developer will markedly promote this kind of fog.

REFERENCES

General

Mees, *The Theory of the Photographic Process*, revised edition, Macmillan, New York, 1954, Chapter 13.

James and Kornfeld, "Reduction of Silver Halides and the Mechanism of Photographic Development," *Chem. Revs.*, **30**, 1–32 (1942).

Sheppard, "Colloid Chemical Aspects of Photographic Development," article in *Colloid Chemistry*, Reinhold, New York, 1944. Vol. V, edited by J. Alexander.

James, "Recent Hypotheses Concerning the Mechanism of Photographic Development," *J. Chem. Education*, **23**, 595–601 (1946).

Glasstone, Laidler, and Eyring, *Theory of Rate Processes,* McGraw-Hill, New York, 1941.

Schwab, Taylor, and Spence, *Catalysis,* Van Nostrand, New York, 1937.

Specific

1. Stauffer, Smith, and Trivelli, *J. Franklin Inst.,* **238**, 291 (1944).
2. Bagdasar'yan, *Acta Physicochim. U.R.S.S.,* **19**, 421 (1944).
3. James, *J. Am. Chem. Soc.,* **61**, 648, 2379 (1939); *J. Phys. Chem.,* **45**, 223 (1941).
4. James, *Phot. Sci. and Eng.,* **1**, 141 (1958).
5. James and Vanselow, *Phot. Eng.,* **7**, 90 (1956).
6. James and Vanselow, *Phot. Sci. and Eng.,* **1**, 104 (1958); Klein, *Z. Elektrochem.* **62**, 505 (1958).
7. James, *J. Chem. Phys.,* **11**, 338 (1943).
8. James, *Science and Applications of Photography. Proceedings of the R. P. S. Centenary Conference, London,* 1953, Royal Photographic Society, London, 1955, p. 155.
9. James, *J. Chem. Phys.,* 11, 183 (1943).

6.

Composition and Reactions
of the Developer

As already indicated, a developing agent must possess the property of being able to reduce sufficiently exposed grains at a substantially greater rate than unexposed or insufficiently exposed grains. Certain reducing agents, however, can be eliminated as possible candidates simply because they cannot reduce silver halide at all or can reduce only a small fraction of it. A simple ferrous salt, such as the sulfate, will serve as an example.

The Oxidation-Reduction Potential

When a solution of the ferrous salt is added to silver bromide, a certain amount of reaction occurs, producing silver and ferric ion. But the ferric ion can oxidize metallic silver. The net reaction is given by the equilibrium equation

$$Fe^{++} + AgBr \rightleftharpoons Fe^{+++} + Ag + Br^- \qquad (6\cdot1)$$

and the point of equilibrium lies far to the left. Only a very small amount of silver bromide is reduced. The equilibrium point of the reaction can be predicted quantitatively from a knowledge of the oxidation-reduction or "redox" potentials involved.

The concept of the redox potential has been used rather widely (and often erroneously) in connection with the theory of development. It will be useful to consider the concept in more detail in connection with the ferrous ion-silver bromide system, just to illustrate what can and what cannot be predicted from it. If an inert electrode, such as platinum, is placed in a solution containing a mixture of ferrous and ferric ions, no chemical reaction with the electrode takes place, but an electric potential is set up between the electrode and the solution. The magnitude of this potential (the redox potential of the ferrous-ferric ion system) is determined by the ratio of the concentrations of the two ions according to the equation

$$E_{Fe} = E_0 + \frac{RT}{f} \log \frac{[Fe^{+++}]}{[Fe^{++}]} \qquad (6\cdot2)$$

where f is the value of the faraday, E_0 is a constant, and the brackets as usual indicate concentrations. Similarly, a silver electrode in a solution containing silver ions can set up a potential which follows the equation

$$E_{Ag} = E'_0 + \frac{RT}{f} \log \frac{[Ag^+]}{[Ag]} \qquad (6\cdot3)$$

where, for most purposes, $[Ag]$ is constant. The equation for a silver-silver bromide electrode in the presence of bromide ions will be the same as $6\cdot3$, or, since the bromide ion concentration determines the silver ion concentration, it can be written:

$$E_{Ag} = E''_0 - \frac{RT}{f} \log [Br^-] \qquad (6\cdot4)$$

If, now, the silver-silver bromide electrode and the excess bromide ions are transferred to the ferrous-ferric ion solution containing the platinum electrode, an electric current will flow when an external electrical connection is made between the two electrodes *provided* the quantity $\Delta E = (E_{Ag} - E_{Fe})$ is not zero. If it is negative, ferric ions will oxidize silver. If it is positive, ferrous ions will reduce silver bromide. In either event, reaction will proceed until ΔE becomes zero. The direction of the reaction is determined by the fundamental thermodynamic principle that such a reaction can proceed only in the direction which leads to a decrease in free energy. The change in free energy to be expected is given by the equation

$$-\Delta F = \Delta E n f \qquad (6\cdot5)$$

where F is the free energy and n is the number of electrons involved in the reaction (one for the reduction of silver ions by ferrous ions).

The thermodynamic considerations show that ferrous sulfate cannot be an effective reducing agent for silver bromide because the ferric ions formed soon bring the net reaction to a halt. An examination of equation 6·2 shows, however, that anything which decreases the ratio $[Fe^{+++}]/[Fe^{++}]$ will decrease the value of E_{Fe} and hence will favor the reduction of the silver bromide. The decrease can be accomplished by adding oxalate, for example, to the solution. The oxalate forms a complex with both ferrous and ferric ions, but the ferric ions are held much more tightly than the ferrous; that is, the dissociation constant of the ferric complex is much smaller than that of the ferrous. The result is a large decrease in the ratio $[Fe^{+++}]/[Fe^{++}]$. For this reason, the solution containing the oxalate is much more effective in reducing silver bromide than a solution containing only a simple ferrous salt.

It should be noted, however, that the thermodynamic considerations do not determine whether a ferro-oxalate solution will be a developer. They show that it can reduce the silver bromide, and they show to what extent the reaction can proceed toward completion. They say nothing about the time which will be required, or whether exposure of the silver bromide to light will hasten the reaction. For example, sodium stannite fulfills the thermodynamic requirements for reaction, but it is not a developer. Apparently little or no activation energy is required for the reaction; in other words, no catalyst is required, and reduction occurs without reference to light exposure. In general, no successful correlation has yet been made between developer activity and the redox potentials of the developers. Indeed, it is often impossible to determine, unambiguously, the redox potential of a developer under practical working conditions.

Classification of Developing Agents According to Structure

Several empirical correlations between developer ability and chemical structure have been suggested, but none includes all known developing agents. A correlation suggested by Kendall[1] has the widest applicability. It has a somewhat larger scope than the earlier correlations of Andresen and Lumière. Kendall associates developer activity with a structural group $a-(C{=}C-)_n b$ where $C{=}C$ represents two carbon atoms joined by a double bond, n is zero or an integer, and a and b may be either hydroxyl ($-OH$) groups, amino ($-NH_2$) groups, or substituted amino groups. (In the substituted amino groups, one or both hydrogens are replaced by certain organic groups such as $-CH_3$, $-C_2H_5$, or

—CH₂COOH.) The symbols *a* and *b* may represent either the same or different groups.

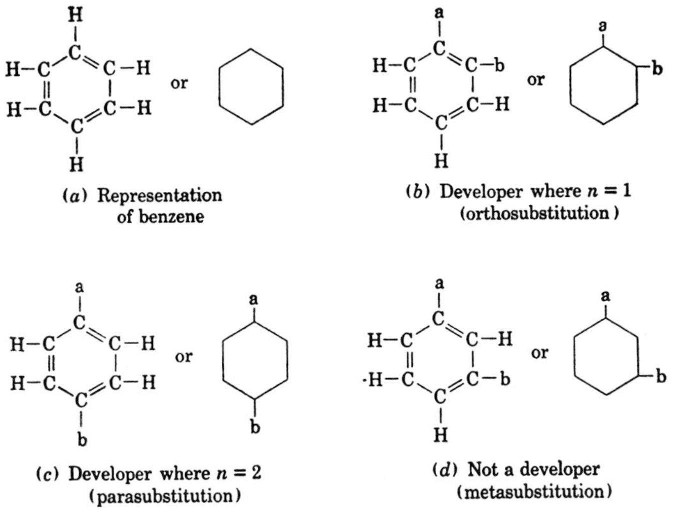

(*a*) Representation
of benzene

(*b*) Developer where $n = 1$
(orthosubstitution)

(*c*) Developer where $n = 2$
(parasubstitution)

(*d*) Not a developer
(metasubstitution)

Fig. 6·1 Substitutions in the benzene ring which will or will not convey developer properties. The symbols a and b represent —OH, —NH₂, or substituted —NH₂ groups. The simple hexagon is used in this book to represent the benzene ring for reasons explained in the preface.

The simplest examples of developers falling under the Kendall classification are those for which *n* is zero. Hydroxylamine, NH_2OH, is a good developer under proper conditions. Two other representatives, hydrogen peroxide ($HOOH$) and hydrazine (NH_2NH_2), show developing properties under more restricted conditions.

The great majority of the developing agents which are included in the Kendall correlation, and indeed the great majority of all known developing agents, are aromatic compounds, principally simple benzene derivatives. Benzene has the structure (in classical representation) shown in Fig. 6·1 (*a*). The entire structure is usually represented by a simple hexagon, and the nucleus of six carbon atoms is referred to as the benzene ring. If two adjacent hydrogen atoms are replaced by the groups *a* and *b*, the resulting compound falls under the Kendall classification for *n* equals one, Fig. 6·1 (*b*). If hydrogens at the opposite ends of the hexagon are replaced by a and b, n equals two, Fig. 6·1 (c). The adjacent positions shown in Fig. 6·1 (b) represent substitutions in the ortho or o-position; those at the opposite ends of the hexagon, Fig. 6·1 (c), substitutions in the para or p-position. Figure 6·1 (d) represents substitution in the meta or m-position, and the resulting compound either *is not* a developer or is a very weak one (with two exceptions, to be noted later in this section).

Because one or more of the hydrogen atoms of the benzene ring can be replaced by certain other atoms or groups without destroying the developer activity, the number of developers belonging to the benzene group is greatly increased. Thus, one or

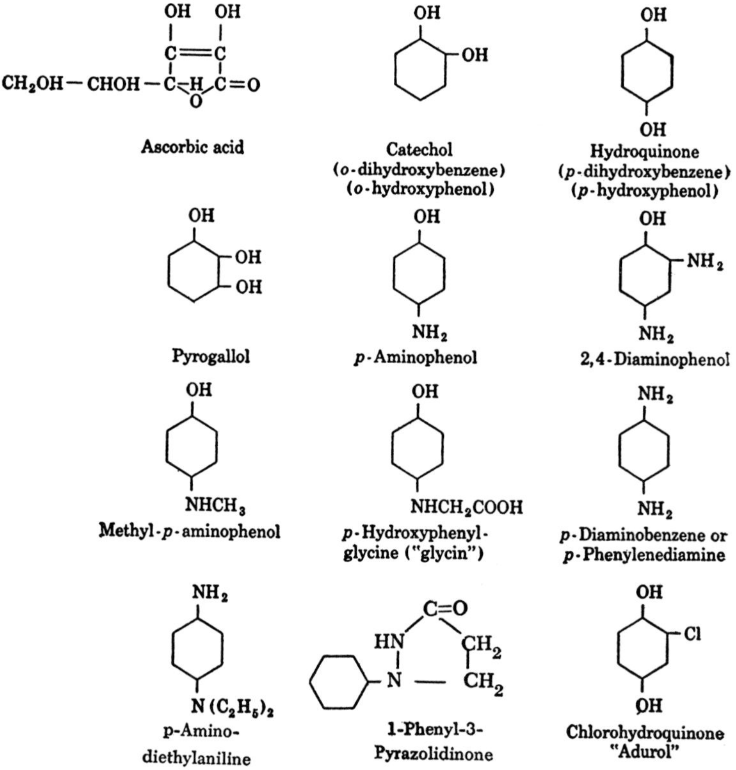

Fig. 6·2 Structures of various developing agents

more hydrogens can be replaced by further hydroxyl or amino groups, or by alkyl groups or halogen atoms, and the compound still will act as a developer. Its developing properties are usually modified, however.

The Kendall classification easily can be extended to the derivatives of naphthalene and the polynuclear aromatic compounds. It also covers certain non-aromatic developers, such as ascorbic acid (vitamin C). It fails to include one important group of developers, however. This group contains compounds characterized by a valence change of a metal during the development process. Various ferro - and molybdo-complex ions, such as the oxalates and malonates, are represented in this group, which includes the historically important ferro-oxalate ion $Fe(C_2O_4)_2^=$. These complexes are oxidized to the corresponding ferri- and molybdi-complexes in the act of reducing silver ions. Certain other developing agents not covered by the Kendall classification include the inorganic substance, sodium dithionite, and two aromatic meta derivatives, trioxymesitylene and oxyaminomesitylene.

Figure 6·2 gives the formulas of some developing agents of outstanding importance, either from a practical or a theoretical viewpoint. The amino compounds are shown as the free bases, although they are usually purchased in the form of salts, which are generally more stable and are generally more soluble in water. They are formed by direct addition of acid molecules to the free base, much as acids add to ammonia to form the ammonium salts. The salts often are sold under trade names. Thus, methyl-p-aminophenol sulfate is known by several names, principally Elon* and metol. Amidol is the dihydrochloride of 2,4-diaminophenol. Phenidone† is 1-phenyl-3-pyrazolidinone.

Dissociation and Ionization of Developing Agents

Although the amino compounds are generally dissolved in the form of salts in preparing developer solutions, the salts become completely dissociated when the solution is made sufficiently alkaline. Only the free bases exist in the practical developing solutions.

Developing agents containing one or more hydroxyl groups ionize in solution. The extent of the ionization depends upon the

---

*"Elon" is a registered trademark of Eastman Kodak Co.
†"Phenidone" is a registered trademark of Ilford, Ltd.

hydrogen ion concentration of the solution. The smaller the hydrogen ion concentration (that is to say, the more alkaline the solution), the greater will be the extent of the ionic dissociation. For example, methyl-p-aminophenol ionizes according to the equilibrium equation

$$CH_3NHC_6H_4OH \rightleftharpoons CH_3NHC_6H_4O^- + H^+ \qquad (6 \cdot 6)$$

The dependence of the ionization upon the hydrogen ion concentration is given by the expression

$$\frac{[CH_3NHC_6H_4O^-]\,[H^+]}{[CH_3NHC_6H_4OH]} = K$$

or

$$[CH_3NHC_6H_4O^-] = \frac{K}{[H^+]}\,[CH_3NHC_6H_4OH] \qquad (6 \cdot 7)$$

where K is a constant for any given temperature. Its value is 4×10^{-11} at 20°C.

From equation 6·7, it follows that the concentration of the ionized methyl-p-aminophenol will equal that of the un-ionized species when the value of the hydrogen ion concentration is equal to K. When the hydrogen ion concentration equals $100\,K$, the concentration of ionized methyl-p-aminophenol will be only one one-hundredth that of the un-ionized form, and so on. Control of the concentration of the ionized form is quite important in development, since the ion is the active developing agent. Consequently, control of the hydrogen ion concentration becomes of major importance to the control of development.

When the developing agent contains a second hydroxyl group, this also may ionize, and such ionization may have an important bearing on the activity of the developing agent. For example, the divalent ion of hydroquinone is the real developing agent; consequently the ionization of the second hydroxyl group of hydroquinone is of major importance.

The ionization of hydroquinone takes place step-wise, and the concentrations of the two ionized forms are related to the hydrogen ion concentrations by the equations

$$\frac{[HOC_6H_4O^-]\,[H^+]}{[HOC_6H_4OH]} = K_1;\ K_1 = 1.3 \times 10^{-10} \text{ at 20°C} \quad (6 \cdot 8)$$

and

$$\frac{[^-OC_6H_4O^-]\,[H^+]}{[HOC_6H_4O^-]} = K_2;\ K_2 \cong 4 \times 10^{-12} \text{ at 20°C} \quad (6 \cdot 9)$$

The concentration of the doubly ionized form can be related to the concentration of the un-ionized form by combining equations $6 \cdot 8$ and $6 \cdot 9$ to give

$$[C_6H_4O_2^=] = \frac{K_1K_2[C_6H_4(OH)_2]}{[H^+]^2} \qquad (6 \cdot 10)$$

For many purposes, it is useful to classify developing agents according to the charge on the active form. Thus, the monovalent ion with a single negative charge is the active agent in a methyl-p-aminophenol (metol) developer, and the divalent ion with a double charge is the active agent in the hydroquinone developer. Table $6 \cdot 1$ lists a number of developing agents according to the charge of the active form.[2] The theoretical basis for the classification already has been given in Chapter 5; applications of it will be made in the next chapter.

Reaction of the Developing Agents with Silver Salts

When a developing agent reduces silver ions to silver, the agent itself is oxidized. The reaction involved in the development of silver halide by hydroquinone in the absence of sulfite can be represented by

$$C_6H_4(OH)_2 \rightleftharpoons 2H^+ + C_6H_4O_2^= \qquad (6 \cdot 11)$$

and

$$C_6H_4O_2^= + 2Ag^+ \rightleftharpoons C_6H_4O_2 + 2Ag \qquad (6 \cdot 12)$$

The hydroquinone is oxidized to quinone at the same time that the silver ion is reduced to silver. The presence of sulfite modifies the reaction, as will be shown in the section on sulfite.

It is believed that the oxidation of an organic compound such as hydroquinone takes place in steps, each involving the transfer

TABLE $6 \cdot 1$

CLASSIFICATION OF DEVELOPING AGENTS ACCORDING TO CHARGE	
Charge	Agent
0	Sym-dimethyl-p-phenylenediamine, p-aminodimethylaniline, diaminodurene, and most of the other derivatives of p-phenylenediamine
-1	Metol, p-aminophenol, hydroxylamine, p-aminophenylglycine
-2	Hydroquinone, chlorohydroquinone, p-hydroxyphenylglycine, metol monosulfonic acid, ferro-oxalate ion, ascorbic acid
-3	Sodium hydroquinone monosulfonate
-4	Potassium hydroquinone disulfonate

of only one electron. On this basis, equation $6 \cdot 12$ should be broken up into two stages. The first involves the formation of semiquinone—a resonance-stabilized radical:

$$\overset{\overset{..}{\underset{..}{O}:}}{\bigcirc} + Ag^+ \rightleftharpoons \overset{\overset{.}{O}:}{\bigcirc} + Ag \qquad (6 \cdot 13)$$

The second is simply the reaction between the semiquinone thus produced and another silver ion to give quinone and a second atom of silver.

The organic developing agents which do not contain hydroxyl groups may react in the un-ionized state. If ionization of the amino takes place, it probably does so only when the developer is in the adsorbed state. The reaction of a typical p-phenylene-diamine, e.g., p-aminodimethylaniline, with silver ion can be represented in the absence of sulfite or coupler (see end of chapter) by the overall equation

$$H_2N{-}\bigcirc{-}N(CH_3)_2 + 2Ag^+ \rightleftharpoons$$
$$HN{=}\bigcirc{=}N^+(CH_3)_2 + 2Ag + H^+ \quad (6 \cdot 14)$$

The reaction probably takes place in two steps, the first being

$$\overset{:N(CH_3)_2}{\underset{:NH_2}{\bigcirc}} + Ag^+ \rightleftharpoons \overset{\cdot N^+(CH_3)_2}{\underset{:NH_2}{\bigcirc}} + Ag \qquad (6 \cdot 15)$$

Other developing agents of the benzene group react in a similar fashion. p-Aminophenol, for example, should yield the quinone-imide

$$O=\!\!\left\langle\!\!\overline{}\!\!\right\rangle\!\!=\!NH$$

but direct identification is difficult because of the great instability of this compound.

The oxidation products of the developing agents vary widely in stability and general reactivity. In the presence of sulfite, however, most of them react rapidly to form sulfonates, and only the sulfonates can be isolated from the conventional sulfite-containing developing solutions.

The Developing Solution

In addition to the developing agent or agents, practical developing solutions usually contain (1) an alkali, added to adjust the hydrogen ion concentration (pH) to the most advantageous value for the particular purpose, (2) a preservative, usually sodium sulfite, and (3) potassium bromide. Other additions may be made for specific purposes.

The Alkali

The chief function of the alkali in development is to adjust the hydrogen ion concentration which, in turn, controls the concentration of the ionized form of the hydroxyl developers, and hence the concentration of the actual developing agent. This is the principal reason for the practical emphasis on pH whenever the developing agent contains the OH group.

The development characteristics of the organic agents which do not contain hydroxyl groups also vary to some extent with the pH. The reason for this is not clear. A possible explanation involves the change in stability of the oxidation product of the developing agent. The reaction represented by equation 6·14 illustrates this idea. Experiment has shown that the addition of various agents which react readily with the quinone-imide oxidation product markedly increase the rate at which development proceeds. It appears, therefore, that the oxidation product is in some way interfering with the development process. The stability of this oxidation product in solution depends markedly upon the hydrogen ion concentration. Increase in pH decreases the stability, and hence increases the rate of removal of the oxidation product by way of decomposition. This, in turn, decreases the extent to which the oxidation product can interfere with the development process. Accordingly, the measured effect of an increase in pH is an increase in the rate of development.

A secondary but very important function of the alkali in practice is to maintain the hydrogen ion concentration at as nearly constant a value as possible. The development reaction is accompanied by the liberation of hydrogen ions. If not controlled, this can produce a large increase in the hydrogen ion concentration (decrease in pH) and, as a consequence, a serious decrease in the rate of development. Accordingly, it is desirable to use an alkali which has a high *buffer capacity*. Even such a buffer cannot completely prevent the change of hydrogen ion concentration during development, but it can greatly decrease that change.

Buffer capacity depends upon the presence in the solution of two components, one which can combine with hydrogen ions and one which can dissociate to give up hydrogen ions. As an example, a mixture of a very weak acid HA and an excess of its ion A^- (added in the form of the sodium or other completely dissociated salt) can act as a buffer. The acid HA can ionize to yield hydrogen ions, and the ion A^- can combine with hydrogen ions to form undissociated acid. The net hydrogen ion concentration of the solution is determined by the usual relation.

$$\frac{[H^+] [A^-]}{[HA]} = K \qquad (6\cdot16)$$

If, now, a small amount of strong acid (hydrogen ion) is added to the solution, the major portion of it will combine with some of the excess A^- to form HA, since K is a constant. Conversely, if a small amount of a strong base, such as sodium hydroxide, is added, the initial removal of hydrogen ion by reaction with the hydroxyl ion of the base is largely compensated by a dissociation of HA. In either event, some change in pH occurs, but it is small in comparison with the change produced in the absence of the buffer.

Several alkalies are available for practical use. Those most commonly employed are sodium hydroxide, sodium carbonate, and members of the borate group. The latter are usually the sodium metaborate (Kodalk) and the sodium tetraborate (borax). The entire pH range from about 8 to 13 can be covered by the proper use of these agents, although the buffering capacity is weak at some points. Excellent buffering can be obtained over the range 8.0 to 10.0 with the metaborate-tetraborate-boric acid system. This system cannot be used, however, for certain developers which have their active groups in the ortho position, because borate forms relatively inactive complexes with them.

Sulfite

The oxidation products of the developing agents usually have an undesirable influence on the course of development. The retarding action of the oxidation products of *p*-phenylenediamines has been mentioned already. Similar but less marked effects are produced by the oxidation products of the *p*-aminophenols. On the other hand, development by hydroquinone actually is accelerated by quinone or its decomposition product. The latter effect also is undesirable for most purposes, as it is uneven and difficult to control.

In addition to the kinetic effects, the oxidation products of most of the organic developing agents decompose in alkaline solution, and the products are usually colored materials which stain the emulsion. It is common practice, therefore, to add a substance which removes the oxidation products rapidly and harmlessly. Sodium sulfite is by far the most satisfactory agent for this purpose.

The overall reaction of silver bromide with hydroquinone in the presence of a sufficient excess of sulfite is represented by the equation:

There is evidence[3] that the semiquinone, formed according to equation 6·13, reacts very rapidly with the sulfite to form the sulfonate. The monosulfonate is a colorless, soluble substance which probably plays no role of significance in the development process. It is a weak developing agent, but its rate of reaction is too small to enable it to compete with hydroquinone under most practical conditions.

The oxidation product of methyl-*p*-aminophenol (metol) reacts with sulfite in a similar manner. Metol monosulfonic acid, again a soluble, colorless product, is formed.[4] In this case, the monosulfonic acid is a fairly strong developing agent. Although its rate of reaction is less than that of the parent substance, it probably takes some part in subsequent development.

The reactions of the oxidation products of hydroquinone and metol are typical of those of most of the aromatic developers. Apart from the few developing agents where reaction between the oxidation product and the sulfite is not possible, reaction usually occurs with the formation of the monosulfonate. When the monosulfonate is oxidized, a quinone or semiquinone is formed which usually can react with a second molecule of sulfite to form a disulfonate.

The stain-preventing action of the sulfite does not carry over to the removal of stain once formed. The stain is not produced by the quinone itself, but by an oxidation and polymerization product (or products) of the quinone. Sulfite will not convert this material into a colorless product.

Sulfite plays another part in the chemistry of the developer solution, this time as a preservative. The organic developing agents in alkaline solution react rather readily with oxygen from the air. Hydroquinone, for example, reacts according to the equation

$$\text{(structure)} + O_2 + 2H^+ \rightarrow \text{(structure)} + H_2O_2 \qquad (6 \cdot 18)$$

The semiquinone is formed as an intermediate step. In the presence of sulfite, the reaction proceeds according to the overall equation

$$\text{(structure)} + O_2 + 2SO_3^= \rightarrow \text{(structure with } -SO_3^-\text{)} + SO_4^= + OH^- \qquad (6 \cdot 18a)$$

The sulfite reacts with either the semiquinone or the quinone to form the sulfonate and also with the peroxide to form sulfate. The sulfite also acts as a preservative by markedly decreasing the *rate* of oxidation of the hydroquinone.

The preservative action of the sufite is not simply a matter of preferential reaction between sufite and oxygen. The rate of uptake of oxygen by a solution containing both sulfite and hydroquinone is many times smaller than the rate of uptake by the hydroquinone alone, other factors remaining constant. The effect is a genuine retardation of the oxidation of the hydroquinone.

Sulfite is a preservative for all hydroquinone derivatives where sulfonate formation is possible. On the other hand, sulfite has no effect on the rate of oxidation of tetramethylhydroquinone (durohydroquinone), where sulfonate formation is not possible. A plausible explanation of the oxidation-retarding effect of sulfite is that sulfite removes or prevents the formation of a catalyst for the oxygen oxidation. Quinone is very probably that catalyst.

A quinone catalysis of the oxidation of durohydroquinone and trimethylhydroquinone actually has been demonstrated by direct experiment. The data on the oxidation of the durohydroquinone can be explained by a simple mechanism.[5] In the absence of a catalyst the oxidation takes place in two steps, a slow one forming the semiquinone, and a rapid one forming the quinone.

$$\text{(durohydroquinone)} + O_2 \xrightarrow{\text{slow}} \text{(semiquinone)} + O_2^- \qquad (6 \cdot 19)$$

$$\text{(semiquinone)} + O_2 \xrightarrow{\text{rapid}} \text{(quinone)} + O_2^- \qquad (6 \cdot 20)$$

The catalysis results from the rapid reaction between the duroquinone thus produced and the original durohydroquinone to give more semiquinone:

$$(6\cdot21)$$

This reaction effectively short-circuits the first or slow step in the oxidation.

The rate of the catalyzed oxidation of durohydroquinone, as expected from this mechanism, is directly proportional to the concentration of the quinone. The same is true of the oxidation of trimethylhydroquinone *for sufficiently small concentrations of quinone.* At higher concentrations, however, the rate approaches a maximum, and further increase in trimethylquinone concentration produces only a very slight increase in reaction rate. In the oxidation of hydroquinone itself the maximum rate probably is reached at such a small concentration of quinone that the catalysis escapes direct measurement.

Sulfite retards the oxidation of many of the other developing agents, again probably by removing or preventing the formation of a catalyzing oxidation product.

It will be noted from equation $6\cdot17$ that the oxidation of hydroquinone by silver ion in the presence of sulfite results in a net formation of acid (liberation of hydrogen ion). On the other hand, the oxidation of hydroquinone by oxygen results in the net formation of base (liberation of hydroxyl ion), as shown by equation $6\cdot18a$. The reaction of hydroquinone as a developer for silver halide thus tends to decrease the pH of the solution, whereas the oxidation of the developer by air tends to increase the pH. This supplies one more reason for the use of a good buffer in the developer solution.

In addition to the functions just considered, sulfite exerts a solvent action on silver chloride and silver bromide. The sulfite ion forms a soluble complex $Ag(SO_3)_2^=$ with silver ion. Some development effects resulting from the increase which large concentrations of sulfite produce in the solubility and rate of solution of the silver salts will be considered in the next chapter.

Bromide

Potassium bromide often is added to the developing solution as a fog restrainer and as an aid to the obtaining of more uniform development. The solubility of silver bromide in water or aqueous solution changes with the concentration of excess bromide ion in a rather complicated fashion, as already mentioned in Chapter 2. Excess bromide ion also is adsorbed by the silver bromide surface. Both factors operate to change the rates of development and fog formation, both relative and absolute. The small amounts of bromide usually added to the developing solution ($0.05M$ or less) generally depress the rate of fog formation to a greater degree than the rate of development; therefore more efficient development is obtained. High concentrations of bromide, under some circumstances, promote fog because of the solvent action upon the silver bromide.

Bromide can exert an effect upon the development characteristics quite apart from its action on fog, as by changing the relative rates of development at the different exposure levels. The action here is complex, but the most important factor appears to involve the charge barrier effect. This subject will be discussed in more detail in the next chapter.

Color Development

In color development of the coupler type, the oxidation product of the developing agent becomes of major importance, and removal of the oxidation product by sulfite is not desired. The primary development process is still the reduction of exposed silver halide grains to metallic silver. The developer or the emulsion layer, however, contains a compound (a coupler) which reacts with the oxidation product of the developing agent to form a dye. The emulsion is coated in several layers, each sensitive to a particular region of the spectrum. By suitable control of the development and by use of several couplers, it is possible to form the proper dye in each layer to give an adequate color representation of the light image producing the original exposure. In the final stages of processing, the silver is removed, and only the dyes remain to form the color image.

The developing agents used for this type of color development are generally members of the p-phenylenediamine group. The parent substance is not a good developer for this purpose, but replacement by alkyl groups of the two hydrogens of one amino group leads to the formation of good color developers. It is possible with a single developing agent to obtain all three basic dyes for three-color photography. Thus, with p-aminodimethylaniline as the developing agent, a yellow dye of formula I is obtained when the coupler is acetoacetanilide; a cyan (blue-green) dye of formula II is obtained with 1-naphthol as coupler; and a magenta dye of formula III is obtained with p-nitrobenzyl cyanide as coupler.

$$(CH_3)_2N-\langle\ \rangle-N=\underset{\underset{CONHC_6H_5}{|}}{C}COCH_3 \qquad I$$

$$(CH_3)_2N-\langle\ \rangle-N=\langle\ \rangle=O \qquad II$$

$$(CH_3)_2N-\langle\ \rangle-N=\underset{\underset{CN}{|}}{C}-\langle\ \rangle-NO_2 \qquad III$$

Nearly all the couplers used in this type of color photography belong to one or the other of two broad groups of compounds originally described by R. Fischer, the discoverer of color development. These groups are (1) phenols and naphthols, which form the cyan indoaniline dyes, and (2) compounds with an active methylene group, which form the magenta and yellow dyes. Kinetic studies indicate that the oxidized developer reacts with the ionized form of the coupler under most practical conditions to form the dyes.

The first stage in the oxidation of the p-aminodialkylaniline developer by the silver halide results in the formation of the semiquinone, as indicated in equation 6·15. It has been suggested that this semiquinone reacts with the coupler, but kinetic studies indicate that it is the fully oxidized form, the quinonediimine, which actually reacts with the coupler. The quinonediimine is formed either as suggested in equation 6·14 or by the reaction of two semiquinone ions to form the quinonediimine and the p-aminodialkylaniline in a reaction analogous to equation 6·21. The reaction between the quinonediimine and a coupler with an active methylene group can be represented as follows:

$$
\begin{array}{ccc}
\overset{\text{H}}{\underset{\text{Y}}{\overset{|}{\underset{|}{\text{X-C:}}}}}\ (-) & \overset{\text{H}}{\underset{|}{\text{N}}} = \langle\hspace{-0.5em}=\hspace{-0.5em}\rangle = \text{NR}_2\ (+) & \overset{\text{H H}}{\underset{\text{Y}}{\overset{| |}{\underset{|}{\text{X-C-N-}}}}}\langle\hspace{-0.5em}\rangle - \text{NR}_2 \\
(\text{coupler}) & (\text{quinonediimine}) & (\text{leuco dye})
\end{array}
$$

The preceding reaction forms the leuco dye (a reduced form of the dye, which may be colorless) rather than the dye itself. There are several possibilities for the oxidation of the leuco compound to the dye. The oxidizing agent might be oxygen from the air, silver ion, or oxidized forms of the developing agent, like quinonediimine or even the semiquinone. We can rule out some of these possibilities. Under optimum conditions, four silver atoms are formed for every dye molecule (except when certain couplers are used which eliminate HCl in the coupling reaction, when only two silver atoms are formed). Oxidation of the leuco dye by oxygen would not give this silver-to-dye ratio. Moreover, dye can be formed at some distance from the silver halide grain, and it is unlikely that enough silver ion would be in solution to do this. It is more likely that the oxidation of the leuco dye is accomplished by oxidation products of the developer.

The observed formation of dye molecules at a distance from the developing silver halide grains requires additional explanation. Quinonediimine molecules formed at the grains are too unstable to diffuse the necessary distance without decomposition. However, Tong[6] has shown that the quinonediimine in alkaline solution undergoes a deamination reaction:

$$
\text{HN} = \langle\hspace{-0.5em}=\hspace{-0.5em}\rangle = \text{NR}_2 \overset{(+)}{} + \text{OH}^- \rightarrow \text{HN} = \langle\hspace{-0.5em}=\hspace{-0.5em}\rangle = \text{O:} + \text{R}_2\text{NH}
$$

The resulting quinone monoimine is stable enough to diffuse some distance away from its point of origin, and it can also react with excess *p*-aminodialkylaniline to form quinonediimine again and *p*-aminophenol. Thus, the quinonediimine which reacts with the coupler at a distance from the silver halide grain can be formed substantially "on the spot" by the reaction of the quinone monoimine with the developing agent.

A little sodium sulfite is added to color developers to preserve the developing agent from oxygen oxidation. The protective action of sulfite is usually not as great for the *p*-aminodialkylanilines as it is for hydroquinone or *p*-aminophenol, but in general large amounts of sulfite cannot be used without adverse effects on dye formation. Hydroxylamine acts as a preservative when used in conjunction with sulfite. On the other hand, copper has a strong catalytic effect upon the oxygen oxidation of the color developers, just as it has on the oxygen oxidation of many other developing agents.

REFERENCES

General

Mees, *The Theory of the Photographic Process,* revised edition, Macmillan, New York, 1954, Chapters 14, 16.

Clerc, *La Technique photographique,* 5th edition, Paul Montel, Paris, 1950, Vol. 1, Chapter 28.

Glafkides, *Chimie photographique,* 2nd edition, Paul Montel, Paris, 1957, Chapter 9.

Koltholff and Laitinen, *pH and Electro Titrations,* Wiley, New York, 1941.

Vittum and Weissberger, "Recent advances in the chemistry of dye-forming development," *J. Phot. Sci.,* **6**, 157-169 (1958).

Specific

1. Kendall, *Proc. IX Intern. Congr. Phot., Paris,* 227 (1935).

2. James, *J. Phys. Chem.,* **43**, 701 (1939).

3. LuValle, *J. Am. Chem. Soc.,* **74**, 2970 (1952).

4. Lehmann and Tausch, *Phot. Korr.,* **71**, 17, 135 (1935).

5. James and Weissberger, *J. Am. Chem. Soc.,* **60**, 98, 2084 (1938).

6. Tong, *J. Phys. Chem.,* **58**, 1090 (1954).

7.

General Kinetics of Development

The simplest study of the kinetics of development, from the theoretical point of view, would be that of the development of a single, typical silver bromide grain by a developing agent in a simple solution. This study has not been carried out. Some experiments by Meidinger and by Rabinovich approach these conditions, however.

Kinetics of Development of Large, Single Grains

Meidinger[1] investigated the kinetics of development of large individual silver bromide grains in a metol-hydroquinone solution. From microscopic observations he determined the rate of initiation of development R_i and the rate of continuation of development throughout the grain R_c. The initiation rate R_i was determined from the time which elapsed between the penetration of the developer to the grain and the appearance of the first traces of reduction visible under the microscope. This rate increased with increasing light exposure until a maximum was reached. In the region of solarization, the rate decreased. The continuation rate R_c, on the other hand, was independent of the exposure. Both R_i and R_c decreased with increasing bromide concentration in the developer, but the decrease in R_i was relatively much greater at low bromide concentrations. Both rates increased when the pH of the developer was increased, and both rates decreased when the developer was diluted with water. Rabinovich and co-workers, using the same type of grain preparation, found that the propagation of development throughout the grain varied markedly according to the composition of the developer.[2] Under some conditions, the radius of the developing area varied exponentially with time; under others, development proceeded in various irregular ways which were not easily studied quantitatively.

Relation between Density and the Size and Number of Developed Grains

The development of a normal photographic emulsion presents a more complex situation. Development rates are usually determined from measurements of changes in optical density. As development proceeds, however, density may increase in either or both of two essentially distinct ways: (1) by increase in the average size of the developed silver particles, that is, by increase in the degree of completion of development of those grains which are developing; and (2) by increase in the *number* of developing or developed grains.

Two extreme cases may be imagined. In the first, all the grains start to develop at the same time; that is, the period of initiation of development is the same for all, and development of any one grain parallels that of any other grain. Increase in density then is caused solely by increase in the size of the silver particles. In the second case, the initiation periods vary in magnitude, and the duration of the initiation period for any given grain is much greater than duration of reaction beyond the initiation period. At any intermediate stage of the gross development of the emulsion, the image is made up essentially of completely or almost completely developed grains. Density then is determined by the number of developed grains. Between these two extremes, the entire range of combinations of the two is possible.

Density increases in proportion to the number of grains developed per unit area when the average size of the silver grains remains constant. If the number per unit area is constant, density increases with increasing size. For grains larger than about 0.2–0.25 micron, the ratio of the mass M of silver per unit area to the diffuse density D increases linearly with the diameter d of the grains:

$$\frac{M}{D} = Bd + C \qquad (7 \cdot 1)$$

The ratio M/D is termed *photometric equivalent;* its reciprocal, D/M, is termed *covering power*.

The behavior of the photometric equivalent during the course of development often indicates why the density is changing,[3] especially if the emulsion has a narrow range of grain sizes. If, with such an emulsion, the photometric equivalent remains essentially constant with increasing density, the increase in density is brought about primarily by an increase in the number of developed grains, and the average size of the silver grains remains essentially constant. If, on the other hand, the photometric equivalent increases as development proceeds, the average silver particle size is increasing according to equation $7 \cdot 1$.

Kinetics of Development under Simplified Conditions

In studying the kinetics of development of a simple emulsion, it is often possible to adjust conditions so that the majority of the grains develop as an ensemble in which the course of development in each grain substantially parallels that of development in any other grain. Development of motion-picture positive film exposed to give ultimate densities which lie well in the shoulder region of the characteristic curve follows this course in some simple developing solutions. This is true of development by sulfite-free hydroquinone solutions[4] of pH 8 to 9, used in the absence of oxygen. Under these conditions, the rate of development by hydroquinone varies approximately as the square root of the concentration of the divalent ion $C_6H_4O_2^=$. This variation holds whether the change in concentration is caused by a change in total hydroquinone content of the solution, or simply by a change in pH.

The rate of development by hydroquinone cannot be described uniquely in terms of the concentration of either the un-ionized hydroquinone or its monovalent ion. It can be described only in terms of the concentration of the divalent hydroquinonate ion. This fact shows that the divalent ion is the active developing agent. The dependence of rate upon the square root of the concentration implies that the ion reacts in the adsorbed state (cf. equations $5 \cdot 5$ and $5 \cdot 6$). Since there is no substantial evidence of adsorption of hydroquinone to silver nuclei, it may be assumed that the adsorption involves the silver bromide or the silver-silver bromide interface. There is independent evidence to support this assumption.

The addition of bromide to the hydroquinone solution decreases the rate of development, and the decrease is much more marked at the start of the reaction than in the later stages. This result is in complete agreement with Meidinger's observations of the effect of bromide on the rate of development of individual silver bromide grains (page 123). Quantitatively, the effect of bromide on the rate at which development starts in the hydroquinone solution is accurately described by the equation

$$\log t = \alpha \log [Br^-] + \text{constant} \qquad (7 \cdot 2)$$

where t is the time of appearance of the image, and α is a fraction.

Quinone, one of the reaction products, accelerates development. Small amounts of sulfite decrease the measured rate because the sulfite removes the quinone formed in the reaction, but such small amounts do not alter the kinetics of development in any other significant way. Large amounts of sulfite, however, introduce complications which will be treated subsequently.

The Induction Period

A definite induction period exists for development by some agents under proper conditions.[5] In the induction period region, *the rate of formation* of density increases with the time of devel-

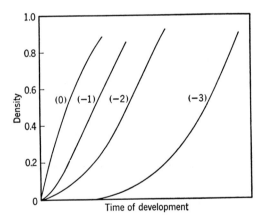

Fig. 7 · 1　Effect of the charge of the developing agent upon the shape of the initial portion of the density-time of the development curve.

opment; as a result, the initial part of the density-time of development curve is concave in shape, as shown by curves (-1), (-2) and (-3) of Fig. 7 · 1. A marked induction period is obtained with the simple, sulfite-free hydroquinone developer used under the conditions described in the preceding section. In this case, a part of the acceleration of development can be attributed to the action of the quinone which is accumulating in the solution, but a marked acceleration persists even when sulfite is added to prevent the accumulation of quinone. Moreover, the acceleration indicated by the density change is *in addition to* the acceleration caused by the increase in the extent of the silver-silver bromide interface. It is probable that, because of the nature of the relation between density and the mass of silver (equation 7·1), the acceleration resulting from the increase in interface will not show up in the density plot. This idea is supported strongly by the fact that, when certain other developing agents (for example, diaminodurene) are used under the same conditions, the density plots do not show induction periods (curve 0, Fig. 7·1) even though the density bears the same relation as before to the mass of silver. A curve with a concave region at the foot is obtained for such a developer only when the mass of silver (instead of density) is plotted against the time of development. Thus, the expected increase in rate with increase in interface is revealed only by the silver plot, not by the density plot.

An induction period is usually obtained if the developing agent acts in the form of a negatively charged ion,[5] and its magnitude depends primarily upon the amount of charge on the ion, not on its chemical nature. Figure 7·1 shows typical curves produced by developing agents of charge 0, −1, −2, and −3.

The induction period can be explained in terms of a change in the magnitude of the charge barrier protecting the individual silver halide grains. In the early stages of development, an increase in the size of the silver speck is accompanied by a decrease in the magnitude of the barrier (see Chapter 5). The local decrease in the barrier permits a larger percentage of the developer ions to reach the solid surface, and the rate of the reaction is increased. The relative effect is greater, the greater the charge of the developing ion and the greater the magnitude of the original barrier. Increase in the halide ion concentration of the developing solution produces an increase in the magnitude of the barrier and hence a corresponding increase in the relative extent of the induction period for the charged developers. Meidinger's observation that the rate of initiation of development is more sensitive to bromide ion concentration than is the rate of continuation of development finds an explanation in this effect of bromide ion on the charge barrier. Uncharged developing agents, on the other hand, are not impeded by the barrier, and hence development by them does not show an induction period.

As already mentioned, sulfite in small amounts decreases the measured rate of development by hydroquinone because it removes quinone which otherwise would accelerate the reaction. Sulfite produces a similar decrease in the initial rates of development by all the *doubly charged* developing ions tested, *except* where the sulfite does not react with the oxidation product. This fact strongly suggests that the accelerating action of the oxidation product is tied up with a decrease in the barrier charge. Such a decrease probably results from adsorption of the oxidation product, or a decomposition product thereof, by the silver halide. When the developing agent is *uncharged*, the oxidation products do not increase but often *decrease* the rate of development: small amounts of sulfite and other substances which remove these products increase the rate of development. The singly charged ions show intermediate results when reaction between sulfite and the oxidation product occurs readily.

The barrier effects discussed thus far originate solely or primarily in the electrostatic action of the adsorbed halide layer. The electric charge of the gelatin also affects the rate of development by negative ions in alkaline solution. When the developer is used in a solution containing a very low total salt concentration, the retarding action of the gelatin charge can be quite significant. This charge is diminished and the rate of development is increased by the addition of neutral salt. Thus, the rate of development of motion-picture positive film by ascorbic acid is increased about sixfold when the potassium ion concentration is increased from 0.05 M to 1.0 M by the addition of potassium nitrate. The effect of salt is considerably greater when the developing agent is doubly charged than when it is singly charged, and potassium salts produce greater acceleration than the corresponding sodium salts.

The Kinetics of Practical Development

The rate of development, as measured under the conditions usually employed in practice, is often a complex quantity. Usually, it is not possible to determine from the available data whether the change in density is primarily a matter of change in the size, or in the number of silver particles, or whether it is because of both. Changes in development conditions may alter the relative importance of size and number without the alteration becoming evident from the simple kinetic data.

Development under the usual practical conditions generally is complicated in other ways. The measured rate often depends upon the interaction and combination of the rates of a number of separate stages, such as rates of diffusion of the developer through the gelatin layer, of penetration of the double-layer barrier, of adsorption of the developing agent, of reduction of silver ions to silver, of solution of the silver halide, and of accumulation or elimination of the reaction products. It is not surprising, therefore, that theoretical interpretations of data obtained under these circumstances are often somewhat ambiguous.

The methods of expressing the rate of development generally fall into three groups. These depend upon (1) the time of appearance of the image, (2) the rate of increase of density for a fixed exposure, and (3) the rate of increase of gamma.

The Watkins formula is sometimes taken as a practical basis for the first method. This formula states that

$$t_D = W \cdot t_a \qquad (7 \cdot 3)$$

where t_D is the time required to obtain the density D, t_a is the time of appearance of the image, and W is the *Watkins factor*. Within limits, W is approximately constant for changes in concentration, temperature, and pH. It varies to some extent with the nature of the emulsion and the amount of exposure, and it varies markedly with the nature of the developing agent. The time of appearance of the image, however, is generally of less practical importance than the rate of increase of density or gamma.

Rate measurements based upon the change of gamma, in turn, are generally of greater practical usefulness than those based upon the change of density. Neither method gives a complete representation of the rate of change of the photographic characteristics, however, since the toe and shoulder regions of the characteristic curve do not always show precisely the same rate of change as the straight portion. The rates of change of density and of gamma sometimes are determined with the aid of approximation equations such as those given in the following section. Useful rates can be obtained, however, simply by measuring the slope of the density- or gamma-time of development curves at some specified value of density or gamma.

The Progress of Development under Constant Conditions

Various formulas have been suggested to represent the progress of development when the developer composition is held constant. The simplest of these is

$$\frac{dD}{dt} = k\,(D_\infty - D) \qquad (7 \cdot 4)$$

where D_∞ represents the density for complete development. It is doubtful whether this formula has any theoretical significance as applied to development. At present, it is best considered as an empirical equation which fits the data over a limited range. Wide departures from it often are observed, and it is not surprising in view of the complex nature of development. Nor is it surprising that none of the various elaborations which has been suggested has led to an expression of general validity. One equation of this kind,[6] in its integrated form, is the following:

$$\begin{aligned} D &= (A \log t + B)\,\log E + C \log t + G \\ &= \gamma \log E + C \log t + G \end{aligned} \qquad (7 \cdot 5)$$

where A, B, C, and G are constants which depend upon concentration, pH, and temperature (and probably the nature of the emulsion as well). The equation holds over a wide range of concentrations of developing agents and of pH for metol-hydroquinone solutions, but only when applied to the straight portion of the characteristic curve and to intermediate stages of development. It fails at very low gamma and at gamma values approaching the maximum.

A simple equation of the same form as $7 \cdot 4$, but expressing the rate of change of gamma instead of density, is of some importance. In its integrated form, the equation is

$$\gamma = \gamma_\infty (1 - e^{-kt}) \qquad (7 \cdot 6)$$

where γ_∞ is the limiting value of γ for the emulsion involved. This equation gives a more accurate representation of the progress of development is most cases than equation $7 \cdot 4$, but it still is not rigorous. The equation is used primarily to determine γ_∞, the ultimate contrast of the photographic material. The value of k in the equation depends markedly upon the nature of the developer, its temperature, and to some extent upon the nature of the emulsion.

Diffusion Effects in Practical Development

Sheppard and Mees showed that the absolute time required for the developer to penetrate the thickness of the emulsion is small, amounting in general to only a few seconds. The composition of the developer in the immediate vicinity of the developing grain, however, may differ considerably from the original composition of the solution when development is rapid. The developing agent is being used up, reaction products are forming, and diffusion is not sufficiently rapid to restore the original developer composition. The latter is shown by the fact that agitation of the developer has an important effect on the rate of rapid development.

If no agitation whatever is used, development by a normally rapid-acting solution becomes noticeably retarded and often uneven in character. Increase in the rate of agitation produces an increase in the rate of development, the latter rate eventually approaching a maximum. Figure 7·2 illustrates the effect. The experiments[7] were carried out with motion-picture positive film and a normal metol-hydroquinone developer (Kodak D-16). Agitation was obtained by the "brush" method, in which a soft, camel's-hair brush is drawn back and forth over the surface of the film.

The absolute rate of diffusion of an individual molecule in the gelatin probably is not affected by such agitation, but the net rate of diffusion is. The net rate of diffusion between the surface of the emulsion and the points where the actual development is occurring (the grains within the emulsion) is determined by the concentration gradient. The rate of diffusion of a particular molecular species is given by the equation

$$\frac{dM}{dt} = A \cdot P \frac{dc}{dx} \qquad (7 \cdot 7)$$

where dM is the amount which diffuses in time dt, A is the area of the film, P is the diffusion coefficient, and dc/dx is the concentration gradient.

In the absence of agitation, a quiescent layer of solution forms along the emulsion surface. Selective diffusion of the developing agent, alkali, and the like into the gelatin tends to change the concentration in this layer of developer. New developer can be supplied only by diffusion from the bulk of the solution. On the

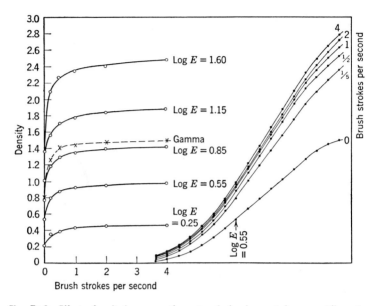

Fig. 7·2 Effect of agitation upon the rate of development by a rapidly acting developer. The characteristic curves obtained for various rates of brushing are plotted on the right-hand side of the figure; gamma and densities for various exposures are plotted, as functions of the rate of brushing, on the left-hand side. (Ives and Jensen.)

other hand, bromide ion being liberated in the development reaction diffuses out toward the quiescent layer, which thus becomes richer in bromide ion than is the bulk solution. Both effects decrease the concentration gradient between the surface of the emulsion and the reaction sites. Agitation disrupts the quiescent layer and keeps the surface of the emulsion in direct contact with developer of the same composition as the bulk of the solution. This, in turn, increases the concentration gradient between the surface and the points where the reaction is taking place within the emulsion, and thus increases the rate of rapid development.

It will be noted that the effect of agitation is of little significance when the rate of development is very small. When the specific rate of the chemical reaction is very much smaller than the rate of diffusion, the former controls the measured rate and the latter is of no importance. On the other hand, if the specific rate of the chemical reaction is very much greater than the rate of diffusion, the molecules of the developer react practically as soon as they reach the reaction sites, and thus diffusion controls the overall, or measured, rate of the development process.

Bromide in Practical Development

Soluble bromides usually retard the rate of fog formation to a greater extent than they retard the rate of development of the latent image, provided the bromide ion concentration does not exceed a few grams per liter. Likewise, bromide ion generally decreases the rate of growth of density in the lower exposure regions to a relatively greater extent than in the higher exposure regions. If development is carried to equal gamma values in a series of solutions varying only in bromide content, the entire characteristic curve is usually displaced with increasing bromide ion concentration toward larger exposure values.

In a series of characteristic curves representing simply a change in development time, it is often found that all the straight line extensions (Fig. 1·3) pass through a common point when they are extrapolated toward the log E axis. When the developer contains little or no bromide, this confluence point generally lies on or very near the log E axis. The exact position and even the existence of the point depends upon both the developer and the emulsion. (Some emulsions fail to give a confluence point with any developer, and a few developing solutions fail to give a confluence point with any emulsion.) Addition of bromide in sufficient quantity shifts the confluence point downward below the axis (Fig. 7·3). The extent of the shift has often been used

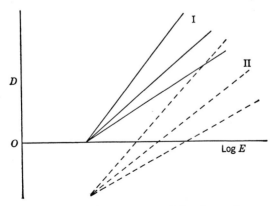

Fig. 7·3 Generalized straight-line extensions of the characteristic curves, showing depression of the confluence point due to bromide. I, no bromide; II, added bromide.

to express the sensitivity of the developing agent to bromide, and this sensitivity in turn has been used as a basis for classifying developing agents. The most extensive work of this sort was carried out by Nietz,[8] and his relative values, sometimes erroneously referred to as reduction potentials, have been widely quoted. These relative values, however, are not constant, as they depend upon the conditions under which they are determined. The bromide effect on development by a single agent can change markedly with a large change in pH or in concentration of the developing agent.

The electric charge effect appears to be one important factor which influences the depression of the confluence point. The available data show a considerably larger depression for the doubly charged agents than for chemically similar singly charged or uncharged agents. It is unlikely, however, that the charge effect is entirely responsible for the differences in bromide depressions between the various developing agents. For example, bromide also may influence the development rate by affecting the adsorption of developing agents to silver bromide or by altering the concentration of the activated complex formed between the developing agent and the silver ion. The search for a complete explanation of the bromide depression is hampered because many of the data in the literature are not comparable and because sometimes important variations in the conditions within a single set of tests have been disregarded.

Effect of Change in Total Concentration of Developing Solution

Simple dilution of a ferro-oxalate developer containing no bromide produces a relatively simple change in development conditions. Primarily, the change is in the concentration of the developing agent, since no sulfite is present and the rate of development is almost independent of pH. Sheppard and Mees found that the rate of development in a ferro-oxalate solution containing little or no bromide varied almost directly with the total concentration. A nearly constant degree of development was obtained when the product of time and concentration was constant regardless of the specific value of either.

Dilution of most of the commonly employed developers produces a more complicated change. Not only is the concentration of the developing agent decreased, but the sulfite concentration, bromide concentration, and total salt concentration are decreased as well. Moreover, the pH is often changed. The complicated change in development rate which can result is well illustrated by Chibisoff's data.

The initial composition of the developing solution was as follows:

Developing agent	0.05 M
Sodium sulfite crystals	100 grams
Sodium carbonate crystals	54 grams
Potassium bromide	1 gram
Water to make	1000 ml

Development was carried out at 15° C. Table 7·1 gives the gamma values obtained when the product of concentration and time of development are constant. Data of this type can be used to determine empirically the dilution required to yield a specified gamma for a given time of development, or conversely the time required for a given concentration. It should not be assumed, however, that a developer formula of substantially different composition from that just given will yield results which are strictly parallel to those shown in Table 7·1.

TABLE 7·1

VALUES OF GAMMA FOR VARIOUS DEVELOPING AGENTS WHEN CONCENTRATION × TIME IS HELD CONSTANT

Concentration	1	0.5	0.25	1	0.5	0.25	1	0.5	0.25
Time	1	2	4	2	4	8	4	8	16
Catechol							0.35	0.60	0.70
Pyrogallol				0.42	0.48	0.52	0.75	0.95	0.81
p-Aminophenol				0.32	0.49	0.63	0.59	0.88	0.94
Metol	0.37	0.56	0.67	0.81	0.98	1.20			
Amidol	0.39	0.60	0.43	0.76	1.12	1.04			

Concentration of the Developing Agent

The rate of development increases with increasing concentration of the developing agent when the other components and the pH of the solution are kept constant. The dependence for developer solutions of simple composition often follows approximately the equation:

$$\text{Rate} = B \cdot C_s{}^n \qquad (7\cdot8)$$

where B is a constant, C_s is the concentration of developing agent in solution, and n is a fraction with a maximum value of unity. A fractional-power dependence can be explained by adsorption of the developing agent (see Chapter 5). A first-power dependence may imply that adsorption is weak (n is approximately unity in the Freundlich adsorption isotherm), that the measured rate is determined by the rate of adsorption of the developing agent, or that the measured rate is determined by the rate of diffusion of the developing agent through the gelatin. In the event that adsorption does not precede reaction, a first-power relation could mean simply that the rate of transfer of electrons to silver ions is proportional to the number of collisions between developer molecules or ions and silver ions, silver, or silver halide surfaces. When a significant amount of solution-physical development occurs, the rate-concentration relation often becomes more complicated.

The value of n in equation 7·8 may change with changing conditions of development by a particular agent. For example, Levenson[9] found that n increased with increasing bromide concentration in a hydroquinone developer of otherwise constant composition. A possible reason for such a change is that bromide ion interferes with adsorption of the organic ion, and the adsorption of the latter by the silver halide is weaker in the presence of excess bromide. A change in n from a fraction to a

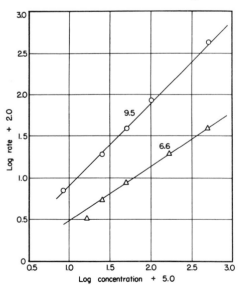

Fig. 7·4 Dependence of development rate upon concentration of Phenidone with no added bromide. Values of pH on curves.

value of unity has also been observed when a shift from a chemical reaction-controlled rate to a diffusion-controlled rate occurred. Figure 7·4 illustrates such a change brought about in a Phenidone developer[10] by a change in pH. In this figure, the logarithm of the development rate is plotted against the logarithm of the concentration. The value of n is given by the slope of the straight line obtained in such a plot, as can be confirmed by taking the logarithm of each side of equation 7 · 8. At pH 6.6, the rate is approximately proportional to the two-thirds power of the concentration, whereas at pH 9.5, the rate varies as the first power of the concentration. At the higher pH, under the conditions used, the rate was controlled by the rate of diffusion.

Diffusion is an important factor in rapid development. At low and moderate concentrations, the rate of diffusion of the developing agent is proportional to its concentration. At high concentrations, however, there is evidence that the rate of diffusion of a developing agent through the gelatin layer can be less than proportional to its concentration in the solution. The absence of a direct proportionality between rate and concentration, therefore, does not always mean that diffusion is not rate-controlling.

Effect of the Alkali

Specification of the pH of a developing solution is of primary importance. Fortunately, pH values can be determined with ease and considerable accuracy now that glass electrode pH meters are available as routine laboratory instruments.

The suitable pH range for practical development varies widely with the nature of the developing agent. Most of the organic agents, especially those containing active hydroxyl groups, do not develop at a useful rate unless the solution is alkaline.

A few organic agents, such as amidol, will develop at a useful rate even in a slightly acid solution. Ferro-oxalate is most useful in acid solution; it shows little dependence on pH over the range of 4 to 7. It cannot be employed at pH values much above 7 unless oxygen is strictly excluded from the system. Dissociation of a hydrogen ion is not involved in the determination of the reaction rate in this case. Increases in alkalinity can influence the development rate of ferro-oxalate only by increasing the gelatin charge barrier effect (an effect which is scarcely noticeable when the total salt concentration is high) and by promoting the formation of ferrous and ferric hydroxides or intermediate hydrolysis products of ferrous and ferric ions.

Figure 7·5 shows[11] the dependence of density upon pH for a fixed exposure and time of development; each curve represents a different developing agent used in a conventional solution containing sulfite. The pH dependence of the agents varies considerably. For example, the change in rate of development by p-aminophenol (curve IV) produced by a given change in pH is

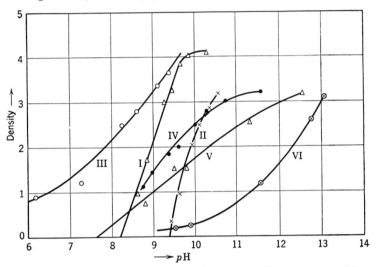

Fig. 7·5 Dependence upon pH of density obtained for a fixed exposure and time of development. I, pyrogallol; II, hydroquinone; III, metol; IV, p-aminophenol; V, p-hydroxyphenylglycine; VI, p-phenylenediamine. (Reinders and Beukers.)

less than one-half of that of hydroquinone (curve II). The pH dependence of the rate of development by Phenidone, not shown in the figure, is even less than that of metol.

The pH dependence of developers which contain the hydroxyl group is largely determined by the ionization of that group, since the ionized form is more active than the non-ionized form. The concentration of the ionized form increases with increasing pH. Metol is a typical example of an agent which contains a single hydroxyl group. The dependence of the concentration of its ionized form on the hydrogen ion concentration is shown in equation 6·7 (page 110). Since pH is the logarithm of the reciprocal of hydrogen ion concentration, this equation can be rewritten in logarithmic form as

$$\log [\mathrm{CH_3NHC_6H_4O^-}] =$$
$$\log [\mathrm{CH_3NHC_6H_4OH}] + p\mathrm{H} + \log K \quad (7\cdot9)$$

where K is the dissociation constant and log K has a value of -10.4 at $20°C$. It is not certain that the increase in rate of development by metol produced by an increase in pH can be wholly accounted for by the increase in concentration of the ion, but is is clear that the ionized form is much more active than the non-ionized form when the two are compared at equal concentrations.

When a developing agent contains two hydroxyl groups, both can ionize and the agent can be present in solution in three forms — the non-ionized, the form with only one hydroxyl group ionized, and the form with both groups ionized. Hydroquinone and catechol are examples of such agents. The doubly ionized form of hydroquinone is by far the most active form, but the singly ionized form may play a part under some conditions.

The p-phenylenediamines apparently do not form active ions in the pH range of photographic interest (although some oxidized forms may ionize), but the rate of development increases with increasing pH over a considerable range. Oxidation products formed during development by p-phenylenediamine and at least some of its derivatives retard development. It has been suggested that increasing the pH favors development by hastening the destruction of these retarding oxidation products, since it is known that their rate of decomposition increases with increasing pH.

The amount of alkali needed to obtain a definite pH depends on the developing agent and its concentration as well as on the amount of sodium sulfite used. Metol, which contains a half mole of sulfuric acid per mole of developing agent, requires enough alkali to neutralize the acid in addition to that needed to raise the pH to a desired value. At high pH, alkali is needed to ionize the hydroxyl groups of both metol and hydroquinone.

The buffering capacity of the alkali is of considerable importance, because the reaction of the developer with silver halide liberates acid. If the buffering action is weak, the pH of the developer may decrease seriously during use, with attendant loss in activity. Actually, the pH of the solution *within* the layer of swollen gelatin determines the actual rate of development of the layer, and the pH of a poorly buffered solution may change much more in this layer than in the bulk solution, particularly in the areas of high exposure level. The photographic effect of such a change in pH is indicated by the observation of Abribat,

Pouradier, and David[12] that the sensitivity and contrast obtained with developers of a given solution pH increase with increasing buffer capacity of the solution.

Data on the effect of various buffers show that the specific nature of the buffer has only a slight effect on the rate of development. Even the slight variation noted may be caused simply by a variation in total salt concentration. One important exception, however, is noted in the use of borate buffers with orthohydroxy developers because a complex is formed between the borate and the $-C(OH)=C(OH)-$ grouping, and the developer activity is markedly reduced as a result. Borate buffers, accordingly, should not be used with pyrogallol, catechol, or other developing agents having two active hydroxy groups in ortho positions.

In practice, several factors enter into the choice of a buffer for a particular developer. Buffer capacity in the desired pH region, solubility of the buffer salts, and cost of the buffer salts are all of importance. Some buffers adversely affect the properties of the fixing bath. Trisodium phosphate, for example, should not be used when a potassium alum fixing bath is employed.

Salt Effects

The rate of development by the charged agents depends upon the total salt concentration and upon the specific nature of the ions formed by dissociation of the salt. Usually this effect is unimportant in practice, since most developing solutions normally contain a rather high salt concentration, and moderate variations have little influence on the development rate. For this reason, the very existence of a salt effect is often overlooked.

The concentration of positive ions (principally sodium) is already $1N$ or greater in the developing solutions commonly employed in practice. An increase in the rate of development by hydroquinone can be achieved in such a solution by the addition of a large amount of potassium nitrate, but considerable variations in sodium ion concentration will produce no detectable change. The salt effect is even smaller in developers containing metol or other singly charged agents. Relatively large variations in salt concentration are of little or no practical significance in such developing solutions, except where large additions of salt produce a marked decrease in the swelling of the gelatin. Sodium sulfate, for example, is often added to the solution to control the swelling of the gelatin when development must be carried out at tropical temperatures. Such additions of sodium sulfate decrease the rate of development under proper conditions, presumably by retarding diffusion of the developer into the emulsion.

Sulfite

The development rates of most of the agents used commercially would be altered if the oxidation products of the agents were allowed to accumulate. Thus, the oxidation products of hydroquinone, pyrogallol, and p-hydroxyphenylglycine accelerate development, while the oxidation products of metol, p-aminophenol, and p-aminodiethylaniline retard development over most or all of its course. Sufite changes the development rates of solutions of these and many other agents simply by combining with the oxidation products to form sulfonates.

Since the amount of sulfite required to remove effectively the oxidation product is usually rather small, the quantities of sulfite normally employed in development are more than adequate. Fairly large changes in sulfite concentration can then be made without changing the rate of development in this way. Some of the substituted p-phenylenediamines are exceptional in this respect, however, and even such agents as hydroquinone and p-hydroxyphenylglycine may show some effects of oxidation products when the overall rate of development is large, even though the sulfite concentration is also large.

With some developing agents, changes in the sulfite concentration can produce a measurable change in development rate as a result of the general salt effect. Sulfite contributes 50 per cent or more of the total salt concentration in most practical developers.

The solvent action of sulfite on silver chloride and bromide undoubtedly has some effect on development rates, but data are not available on this point for developers of the conventional composition. A more important practical aspect of this solvent action is the tendency of high-sulfite developers to give less graininess, other things being equal, as discussed in a later section of this chapter,

Large concentrations of sulfite can change the relative rates of development for different exposures, and in this way change the measured emulsion speed for incomplete development. The effect is illustrated in Fig. 7·6 by some data obtained with ascorbic acid as developing agent. The measured speed (expressed as $1 - \log i$) is plotted against sulfite concentration for development carried to a constant gamma. Sulfite produced a marked

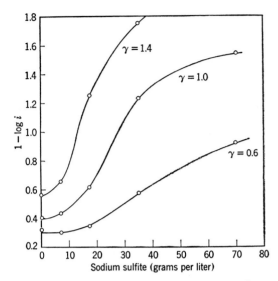

Fig. 7 · 6   Variation of emulsion speed with sulfite content of an ascorbic acid developer.

increase in the measured speed for each of the three gamma values represented. An increase of this type, however, has been obtained only when the active developing agent was a negative ion. It is probable that the charge barrier effect once more is involved. The solvent action of the sulfite may disrupt the adsorbed bromide ion layer and in this way make the latent image centers formed by the smaller exposures more accessible to the developer ions than they were originally.

The Temperature Coefficient

The rate of most chemical reactions increases with increase in temperature, and development is no exception. Because the variation of rate with temperature is often large, adequate temperature control is of considerable practical importance.

The temperature dependence of development varies considerably according to the composition of the developer and the photographic material used. The temperature coefficient (that is, the factor by which the rate of development increases when the temperature is increased 10° C) can be as low as 1.25-1.3 for some developer-emulsion combinations and as high as 4 for others. Figure 7 · 7 illustrates the temperature dependence of development by several agents used in the formula given on page 135. A change in developer composition, however, could change even the relative behavior of the various agents.

Several factors can combine to determine the net effect of temperature on development.[13] Under certain conditions, one factor alone can dominate and mask the presence of the others, but under most practical conditions, several are involved. These include one or more of the following.

An increase in temperature increases the specific rates of the chemical reaction or reactions of development. If a particular chemical reaction is rate-controlling, the temperature dependence over a limited range can be expressed by the Arrhenius equation [Eq. 5·3, p. 88]. An increase in temperature also increases the rate of diffusion of the developer components and reaction products through the emulsion layer. The rate of development in some solutions depends primarily on the chemical reaction and in others primarily on diffusion. Sometimes the rate depends on the chemical reaction at low temperatures, on

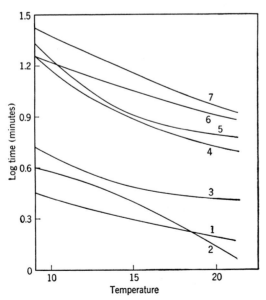

Fig. 7·7 Dependence of time of development required to obtain a fixed gamma upon temperature of the developing solution. 1, amidol; 2, metol; 3, pyrogallol; 4, p-aminophenol; 5, catechol; 6, hydroquinone; 7, p-hydroxyphenyglycine. (Chibisoff.)

diffusion at high, and on both in varying degrees at intermediate temperatures.

At constant pH, the degree of ionization of the organic developing agents which contain hydroxyl groups increases with increasing temperature. Since the ionized form is generally more active than the un-ionized, this means that the concentration of effective developing agent increases with temperature. On the other hand, the pH of a buffer solution of fixed composition generally decreases with increasing temperature. The influences of temperature on the degree of ionization and on the pH thus act in opposite directions, but a net increase in ionization usually occurs.

The quantitative effect of temperature can depend upon the amount and kind of exposure of the photographic material. The temperature dependence often increases with decrease in the amount of the exposing light. It may vary with the composition of the photographic material as well.

The temperature dependence varies with the developing agent, and it often decreases with increasing pH for a particular agent. The latter change is connected with the previously mentioned increase in the degree of ionization as pH increases, which causes a decrease in the *relative* effect of temperature on the concentration of the ionized form. The temperature dependence is generally greater when the developer contains soluble bromide than when it does not.

A change in temperature can influence the relative amount of solution-physical development. The temperature dependence of solution-physical development is often, though not always, greater than that of direct development.

The rate of fog development is more dependent on temperature than the rate of latent-image development. The higher the temperature, the greater will be the fog obtained in development to a particular gamma. The swelling of the gelatin also increases with increase in temperature, and the emulsion layer becomes more susceptible to physical damage.

Cationic Development Accelerators

Development by some agents is markedly accelerated by the presence of small amounts of certain quaternary ammonium salts which ionize to give a positively charged organic ion. Two effective salts of this type are α-picolinium-β-phenylethyl bromide and lauryl pyridinium bromide. In the pyridinium series of quaternary salts, the magnitude of the acceleration increases with increasing size of the aliphatic chain from methyl (CH_3) to lauryl ($C_{12}H_{25}$), and the amount of quaternary salt required to produce a noticeable effect decreases. The basis for this type of development acceleration appears to lie in the charge effect. The positively charged quaternary ions are adsorbed by the silver halide, and a good correlation has been observed between the degree of acceleration and the degree of adsorption of the quaternary ion in a simple series such as the pyridinium series. Moreover, the acceleration depends on the charge of the developer ion. The rate of development by uncharged agents, such as members of the p-phenylenediamine series, is either not affected by the quaternary ions or is even decreased. Among the negatively charged developers, the accelerating effect of a given quaternary ion increases with an increase in the charge. The positively charged quaternary ion evidently promotes adsorption of the negatively charged developer ion and thereby accelerates development. Certain other positively charged organic ions, such as the ions of sensitizing dyes, act in a similar way, but the net effect of strongly adsorbed dyes appears to be complicated by other factors.

Superadditive Combinations of Developing Agents

A combination of two developing agents sometimes shows greater photographic activity than would be expected from the activities of the separate agents. Such combinations are said to be *superadditive.*

Two types of superadditivity can be distinguished. In both, the density developed in a given time by a solution which contains the two agents, A and B, is greater than the sum of the densities produced on separate strips of film, one developed in a solution which contains the same amount of A as used in the combination and the other developed in a solution which contains the same amount of B. All solutions are of the same pH and the same composition except for the developing agent, and the film strips have received the same exposure. In the first type of superadditivity, the *maximum rate* of growth of density in the solution which contains both A and B does not exceed the sum of the maximum rates in the solutions of the separate agents. In the second and more important type of superadditivity, the maximum rate of growth of density in the solution of the two agents does exceed the sum of the rates in the separate solutions.

The first type can be obtained when developer B shows a relatively large induction period and A shows little or none. It can be explained by the simple assumption that A starts development of the grains and thus shortens the time required for B to act with maximum efficiency in the combination.

The two developing agents of the combination which exhibits the second type of superadditivity also generally show marked differences in their induction periods, but the simple explanation given for the first type is inadequate. The mechanism of this second type is still in doubt. One suggestion is that A is the active developing agent and that B acts in the combination primarily to regenerate A by reducing the oxidized form of the latter. One condition under which regeneration could lead to rate supperadditivity would be that the oxidation product of A inhibit development and that it not be adequately removed by the sulfite. Another suggestion is that the oxidation product of A may be a positively charged ion, which could then accelerate development by B (see preceding section). The two developing agents in a superadditive pair generally consist of an agent which is active in the form of a multiply charged negative ion (e.g., hydroquinone) and an agent which is active as an uncharged molecule (Phenidone at low pH) or a singly charged ion (metol or Phenidone at higher pH), and a positively charged oxidation product of the latter could markedly accelerate development by the developing agents which act in the form of a multiply charged negative ion. Other explanations of superadditivity have also been suggested in the literature.[14]

The best-known examples of superadditivity among the commercial developers are the combinations of hydroquinone and metol and of hydroquinone and Phenidone.

Kinetics of Solution-Physical Development

Under most conditions of practical development, where solution-physical development is taking place to some extent along with the direct development, the rate of the solution-physical development depends upon the composition of the solution in quite a different way from the rate of direct development. The rate of solution-physical development by a metol developer, for example, is almost independent of pH in the alkaline solution, whereas the rate of direct development increases markedly with increasing pH. Consequently, solution-physical development plays a relatively greater part in total development at low pH than it does at high.

The rate of solution-physical development increases with increasing sulfite content. Small amounts of thiocyanate and ammonia also markedly increase the rate. Although ammonia has less solvent action for silver bromide than an equivalent amount of sulfite in terms of equilibrium solubility, it increases the rate of solution by a much greater factor.

Small additions of bromide (e.g., a few tenths of a gram of potassium bromide per liter) decrease the rate of solution-physical development, but larger amounts increase it. The temperature coefficient is relatively high, but it depends to some extent on the solvent. Activation energies in the range 15-20 kcal/mole have been reported for various solvents.

The Relation of Kinetics to Structure

Developing agents can be classified on the basis of a rough correlation between development kinetics and chemical structure.[14] The classes include (1) agents with only hydroxyl groups as "active" groups, (2) agents with both hydroxyl and amino active groups, (3) agents with only amino active groups, (4) metal ions, and (5) metal ion complexes in which the metal has a variable valence.

Most agents of class (1) are aromatic compounds, although some developers of this type, such as ascorbic acid, are aliphatic compounds. The agents in which the hydroxyl groups are in the para position to each other are generally most active in the form of the doubly charged ion, show a marked dependence of rate on pH, and have a relatively large induction period. Their action is markedly accelerated by active quaternary salts during the early stages of development. The oxidation product or products of many of these agents accelerate development, and sulfite retards it. Agents with the hydroxyl groups in the ortho position show properties in between those of the para hydroxy compounds and the corresponding compounds of class (2) in which an amino and a hydroxyl group are in the para position to each other. The ortho compounds, however, generally resemble the para hydroxy compounds more closely with respect to curve shape, influence of quaternary salts, and influence of oxidation products.

Most agents of class (2) are aromatic compounds. Those in which the amino and hydroxyl groups are in the para position generally show small induction periods. Quaternary salts accelerate development, but the maximum acceleration does not exceed two- to three-fold if the developer molecule does not contain ionized groups other than the hydroxyl. The ion formed by ionization of the hydroxyl group is more active than the un-ionized molecule. The oxidation products sometimes accelerate development slightly during the induction period, but generally decrease the rate of development in the later stages. If the compound contains a radical with a carboxylic acid or a sulfonic acid group as a substituent of the amino group, the induction period is increased and the general photographic properties are shifted towards those of the para hydroxy compounds of class (1). A sulfonic acid group in the ring produces a similar but smaller shift. Kinetic data are scarce on compounds of class (2) in which the active groups are in the ortho position, and do not warrant general conclusions.

Compounds of class (3) are mostly aromatic. The agents in which the amino groups are in the para position and the molecule contains no ionized group generally develop without an induction period, although some show a small one. Development is not accelerated by quaternary salts and is often retarded by them; it is generally retarded by oxidation products and accelerated by sulfite. The presence of an ionized group shifts the photographic properties towards those of class (2). Agents of class (3) in which the active groups are present only in the ortho position are generally very weak developers.

The dependence of the rate of development on pH is generally less for class (2) developers than for class (1), and still less for class (3).

Phenidone (1-pheny-3-pyrazolidinone) and its derivatives should probably be placed in a special section of class (2). They can ionize, but the un-ionized form appears to be quite active as well as the ionized form. These compounds develop without an induction period, and their action is not accelerated by quaternary salts. They resemble the p-aminophenols of class (2) in some properties and the p-phenylenediamines of class (3) in others.

Vanadous ion is the only representative of class (4) about whose photographic properties we have any details. This agent develops without an induction period and shows little dependence upon pH so long as the pH is low enough to keep the vanadous ion from hydrolyzing. The rate of development seems to be largely determined by the rate of diffusion through the gelatin.

The members of class (5) which have been studied in detail generally show considerable induction periods when the complexing ion is present in sufficient excess. The rate of development is increased by quaternary salts, but it shows relatively little dependence on pH. These agents must be used at a pH sufficiently low to prevent precipitation of the metal hydroxides and a breakdown of the metal ion complex.

Fine-Grain Development

The graininess of the developed image depends to some extent on the developer. In a later chapter, the subject of graininess will be dealt with in detail. For the present purposes, graininess may be defined simply as the inhomogeneity of the image as seen by the observer. It becomes particularly evident in large-scale enlargements and in motion-picture projections viewed close to the screen.

The outstanding developing agent which, by itself, gives low graininess (fine-grain development) is p-phenylenediamine. The exact reason for this is unknown. p-Phenylenediamine has a strong solvent action for silver halide, however, which favors the physical type of development. Moreover, the addition of its isomer, m-phenylenediamine (not a developer) to low-activity solutions of certain developing agents reduces the graininess of the developed silver image, probably because of the solvent action of the diamine.

Apart from p-phenylenediamine and possibly o-aminophenol, the developing agents themselves show little difference in the graininess of the images they develop. Fine-grain development is largely a matter of the composition of the developing solution. Relative rates of direct development, solution of the silver halide, and physical development bear an important relation to the graininess produced. Solutions of low or moderate rates of development give reduced graininess when certain silver halide solvents are present. Typical solvents include sodium sulfite (in large amounts), ammonium chloride, certain organic amines, and potassium or ammonium thiocyanate. Kodak D-76 and D-23 are representative of the developers which depend solely upon sodium sulfite; DK-20 represents a group containing thiocyanate.

The action of the fine-grain developers appears to depend upon the proper balance of development rate and solvent action. The developers just listed largely lose their fine-grain action if the *p*H of the solution is increased to the point where they become rapid developers. Moreover, if the solvent action is increased too much, as by addition of sodium thiosulfate, graininess is adversely affected.

Microscopic examination[15] of the developed and developing grains has shown definite differences between the action of the fine-grain developers and of the high-activity, low-solvent developers. The solvent action in DK-20 is marked on grains which do not develop. In the preliminary phase of development of silver bromide grains which contain no iodide, some grains start to develop in the manner of normal chemical development, but the main part of development appears to be an intensifier action in which silver is deposited by solution-physical development on grains which are already partially developed. The final silver grains are, in general, larger than the original silver bromide grains if development is continued sufficiently. Development of grains with an iodide content that is customary in negative emulsions appears to be largely solution-physical, but on the average the developed grains are smaller than the original ones. Many more development centers are formed by DK-20 than by the high-activity, low-solvent developers.

Meidinger[16] observed that the mean time for reduction of grains by a fine-grain developer was much greater than for an active metol-hydroquinone developer. Although the former started to develop about the same number of grains as the latter, it only partially reduced the grains during the normal time of development, whereas the active developer reduced the grains completely.

Latensification by Chemical Treatment

The effective photographic speed of an emulsion for normal development can often be increased to some extent by suitable treatment after the image-forming exposure has been made. This effect is termed *latensification*. The secondary low-intensity exposure technique described in Chapter 4 (p. 72) represents one type of latensification. Other kinds of treatment which can produce latensification under proper conditions can be divided into three general classes: (1) treatment with metallic agents, such as mercury vapor and gold salts, (2) compounds of suitable redox potential, such as hydrogen peroxide and sodium perborate, and (3) sulfur dioxide, bisulfite ions, and certain amines. The mechanism of these three kinds of latensification is uncertain, but type (1) may involve the addition of mercury or gold atoms to latent image centers, or the replacement of some silver by mercury or gold, and type (2) may involve the reduction of silver ions to silver with a corresponding increase in the size of the latent image centers.

The effectiveness of any latensification depends on the development conditions. The degree of latensification decreases with increasing degree of development and may be negligible for prolonged development in a solution of high activity. Latensification also depends on the nature of the latent image, and it is more effective for image exposures of short duration and high intensity. Gains in speed are seldom more than two-fold and may be considerably smaller.

Fog

It is desirable to regard fog as characteristically different from the density produced by image development. In the presence of a developed image, however, it is usually impossible to separate quantitatively the densities arising from the two sources. The amount of fog in a given area must decrease with increasing image density, because some of the grains which might have been reduced as fog have developed as image. To add to the difficulty of separation, the optical density of fog usually does not bear exactly the same relation to the mass of silver as the image density does. Under some conditions, the difference may be negligible; under others, it may be considerable. There is no assurance that the photometric equivalent (M/D) of the fog, determined in the absence of the image, is the same as that of fog formed in the presence of the image. It is quite likely that the presence of the developing image changes to some extent the form, distribution, or amount of fog silver, particularly when a considerable amount of silver halide solvent action is occurring. For example, silver ions in solution which, in the absence of an image, would produce fog nuclei by reduction may, in the presence of an image, simply develop out upon the image centers.

Fog generally has a complex origin. Emulsion fog and developer fog often are produced simultaneously, and other types may be superimposed upon them under certain conditions. Experimentally, a partial separation between emulsion fog and development fog can be made by use of emulsions specially prepared for the purpose; limited kinetics studies have been made in this way. These have indicated a marked difference in the effect of sulfite on the two types of fog produced when hydroquinone is used as developing agent. A small amount of sulfite decreases the rate of emulsion fog formation, just as it decreases the rate of development. On the other hand, the sulfite *increases* the rate of developer fog formation. The quinone formed in the initial stages of the fogging reaction evidently interferes with the further formation of developer fog, probably by destroying incipient catalytic centers. Substances other than sulfite which remove quinone produce a similar increase in this type of fog.

With most developers, both types of fog formation are more sensitive than image development to changes in the bromide content of the solution. Accordingly, bromide is often used as an *anti-foggant* in development. Certain other substances, such as 6-nitrobenzimidazole, have a similar action, either separately or in combination with bromide.

In most cases of practical development, high concentrations of sulfite tend to promote fog formation, particularly when the rate of development is low. This effect probably is associated with the solvent action of the sulfite, because other silver halide solvents, such as ammonia, thiosulfate ion, and thiocyanate ion exert a similar action. A small amount of sodium thiosulfate, accidentally transferred to the developer from the fixing bath, can result in a considerable increase in fog under proper conditions.

The physical character of the fog can be changed by the solvent action. This change may be accompanied by a change in appearance and in the photometric equivalent. In extreme cases, the color of the fog is yellow or even grayish white in reflected light, and reddish in transmitted light. The photometric equivalent is considerably larger than that of image silver, and it may even amount to several times the latter.

The origin of other types of fog, such as aerial fog and sulfide fog, has been discussed already. These types appear largely as a result of accidential circumstances in practical development, and a discussion of the kinetics of formation would involve an expenditure of space quite out of proportion to their practical or theoretical importance.

REFERENCES

General

Mees, *The Theory of the Photographic Process,* revised edition, Macmillan, New York, 1954, Chapter 15.

Chibisoff, "Theory of the Photographic Process," *Kinophotoizdat,* Moscow, 1935 (in Russian).

Specific

1. Meidinger, *Physik. Z.,* **36,** 312 (1935).
2. Rabinovich, Bogoyavlenski, and Zuev, *Acta Physicochim, U.R.S.S.,* **16,** 307 (1942).
3. Sheppard and Ballard, *J. Franklin Inst.,* **206,** 659 (1928); James, *ibid.,* **240,** 83, 229 (1945).
4. James, *J. Phys. Chem.,* **44,** 42 (1940).
5. James, *J. Franklin Inst.,* **240,** 15 (1945).
6. Elvegard, *Z. wiss. Phot.,* **41,** 81 (1943); **42,** 65 (1944).
7. Ives and Jensen, *J. Soc. Motion Picture Engrs.,* **40,** 107 (1943).
8. Nietz, "The Theory of Development," Monograph 2 on *Theory of Photography,* Eastman Kodak Co., Rochester, N.Y., 1922.
9. Levenson, *J. Phot. Sci.,* **1,** 117 (1953).
10. James and Vanselow, *Phot. Sci. and Tech.* (2) **1,** 77 (1954).
11. Reinders and Beukers, *Ber. VIII intern. Kongr. Phot., Dresden,* 171, (1931).
12. Abribat, Pouradier, and David, *Sci. et inds. phot.,* **20,** 121 (1949).
13. James, *Phot. Sci. and Tech.,* (2), **2,** 81 (1955).
14. Levenson and James, *J. Phot. Sci.,* **2,** 169 (1954).
15. Loveland, private communication.
16. Meidinger, *Z. Naturforsch.,* **6a,** 275 (1951).

Fixing and Washing

Only a portion of the total silver halide of the original emulsion is reduced to silver during the development of a normal photograph. The remaining silver halide impairs both the immediate usefulness of the photograph and its permanence, and hence should be removed. In the fixing process, the residual silver halide is dissolved out of the film without damaging the metallic silver of the image.

Some Factors Affecting the Solubility of Silver Halides

The solubility of silver halide in the fixing solution can be treated simply as an equilibrium problem, without reference to the mechanism of solution. Let us consider first the solubility of silver halide in pure water. The amount that dissolves is controlled by the product of the concentrations of silver and halide ions, that is, by the solubility product. This is a constant for any given temperature:

$$[Ag^+] [X^-] = K \text{ at constant temperature} \qquad (8 \cdot 1)$$

The values of K for silver bromide and silver chloride are of the orders of 10^{-13} and 10^{-10}, respectively, in the region of normal processing temperatures ($18°$ to $24°C$). If neither silver nor halide ion is in excess, the solubility in terms of moles per liter is given by the square root of K. If a slight excess of halide ion is present (not enough to form complex ions to any significant extent) the solubility will be even less. In either event, the solubility is so small that washing the silver halide out of the emulsion with pure water is not in the least feasible.

According to equation $8 \cdot 1$, the solubility of silver halide in water can be increased by any device that will reduce the concentration of either silver ion or halide ion. If the concentration of silver ion, for example, is decreased by the addition of some agent that will form a complex with it, the halide ion concentration must increase in order that K of equation 8·1 remain constant. This increase in halide ion concentration is brought about by the solution of more silver halide. Hence, the solubility of the silver halide is increased by the addition of the complex-forming agent. The function of the fixing agents is to form complexes in which the silver ions are tightly bound. Examples of such complex-forming substances have been encountered already in preceding chapters. Thus, sulfite forms the soluble complex $Ag(SO_3)_2^=$, ammonia forms the complex $Ag(NH_3)_2^+$, and halide ions in considerable excess form soluble complexes of uncertain composition. A number of other substances are known which form complexes of the general formula $AgA_2^{(2n-1)-}$, although this is not the only form which silver complexes can take. The complex is dissociated slightly into silver ions and A molecules or ions according to the relation

$$\frac{[Ag^+][A^{n-}]^2}{[AgA_2^{(2n-1)-}]} = K' \qquad (8·2)$$

This equation determines the permissible silver ion concentration in the solution, provided the substance **A** does not form other complexes with silver ions and thus introduce further complications in the quantitative formulation. In general, the smaller the silver ion concentration, as given by equation 8·2, the greater will be the solubility of silver halide in a solution of **A**.

Sulfite and ammonia are not strong solvents for silver bromide, since K' is too large in each of them. It is of the order of 10^{-8} for ammonia and 10^{-9} for sulfite in the temperature range of 18° to 24°C. Certain other substances form complexes which have much smaller dissociation constants and hence are much stronger solvents for silver bromide. Thus, thiosulfate ion forms a complex having a dissociation constant of the order of 10^{-14}, and cyanide ion forms a complex having a constant of about 10^{-19}. Solutions of either substance in sufficient concentration act as strong solvents for silver bromide. It is evident that the bromide is more soluble in a cyanide solution than in a thiosulfate solution of equal concentration, but the cyanide is objectionable for photographic use because of its poisonous nature. The thiosulfates, particularly in the form of sodium salt (hypo), are used almost exclusively as fixing agents in practice.

The existence of two silver thiosulfate ion complexes of the formulas $Ag(S_2O_3)_2^=$ and $Ag(S_2O_3)_3^{\equiv}$ seems well established.[1,2] Chateau and Pouradier[2] calculated the dissociation constants of the two complexes to be 3.5×10^{-14} and 7.0×10^{-15}, respectively, at $20°C$. Both complexes are probably formed during fixation in baths of the usual composition. The various complex salts which have been isolated in solid form need not be considered as playing a role in fixation. At least four of these salts have a stable existence at room temperature, but they dissociate into ions in solution. However, one salt contains $AgS_2O_3^-$, which probably is the *initial* complex formed in fixation.

Since silver iodide has a solubility product of only 10^{-16} at $20°C$, iodide ions greatly depress the solubility of silver bromide in thiosulfate solution. Even the small percentages of silver iodide present in most negative materials have a marked effect upon the total solubility of silver salt in the fixing bath.

Ideally, a fixing agent should dissolve the silver halide without attacking the silver of the image. Sodium thiosulfate does not completely fulfill this requirement, inasmuch as it does attack the silver to some extent, the rate of solution being greatest when the silver is in the finest state of division. The rate is materially increased by the presence of oxygen, which may play an essential part by oxidizing the silver. In appreciably acid solutions which also contain bisulfite, sulfur dioxide apparently plays the part of an oxidizing agent in increasing the rate of solution of the silver, and the action becomes very marked in strongly acid solutions. Ammonium thiosulfate solutions appear to attack the silver image more readily than sodium thiosulfate solutions. In practice, however, the amount of silver dissolved by the conventional fixing bath is usually of little importance unless fixation is prolonged considerably beyond the time normally required for removal of the silver halide. A notable exception is post-fixation physical development, where the solvent action can destroy much of the latent image.

Rate of Fixation

The total solubility of silver halide in a thiosulfate solution determines the maximum capacity of that solution to dissolve the silver halide. However, the practical usefulness of the solution as a fixing bath is determined primarily by other considerations. One of these is the rate of fixation, or the total time required to fix a given type of emulsion in the bath in question.

Sheppard and Mees[3] investigated the kinetics of fixation of a silver bromide emulsion in dilute solutions of sodium thiosulfate. They found that the rate was not altered by the addition of 0.1 M potassium bromide to the solution, but was substantially increased by agitation. These findings suggested that the rate is determined to an important extent by a diffusion process.

Most of the experimental work which has been done on the kinetics of fixation is based upon determinations of the clearing time, that is, the time required for the disappearance of the last visible trace of silver halide. Measurement of the clearing time involves the determination of the point at which the fixing rate becomes negligible so far as the eye can judge. It is not entirely satisfactory as a quantitative measure of the fixing rate. Results

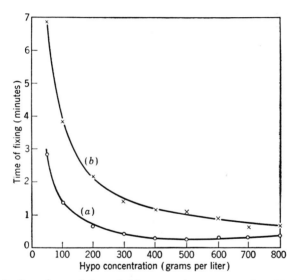

Fig. 8·1 Dependence of time of fixing upon hypo concentration. (a) Fine-grain emulsion. (b) Coarse-grain emulsion. (Russell.)

based on this method usually have at least semi-quantitative value, however, and the clearing time is obviously of direct practical interest. It has been found to vary with (1) the nature of the emulsion, (2) the thiosulfate concentration, (3) the nature of the cation, (4) temperature, (5) agitation, (6) the degree of exhaustion of the fixing bath, and (7) the presence of other salts.

The clearing time varies considerably with the size of the silver halide grains, being shorter for fine-grain emulsions than for coarse-grain ones, other things being equal. This is shown by Fig. 8·1, where curve (*a*) represents data for a fine-grain emulsion, curve (*b*) a coarse-grain emulsion. The result is to be expected if rate increases with halide surface. Fine-grain emulsions present a greater total area per unit weight of silver halide. Likewise, the clearing time varies with the mean diffusion path in the emulsion, and so it is larger for thick emulsions than for thin ones. The hardness of the gelatin has very little effect, if any.

The variation of clearing time with concentration of thiosulfate is also illustrated in Fig. 8·1. The time decreases rapidly with increasing concentration at first, but subsequently it levels off and shows little change beyond 300 to 400 grams per liter. The shape of the curve at the higher thiosulfate concentrations, however, sometimes departs markedly from that shown in Fig. 8·1. Many of the older data in the literature show a region of optimum concentration where the measured clearing time was a minimum. This optimum region usually occurred at about 300 to 400 grams per liter, and at higher concentrations the clearing time increased markedly. At least some of these data, however, apply to the time required to clear film which had been introduced directly into the thiosulfate solution without prior development. Conditions are not specified for the remaining data of this kind.

Alnutt[4] observed that, under otherwise identical conditions, curves showing optimum concentrations were readily obtained when dry film was introduced into the fixing solution, and curves showing no optimum were obtained when the film was first soaked in developer or in plain water. (The soaked film, of course, corresponds more closely than the dry to practical fixing conditions.) However, Alnutt found that the temperature of the fixing bath influences the shape of the concentration curve. His data for prewetted film show evidence of an optimum concentration when the temperature of a sodium thiosulfate solution was at 15°C, but no evidence of an optimum at high temperatures. His data for ammonium thiosulfate solutions show a definite optimum at 15°, but none at 25°. It is possible that the shape of the concentration curve may vary also with the nature of the photographic emulsion and the *p*H of the solution, but these factors have not been investigated adequately.

The cause or causes of the optimum have not been established with certainty. Sheppard has suggested that a balance between the effects of two opposing influences is involved. The first is the normal mass action effect of increasing concentration. This is predominant at the lower concentrations, where increase in thiosulfate concentration produces a corresponding increase in the fixing rate. The second is the effect of salt in depressing the swelling of the gelatin. When the decrease in swelling counterbalances the mass action effect, the rate of fixing reaches its maximum value. If this explanation is correct, the shape of the concentration curve should be influenced by pH changes and by the addition of a neutral salt such as sodium sulfate.

The rate of fixing, particularly of emulsions containing iodide, is dependent upon the nature of the cation. As indicated by the data in Fig. 8 · 2, the clearing time of a typical negative emulsion in ammonium thiosulfate solution is quite substantially shorter than that in sodium thiosulfate solution of equal concentrations. Lithium thiosulfate, on the other hand, is somewhat slower in its action than sodium thiosulfate. The fixing rates of potassium and calcium thiosulfates, as indicated by other data, are considerably slower than that of the sodium salt.

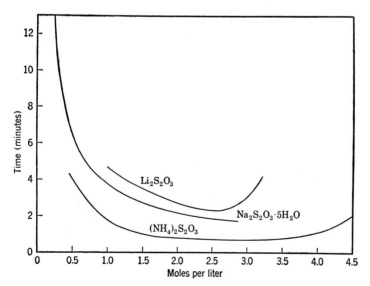

Fig. 8 · 2   Dependence of clearing time upon the concentration of various thiosulfates at 20°C. (Curves based upon data by Alnutt.)

Because of its faster action on emulsions containing iodide, ammonium thiosulfate is used commercially in the formulation of rapid-fixing solutions. Baths which are satisfactory in general properties can be prepared with ammonium in place of sodium thiosulfate, and the substantially shorter fixing times required by such solutions offer a distinct advantage wherever it is important to fix the emulsion in the shortest possible time. However, ammonium thiosulfate offers no practical advantage over the sodium salt in the fixing of the usual paper emulsions (chloride, chlorobromide, or pure bromide).

Ammonium thiosulfate suffers the disadvantage that it is less stable in the solid form than the sodium salt. Moreover, the solid residue obtained by evaporation of partially exhausted fixing baths containing ammonium thiosulfate is less stable in the presence of light than that obtained from the corresponding sodium thiosulfate baths. However, a photographic image fixed by ammonium thiosulfate does not lose stability on this account, provided the emulsion is given a normally thorough washing.

The clearing time decreases with increasing temperature. Apparently, the action is twofold. Both the swelling of the gelatin and the normal rate of diffusion in solution increase with increasing temperature. The net effect on the rate of fixation varies with the experimental conditions and with the concentration of the thiosulfate. The increased swelling of the gelatin, however, may seriously threaten the mechanical stability of the film if the temperature becomes too high, and the best working temperature for most purposes lies in the range of 16° to 24°C.

The clearing time is decreased by agitation, the reason being similar to that already given for rapid development. Agitation increases the rate of supply of fresh solution to the surface, and thus it increases the thiosulfate concentration gradient between the surface of the gelatin and the silver halide grains within.

The clearing time can be changed by the addition of salts other than the thiosulfate. For example, the addition of ammonium chloride to sodium thiosulfate solution under proper conditions decreases the clearing time of emulsions that contain iodide. The effect depends upon both the concentration of thiosulfate and the concentration of ammonium chloride. It is most marked at low thiosulfate concentrations, and an optimum ammonium chloride concentration is observed for any particular thiosulfate concentration.

Strauss found that sodium chloride accelerated fixing to some extent, but that sodium bromide retarded it. The effect of bromide was not marked, however, and Sheppard and Mees had found that 0.1 M bromide was without measurable effect at low thiosulfate concentrations. Sodium iodide has a powerful retarding effect upon the fixing process. Since most commercial silver bromide emulsions, particularly the negative materials, contain silver iodide, the accumulation of iodide in the bath during repeated use can become an important factor in determining the useful life of the bath under practical working conditions.

The clearing time changes with the degree of exhaustion of the fixing bath. The change in time is in the direction to be expected from a knowledge of the change in composition of the solution. These changes, and the accompanying alterations in the properties of the fixing bath, will be considered subsequently.

The clearing time does not in general represent the time when all the silver halide has been converted into silver thiosulfate complex. Small residues of silver halide still remain. It is desirable to extend the fixing time well beyond the clearing time for two reasons, firstly to allow conversion of the invisible silver halide residue into thiosulfate complex, and secondly to decrease the concentration of the complex and of halide ion in the gelatin layer. The evidence in general indicates that the fixing may be regarded as complete for practical purposes if the time is extended to about twice that required for clearing. This criterion, however, is a practical one rather than a universally applicable principle.

The Acid Fixing Bath[5]

The fixing agent in straight black-and-white photography is commonly employed in an acid solution. (This is not true for color photography because acid may adversely effect the dyes formed in coupler development.) The acid serves a dual purpose. (1) It permits the direct use of potassium alum (potassium aluminum sulfate) or chrome alum (potassium chromium sulfate) as hardeners in the fixing bath. These materials are not effective as hardeners in neutral or alkaline solution. (2) It neutralizes any alkaline developer which may be carried over, thus quickly stopping development and preventing the formation of stain. If the developed film were transferred directly to an *alkaline* thiosulfate solution, the reducing action of the developer in combination with the solvent action of the thiosulfate might lead to the formation of dichroic fog. Furthermore, stain might be formed by oxidation products of the developing agent which are not adequately removed by the now diluted sodium sulfite.

The use of acid, however, entails certain complications. Thiosulfate ion is unstable in acid solution, decomposing primarily according to the equation

$$S_2O_3^= + H^+ \rightleftharpoons HSO_3^- + S \qquad (8 \cdot 3)$$

In addition to bisulfite ion (or sulfur dioxide) and sulfur, various polythionic acids and hydrogen sulfide have been identified among the decomposition products. The hydrogen sulfide yield is very low, possibly because of its reaction with sulfur dioxide to·give free sulfur.

Decomposition of the acid thiosulfate solution can be greatly retarded by the use of a preservative, provided the pH of the solution is not too low. Bisulfite (often added as sulfite, but existing largely as bisulfite in the acid solution) acts as an effective preservative. The basis for the preservative action is implied in equation $8 \cdot 3$. The addition of bisulfite ion shifts the equilibrium toward the left, in accordance with the principle of mass action.

Even in the presence of sulfite, sulfurization will occur eventually. The sulfurization life of the bath, that is, the time that can elapse before sulfur begins to precipitate, depends markedly upon the hydrogen ion concentration. The accelerating effect of hydrogen ions on the decomposition is indicated by equation $8 \cdot 3$. In practice, the thiosulfate bath is generally used above a pH of 4.0, except when chrome alum is added as hardener. The chrome alum fixing baths are generally somewhat more acid, but the use of a lower pH is at the expense of a loss in stability.

The hardener is used in the fixing bath to decrease the hazard of mechanical injury to the gelatin layer. The latter, in a swollen condition, is easily scratched, torn, or distorted by mechanical action. Unhardened gelatin is most susceptible to such action during the washing process and during transfer from the washer to the drying apparatus. During fixation the swelling will be repressed to a considerable extent, either by the salt present or by virtue of a pH lying in the region of the isoelectric point. During washing, however, the salt is removed, and the pH generally rises progressively to a value well above the isoelectric point. The gelatin thus will swell to the maximum for that pH and temperature. The use of a hardener in the fixing bath restrains the swelling and thus reduces the danger of mechanical injury. Hardening becomes more important the higher the processing temperature, as the swelling increases rapidly with temperature.

The decrease in swelling of the gelatin layer can be used as a practical measure of hardening. The swelling can be measured either by the change of weight of the gelatin layer or by the change in thickness (volume). A more convenient but somewhat more arbitrary method involves the change in melting temperature of the gelatin. The simplest measurements of melting temperature are made by placing strips of film in a water bath, raising the temperature of the bath at a definite rate, and noting the temperature at which the gelatin layer melts or shreds off the film support. The measured temperature depends somewhat upon both the rate of heating and the extent of agitation.

The hardening agent generally used in the fixing bath is potassium alum, $KAl(SO_4)_2 \cdot 12H_2O$. The extent of the hardening produced varies with both concentration and pH. This is illustrated by the schematic curve in Fig. 8·3, which shows that the hardness increases with pH until a maximum is reached beyond which it decreases. Little or no hardening action is obtained in alkaline solution.

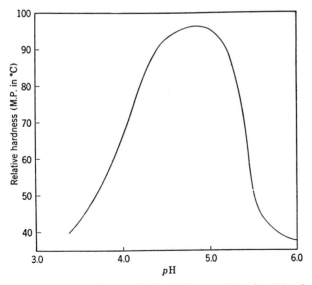

Fig. 8·3   Variation of hardening with the pH of a potassium alum fixing bath.

The mechanism of hardening is not completely understood. It is probable that some type of aluminum-gelatin complex formation occurs, in which the aluminum ion (or possibly an intermediate hydrolysis product) reacts with the $-COO^-$ groups of the gelatin chains to form cross-linkages between the polypeptide chains (see Chapter 2). This reaction increases the forces holding the chains together in the three-dimensional network of the rigid jelly. According to this view, three factors operate to produce a maximum in the hardening curves: (1) the free $-COOH$ groups of the gelatin end and side chains become increasingly ionized to $-COO^-$ with increasing pH; (2) the concentration of aluminum ions decreases with increasing pH because of the formation of the insoluble hydrous alumina, $Al_2O_3 \cdot x(H_2O)$, and related basic aluminum sulfites and sulfates; (3) the formation of colloidal alumina particles at the surface of the gelatin inhibits the penetration of aluminum ions into the gelatin because the colloid adsorbs the ions. The last two effects diminish the rate of hardening and, as they increase in magnitude, they eventually outweigh the first effect, and thereby account for the existence of the maximum in the hardening curve.

Any other factor which restrains penetration or reduces the concentration of aluminum ions should also decrease hardening. Thus, polycarboxylic acids (such as citric) and hydroxycarboxylic acids (such as lactic) inhibit hardening by binding the aluminum ions into complexes.

Besides aluminum, only chromium is of much practical importance as a hardener for the photographic emulsion during processing. The chromium is generally used in the form of chrome alum, $KCr(SO_4)_2 \cdot 12H_2O$. The mechanism of chromium hardening is still a subject of controversy. An optimum pH which is lower than that for aluminum is observed in chromium hardening, and it corresponds approximately to the point at which chromic oxide and the basic chromic sulfate start to form. Probably the chromic ion is the chief hardening agent, and apparently it can form cross-linkages between the polypeptide chains by reacting with either the $-COO^-$ group or the NH_2 group.

It has been noted already that the stability of thiosulfate in solution is an important consideration in the determination of a lower practical limit to the pH of the fixing solution. There are other limiting factors to consider, however. Decrease in pH beyond the optimum for hardening is accompanied by a decrease in hardening, and too low a pH is a disadvantage to the subsequent washing process. On the other hand, several factors enter to set a rough upper limit to the permissible pH of the practical solution. If the pH is too high, the bath is no longer effective in preventing stain. Increase in pH beyond the optimum is likewise accompanied by a loss in hardening power. Finally, if the pH becomes too high, the hardening agent tends to sludge out in the form of the hydrous oxide and related basic salts. The useful range of pH for the potassium alum fixing bath generally lies in the region of 4 to 6. The chrome alum baths are generally used in the region of 3 to 4 to obtain optimum hardening and low sludging tendency.

Since contamination from the developer tends to increase the alkalinity during use, the solution should be well buffered against an increase in pH. This is accomplished by use of mild acids, such as acetic, or acid salts, such as sodium bisulfite, to adjust the pH to the desired value. Boric acid, used in aluminum-containing fixing baths in the presence of acetic, propionic, or butyric acid, contributes specific properties by extending the useful hardening life and decreasing the sludging tendency as the pH of the bath increases by contamination with the developer. An acid that forms a relatively undissociated complex with the hardening agent should not be used, since such an acid will adversely affect the hardening properties of the solution.

Washing

The fixed photographic material contains considerable amounts of thiosulfate. Removal of this ion will result in a marked improvement in the stability of the silver image. The principal purpose of washing is to remove the thiosulfate, together with the usually small but not negligible amount of soluble silver thiosulfate complexes which remain in the film. When film or plate materials on stable supports are adequately fixed and washed, their silver images are permanent for practical purposes. If, however, the washing has been insufficient, the color (tone) of the silver image may change upon being kept at high humidity, and particularly at both high humidity and high temperature. This color change is known as fading. It is a result of a reaction between the thiosulfate and the finely divided silver, leading to the formation of yellowish or brown silver sulfide. An overall yellowish stain, particularly noticeable in the clear portions, can result from decomposition of the silver thiosulfate complex to form silver sulfide.

The washing of photographic materials coated on water-impervious supports, such as glass or cellulose nitrate or acetate film, is a straightforward process, and the thiosulfate can be adequately eliminated by a practical washing procedure. In the following discussion, the use of films or plates is implied unless otherwise stated. Washing of materials coated on fibrous supports, such as paper, represents a special case where complete removal of the thiosulfate is not possible by the ordinary washing process. The treatment of such materials will be considered separately.

At the outset, it will be useful to distinguish two extreme types of washing. In the first type, the film (or plate) is placed in a vessel of water and allowed to stand, either with or without stirring, until equilibrium is attained. At the equilibrium point, the rate of passage of thiosulfate from the film to the water equals the rate of passage from the water to the film. The amount of thiosulfate originally present in the film will be reduced to a definite fraction of the original amount, the magnitude of the fraction depending upon the volume of the water in the vessel. The vessel is now completely emptied and filled with water. When equilibrium is again attained, the amount of thiosulfate in the film has again been decreased, and by the same fractional amount as in the first washing. If the process is continued, the amount of thiosulfate in the film decreases exponentially with increasing *number of changes* of water.

In the second type, a continuous supply of fresh water is maintained at the film surface as, for example, by directing a rapidly flowing stream of fresh water against the surface. The rate of washing then is a continuous function, and is determined by the rate of diffusion of the thiosulfate from the gelatin layer. The rate of diffusion can be expressed simply by the equation

$$\frac{dM}{dt} = A \cdot P \frac{dc}{dx} \qquad (8 \cdot 4)$$

where dM is the amount of thiosulfate which diffuses in time dt, A is area of the film, P is the diffusion coefficient, and dc/dx is the concentration gradient in the gelatin layer. When a particular film is processed in a specified manner and washed under

conditions of constant temperature and pH, the diffusion coefficient is substantially constant and the rate of washing (removal of thiosulfate) is determined by the concentration gradient. If a continuous supply of fresh water is actually maintained
at the gelatin surface, the concentration of thiosulfate in this
water layer is zero, and the effective gradient has its maximum
value for whatever concentration of thiosulfate may be in the
gelatin layer. If the water layer at the surface contains thiosulfate, the concentration gradient will be smaller, and the rate of
washing will be smaller.

Virtually all practical washing practices involve compromises
between the two types just described. The water may be changed
at regular intervals, but without allowing time for equilibrium.
Then, both the frequency with which the water is changed and
the rate of diffusion will affect the time required for washing.
Other washing devices maintain essentially a continuous flow.
It is possible to approach quite closely conditions where the
concentration gradient is proportional to the amount M of thiosulfate remaining in the film. Integration of equation $8 \cdot 4$ shows
that, under such conditions, the concentration of thiosulfate in
the film drops exponentially with increasing washing time.

Factors Affecting the Diffusion-Controlled Rate of Washing

The rate of washing increases with the temperature of the
wash water. However, high temperatures produce excessive
swelling of the gelatin and thus increase the danger of mechanical damage to the emulsion. A wrinkling or reticulation of the
gelatin often is obtained when the temperature of the water is
too high, and excessive swelling of the gelatin may even retard
washing. For most practical purposes, the temperature should
be kept well below the region where reticulation occurs, and
the temperature should be approximately that of the fixing bath.

The rate of washing depends upon the pH of the water and
upon the composition of the fixing bath. Treatment of partially
washed materials with dilute alkaline solution (preferably 0.03
to 0.3 per cent ammonia) for a few minutes appreciably increases
the rate of subsequent washing. A controlled addition of ammonia to the wash water sometimes is used to effect the same result. Alkaline treatments have the disadvantage, however, that
they often remove or decrease hardening and thus promote softening and excessive swelling of the gelatin.

The change in the rate of washing with pH probably is associated with the change in the electrical state of the gelatin. At pH values below the isoelectric point, the positive charge of the gelatin tends to retain a negative ionic atmosphere within the layer. In alkaline solution, where the gelatin is itself negative, the opposite is true.

The rate of washing of film fixed in an alum fixing bath often is lower than that of film fixed in a non-hardening bath.[6] The effect of alum on washing depends upon the pH of the fixing bath and the kind of alum present. With potassium (aluminum) alum, the retarding effect is strong at pH 4.1 and decreases with increasing pH until a value between 4.7 and 5 is reached. At higher pH, the rate of washing shows little or no dependence upon the presence or absence of alum. The reason for the effect of alum on washing is not clear. The retarding action does not parallel the increase in hardening of the gelatin. Indeed, the latter often is at a maximum at a pH of around 5, whereas the effect of the alum upon washing is insignificant at that pH. Moreover, chrome alum does not exert nearly so great a retarding action as the corresponding aluminum compound. Adsorption of the thiosulfate to alumina or to the hardening complex has been suggested, but adequate proof of adsorption has not been obtained. Another possible factor is that of the influence of alum on the pH of the gelatin layer. Alum acts as a buffer in the pH range where the retarding effect is pronounced, and thus it may retard washing by retarding the adjustment of the gelatin pH to that of the wash water.

The rate of washing in certain salt solutions, such as sodium sulfate solution or sea water, is greater than that in plain water. However, the salt from sea water must be largely removed by subsequent washing, because small quantities of thiosulfate are destructive in the presence of chloride ion. A 2% sodium sulfite solution, or the corresponding sulfite solution which has been neutralized by the addition of bisulfite, is considerably more effective than sodium sulfate or sea water as a washing aid.[6]

Washing involves not only removal of thiosulfate ion, but removal of residual silver salts as well. However, the quantity of the residual silver salts already should have been lowered to a practical minimum by adequate fixation, as described on page 161. It is good practice in washing studies to compare results obtained with two widely different fixing times to insure that the washing rate is independent of the fixing time.

Removal of the silver thiosulfate complex by washing usually follows rather closely the removal of thiosulfate ion. Factors that produce a change in the rate of elimination of one produce a similar change in the rate of elimination of the other. An exception to this general statement appears in some experiments by Crabtree, Eaton, and Muehler[7] on washing film which had been fixed in a partially exhausted bath of pH 4.1. The bath contained potassium (aluminum) alum as hardener. The data show that small quantities of silver salt were retained by the film even after prolonged washing, and that the amount of silver salt retained depended upon the amount of film which previously had been fixed in the bath. If the pH of the fixing bath was raised above 5, however, the silver salt was completely eliminated by washing. No retention of silver was observed at any pH or following any degree of exhaustion when the fixing bath contained no hardener.

Washing of Papers

The washing of paper prints is more complicated from the theoretical viewpoint than the washing of film or plates. The initial rapid diffusion, which follows equation 8·4 rather closely, eventually degenerates into a very sluggish process. Although the main bulk of the thiosulfate can be removed within the first two or three minutes of washing, a harmful residue remains behind which will not be reduced to a tolerable amount in less than 30 to 60 minutes, depending upon the thickness of the paper support. Residues of the order of 64 milligrams of $Na_2S_2O_3 \cdot 5H_2O$ per square meter (0.04 mg per sq in.) may remain in single-weight prints after 6 hours of washing; this quantity is not significantly lowered by prolonging the washing up to 20 hours.

The washing of the usual photographic paper represents a compromise between the washing of at least two different parts: the gelatin layer and the paper base. The washing of the gelatin layer follows the same pattern as that of film or plates, as discussed previously. The washing of the paper base, particularly in its later stages, is the sluggish process. For this reason, factors that affect washing of the gelatin only do not affect the washing of paper prints except during the earliest part of the process.

Figure 8·4 shows the general form of the washing curve in the later stages, where the washing of the paper predominates. The rate of elimination of thiosulfate approaches zero while ap-

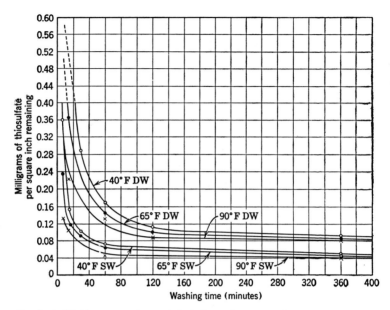

Fig. 8·4 Washing curves for typical single-weight (SW) and double-weight (DW) photographic papers. (Crabtree, Eaton, and Muehler.)

preciable amounts of thiosulfate still remain in the paper. Double-weight (DW) paper may retain up to double the amount retained by single-weight paper.

The thiosulfate retained by the paper after prolonged washing appears to be adsorbed. Adsorption is strongly suggested by some experiments of Crabtree, Eaton, and Muehler, in which the thiosulfate content of paper which had been soaked for varying times in a dilute thiosulfate solution was determined. The paper was prepared in the same way as normal photographic paper, except that the silver halide was omitted. Table 8·1, in which the thiosulfate concentrations have been calculated from their published data, gives some typical results. The solution used contained 0.400 grams sodium thiosulfate pentahydrate per liter.

The data in Table 8·1 show that the amount of thiosulfate taken up by the paper increases steadily with increasing time, whereas the total amount of solution in the paper becomes essentially constant within a few minutes. The data do not indicate whether the adsorption is by the paper fibers or by the sizing.

TABLE 8·1

UPTAKE OF THIOSULFATE BY PHOTOGRAPHIC PAPER BASE

Time of Treatment, Minutes	Weight of Absorbed Solution, Milligrams per Square Decimeter	$Na_2S_2O_3 \cdot 5H_2O$ in Milligrams per Square Decimeter
5	700	0.31
15	770	0.34
30	830	0.74
60	770	0.99
120	830	1.53
330	830	2.15

The extent to which washing should be carried to assure permanence of the image depends upon the degree of permanence desired. Film and prints destined for archival use require the maximum degree of permanence obtainable and, on the basis of results from accelerated fading tests, this means practically complete elimination of thiosulfate and silver complexes. Film and prints for ordinary commercial and amateur use do not require such stringent elmination. Crabtree, Eaton, and Muehler[7] have suggested the following values as the "maximum permissible concentration of thiosulfate" (as $Na_2S_2O_3 \cdot 5H_2O$) for commercial and archival use:

| Material | Commercial Use | | Archival Use |
	Mg per sq. in	Mg per sq dcm	Mg per sq dcm
Motion-picture film			
Fine-grain duplicating positive	0.02	0.30	0.08
Normal fine-grain release positive	0.05	0.80	0.15
High-speed negative	0.20	3.0	0.80
Film used by photofinishers and amateurs	0.15–0.25 [1]	2.3–3.9 [1]	0.80 [1]
Industrial type A x-ray film	0.15–0.25 [1]	2.3–3.9 [1]	0.80 [1]
Paper			
Double-weight	0.20–0.25	3.0–3.9	Nil
Single-weight	0.10–0.15	1.5–2.0	Nil

[1] Data apply to coatings on one side of the film.

When it is necessary to reduce the thiosulfate content of paper beyond that which can be attained by normal washing, as when storage conditions are adverse or when the material is destined for archival use, recourse must be had to the use of chemical agents. Alkaline baths are sometimes used as "assists" to promote the leaching out and subsequent washing away of thiosulfate, but the complete removal of thiosulfate is not obtained in this way unless the alkaline baths are employed for excessive times. It is preferable to use *hypo-eliminators* which quantitatively oxidize the thiosulfate to the innocuous sulfate without attacking the silver image. Chemical agents that convert thiosulfate to tetrathionate are not satisfactory, since tetrathionate easily effects sulfiding of silver images.

Muehler's hydrogen peroxide-ammonia mixture is quite effective as a hypo-eliminator. In practice, the well-fixed prints, which have been washed in plain water for 15 to 30 minutes, are treated for 5 to 6 minutes in the eliminator solution and finally washed about 5 minutes. The solution, which has a pH value in the range 9.8 to 10.2, reacts quantitatively with the thiosulfate according to the equation

$$Na_2S_2O_3 + 4H_2O_2 + 2NH_4OH \rightarrow$$
$$Na_2SO_4 + (NH_4)_2SO_4 + 5H_2O$$

Sodium chlorite in a suitably buffered, mild acid solution is another promising hypo-eliminator. Eliminators of this type are not required for the treatment of film and plate materials, however, and their use with such materials may even be disadvantageous because of their tendency to soften and blister the usual film or plate emulsion.

Complete removal of the silver thiosulfate complex has special importance for white papers, since small amounts can produce a noticeable stain upon decomposition. The practice of following the initial fixation by a treatment in a second bath of fresh fixing solution is useful in promoting complete removal of the silver salt.

Stabilization

The fixing and washing processes are sometimes replaced by a single step, called *stabilization*. This process may be employed when it is desired to obtain a usable (for some purposes) record in a minimum time. The stabilizing agents can be divided into two classes. The agents of the first class depend upon the same process as fixation; they form soluble complexes with silver ion. For stabilization, these complexes must be relatively insensitive to light and relatively stable to heat and humidity. An acid thiourea solution acts in this way, and a solution of 5 per cent sodium bisulfite and 30-60 per cent sodium thiosulfate is a suitable stabilizer for film. An excess of the agent is necessary for stability of the complex, however, and partial removal of stabilizer by incomplete washing may result in loss of stability of the image.

The agents of the second class form insoluble complexes or compounds with silver ion. Agents of the general formula RSH, where R is an aliphatic, aromatic, or heterocyclic radical, will form salts of the formula RSAg. Many of these compounds are relatively insoluble and are stable to light. They are usually opaque, however, and often colored, but they may be useful for stabilizing photographic papers none the less.

REFERENCES

General

Mees, *The Theory of the Photographic Process,* revised edition, Macmillan, New York, 1954, Chapter 17.
Clerc, *La technique photographique,* Paul Montel, Paris, 5th edition, 1950, Vol. 1, Chapter 29.
Glafkides, *Chimie photographique,* 2nd edition, Paul Montel, Paris, 1957, Chapter 11.
Baines, "Fixation—The Chemistry of the Hypo Bath," *J. Phot. Sci.,* **3,** 175-9 (1955).

Specific

1. Bassett and Lemon, *J. Chem. Soc.,* **1933,** 1423.
2. Ölander and Adelsohn, *Svensk Kemi Tid.,* **58,** 33 (1946); Chateau and Pouradier, *Sci. et inds. phot.,* **24,** 129 (1953).
3. Sheppard and Mees, *Investigations on the Theory of the Photographic Process,* Longmans, Green and Co., London, 1907.
4. Alnutt, *J. Soc. Motion Picture Engrs.,* **41,** 300 (1943).
5. Sheppard, Elliott, and Sweet, *J. Franklin Inst.,* **196,** 45 (1923).
6. Henn, King and Crabtree, *Phot. Eng.,* **7,** 153 (1956).
7. Crabtree, Eaton, and Muehler, *J. Soc. Motion Picture Engrs.,* **42,** 9 (1943); *J. Franklin Inst.,* **235,** 351 (1943).

9.

Sensitometry I, Exposure and Development

Photographic *sensitometry* is the science of measuring the sensitivity of photographic materials. It consists of the quantitative measurement of the relation between the density of the photographic image and the treatment to which the material has been subjected. The methods of exact sensitometry have become important to the users as well as to the manufacturers of photographic materials.

The trend in modern sensitometry is to obtain data which can be interpreted in terms of practical results. All methods of measuring sensitivity require a standard light source, a method of giving a graduated set of known exposures, a method of development that will give reproducible results, and a method of interpreting the response of the material to the process of exposure and development. If the results are to have practical significance, the radiant energy of the light source, time and intensity of the exposure, and the developer formula and development conditions must be in accordance with those used in practice. In addition, the response of the film must be interpreted in terms of that required from the material as it is commonly used. The above requirements will of course be different for different photographic materials, and will in fact depend upon the use for which they are intended.

Sensitometers

The instrument used to produce a precise set of graded exposures on a photographic material is called a *sensitometer*. The essential elements of a sensitometer are shown in Fig. 9 · 1. A light source of known luminous intensity which is emitting radia-

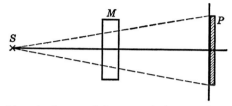

Fig. 9 · 1   Schematic diagram of the essential elements of a sensitometer.

tion of a known spectral composition is shown at S. The photographic material P is illuminated by the light source in such a manner that all points on the surface receive the same amount of radiant energy per unit time. The exposure-modulating device M is placed between the light source and the photographic material.

Light Sources

It is very important that the spectral composition of the light source used in a sensitometer be both *known* and *appropriate*. The spectral sensitivity curves for three typical photographic emulsions are shown in Fig. 9 · 2, together with the energy distribution for average noon sunlight and for light from a tungsten source. Curve A is for an ordinary blue-sensitive emulsion, B is for an orthochromatic blue-green-sensitive emulsion, C is for a panchromatic emulsion, D is the energy distribution for mean noon sunlight, and E is the energy distribution for a tungsten light source. If the ordinates of curves A, B, and C, respectively, are multiplied by the corresponding ordinates of curve D, the curves A_d, B_d, and C_d shown in Fig. 9 · 3 are obtained. The curves A_e, B_e, and C_e, as shown in the same figure, are obtained when the ordinates of curves A, B, and C are multiplied by the corresponding ordinates of curve E. A comparison of the areas under curves A_d and A_e in Fig. 9 · 3 gives the relative effectiveness of sunlight and tungsten light as a source for use with a blue-sensitive emulsion. In a similar manner, a comparison of the areas under the other two sets of curves in this figure gives the relative effectiveness of sunlight and tungsten light when used as a light source with an orthochromatic emulsion and a panchromatic emulsion, respectively. It is apparent from Fig. 9·3 that the energy distribution of the light source used for exposure is an important factor in sensitometry, since both the absolute and the relative responses of photographic materials to exposure depend markedly on the energy distribution of the light source.

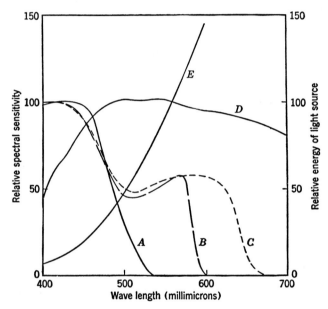

Fig. 9·2   Spectral sensitivity curves (A, B, C) for three typical photographic materials together with the energy distribution curves for mean noon sunlight (D) and a tungsten light source (E).

In practical sensitometry, the light source used to expose a given photographic material in the sensitometer must emit radiation which is *equivalent spectrally* to that used in practice to expose this same material. The light sources used in early sensitometric investigations had been developed as standards of luminous intensity rather than to be a spectral match for the light sources used in taking pictures. Among the sources which have been used are the standard candle, the Hefner lamp, the acetylene flame, and the standardized incandescent lamp. Of these sources, the calibrated incandescent lamp offers many practical advantages. However, the highest filament temperature of modern incandescent lamps is only about 3400°K, whereas the effective equivalent color temperature of the sun is approximately 5400°K. In order to obtain a spectral match between the radiation from an incandescent lamp and the several light sources used to make photographs, it is necessary to introduce a selectively absorbing filter between the light source and the exposure plane of the sensitometer.

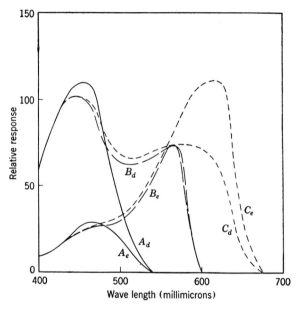

Fig. 9·3 The relative responses of photographic materials to mean noon sunlight and to a tungsten light source.

It is relatively easy to obtain a spectral match between the light source in the sensitometer and the artificial light sources used in practice; it is more difficult to obtain a spectral match between an artificial light source and sunlight. Dyed gelatin filters, such as the Wratten No. 79, give approximately the desired radiation when used in combination with the correct controlled source. These gelatin filters, although very stable, are not reproducible with sufficient precision to be useful in a primary standard. The International Congress of Photography in 1928 adopted a resolution defining the international unit of photographic intensity as one visual candlepower of radiation of the quality emitted by a 2360°K source screened with a Davis-Gibson liquid filter to an approximate match with sunlight, although the current trend is to use a 2850°K source filtered to *daylight*. The Davis-Gibson filters are fairly stable and reproducible. The formula for converting a 2360°K radiation to sunlight is:

SOLUTION A

Copper sulfate, $CuSO_4 \cdot 5H_2O$	3.707	grams
Mannite, $C_6H_8(OH)_6$	3.707	grams
Pyridine, C_5H_5N	30.0	cc
Water (distilled) to make	1000.0	cc

SOLUTION B

Cobalt ammonium sulfate, $CoSO_4 \cdot (NH_4)_2SO_4 \cdot 6H_2O$	26.827	grams
Copper sulfate	27.180	grams
Sulfuric acid (sp gr 1.835)	10.0	cc
Water (distilled) to make	1000.0	cc

Each solution is used in a cell 1.0 cm thick, the cells being in tandem.

Modulation of Exposure

Since exposure is the product of time and intensity, sensitometers may employ either a time-scale or an intensity-scale modulation system. Exposure is usually expressed in meter-candle-seconds and can be impressed either continuously or intermittently. Instruments for controlling exposure have been classified by L. A. Jones[1] into intensity-scale and time-scale sensitometers, subdivided as follows:

Type I.   Intensity-scale (sensitometers); I variable, t constant

        A. Exposure intermittent
            1. Wedged exposure
            2. Stepped exposure
        B. Exposure non-intermittent
            1. Wedged exposure
            2. Stepped exposure

Type II. Time-scale (sensitometers); I constant, t variable

        A. Exposure intermittent
            1. Wedged exposure
            2. Stepped exposure
        B. Exposure non-intermittent
            1. Wedged exposure
            2. Stepped exposure

Sensitometers using intermittent exposures were in general use until about 1920, but they have the very serious fault that a photographic material does not add intermittent exposures arithmetically for anything less than a critical frequency. This is shown in Fig. 9·4, where the two sensitometric curves represent data on the same material derived from intermittent and nonintermittent exposures of identical magnitude. In general, different values of gamma and inertia will be obtained from intermittent and non-intermittent exposures of the same material. Since the intermittency effect is associated with reciprocity failure (see Chapter 4), it is not the same for different materials, and the relative sensitometric values for different materials as obtained with intermittent exposures may not be the same as those obtained with non-intermittent exposures. To simulate the common practice in exposing photographic materials, the modulating device in the sensitometer must therefore be of the non-intermittent type. The exception would be an intermittent exposure device which impressed the exposures at a rate above the critical frequency.

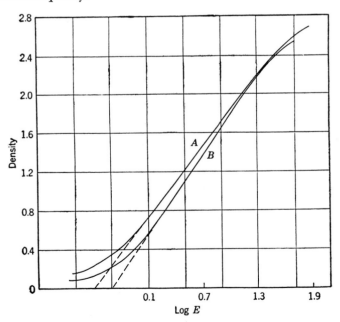

Fig. 9·4 Sensitometric curves from (A) non-intermittent and (B) intermittent exposures on a single material.

In comparing time-scale and intensity-scale sensitometers it is again necessary to point out that, if the sensitometric data are to be applied to the practical use of photographic materials, the data must be obtained under conditions similar to those under which the material is to be used. For most negative materials, this means a short, continuous, intensity-scale exposure at a relatively high level of intensity. In astronomy, however, it means long exposure times at a very low level of intensity. Sound recording is an example of the opposite extreme where the exposure given the photographic material is of the order of 1/20,000 second at very high levels of intensity.

The importance of selecting the proper intensity level is demonstrated by Fig. 9·5, which illustrates again the reciprocity law failure discussed in Chapter 4. The curves in this figure show the values of log It required to produce densities of 0.2, 0.4, 0.7, 1.0, 1.5, 2.0, and 2.5, respectively, for various values of log I. If time-

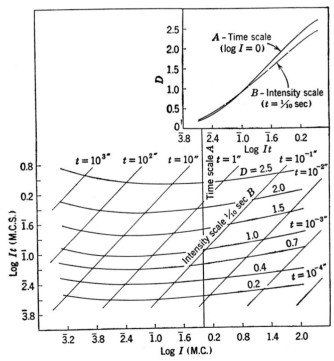

Fig. 9·5   Reciprocity failure curves for a panchromatic emulsion.

scale and intensity-scale sensitometers were to give the same sensitometric data, these curves would have to be straight lines parallel to the log I axis. Any ordinate across the curves, such as A, represents the data obtained with a time-scale sensitometer. Likewise, any line drawn through the curves at an angle of $45°$ to the coordinates, such as B, represents the data obtained with an intensity-scale sensitometer. If the density values are plotted against the exposure It for the set of intercepts produced by the lines A and B, respectively, the curves shown in the inset of Fig. $9 \cdot 5$ are obtained. These curves, which are the characteristic curves as obtained with time-scale and intensity-scale sensitometers, show the large differences that can occur between the two types of measurements. It should be noted that these two curves apply to only one level of intensity for the time-scale curve and to only one time for the intensity-scale curve. A complete set of curves could be drawn for both scales by employing the other lines parallel to A and B. It is clear that the curves within a given set can differ from each other appreciably.

Time-Scale Sensitometers (Type II)

Despite their many disadvantages, time-scale sensitometers were the earliest to be adopted in practice because of the difficulty of obtaining satisfactory instruments using an intensity scale. Until relatively recent years, it has been very difficult to obtain unvarying light sources and a strictly reproducible intensity modulator. These experimental difficulties led Hurter and Driffield to perform their classical work on sensitometry with a sensitometer employing a rotating sector disk giving intermittent exposures on a time-scale basis. Since the exposure is made by allowing the sector disk to make several revolutions, the long-period variations in light intensity act upon the whole of the strip at the same time and do not affect the relative exposures given each strip. A typical sector disk is shown in Fig. $9 \cdot 6$. Since each successive aperture is one-half as large as the preceding one, the innermost ring gives an exposure of half of the total time of operation; the next, one-fourth; the next, one-eighth; and so on, there being nine sectors in all in this particular disk.

As soon as it was possible to maintain the light source at a constant intensity for a period of time long enough to make an exposure, the errors arising from the intermittency effect could be eliminated by driving the disk at such a speed that it made the exposure in a single revolution. Such a sensitometer was

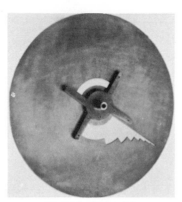

Fig. 9·6   Sector disk.

designed by L. A. Jones[2] particularly as a control instrument for use with motion-picture film. A schematic diagram of this instrument is shown in Fig. 9·7. The lamp house contains a carefully standardized tungsten filament lamp of a precision type. The light, after passing through a filter, is reflected by a mirror to the exposure plane. The exposure modulator is a cylindrical drum which makes one revolution for each exposure. The drum is driven by a synchronous motor to assure accurate exposure times, and it has twenty-one apertures increasing as powers of $\sqrt{2}$. For ordinary work, gelatin filters are placed between the light source and the exposure plane to produce a source-filter combination giving radiation comparable with that used in practice for the particular material being exposed. When desired,

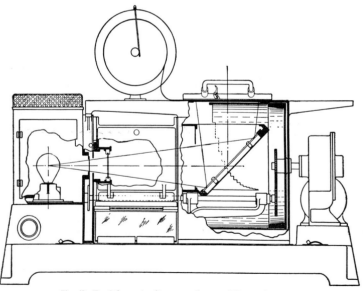

Fig. 9·7   Schematic diagram of type II-B sensitometer.

however, a Davis-Gibson filter can be used in place of the gelatin filters. Other similar non-intermittent time-scale sensitometers have been described which give longer or shorter exposure times by employing different types of sector wheels.

Intensity-Scale Sensitometers (Type I)

With the advent of steady light sources and reproducible intensity modulators, intensity-scale sensitometers have largely replaced time-scale sensitometers. By employing an exposure time in agreement with that used in practice and varying the intensity sufficiently to obtain a range of densities, the sensitometric data derived are directly applicable to the photographic material under practical operating conditions. The time of exposure would, of course, be different for different materials, depending upon the purpose for which the material is commonly used. The exposure time is commonly controlled by single-aperture sector disks, rotating drums with a single opening, or, when longer exposures are required, electronic time-control switches.

The most common method of modulating the intensity of the light falling on the sample employs an accurate step tablet or optical wedge. The exposure is made with these variable-density step tablets or wedges in contact with the photographic material. These wedges and tablets can be made by properly casting gelatin containing dyes or colloidal carbon. In practice, it is very difficult to make wedges or tablets that do not modify the spectral composition of the light falling on the sample. Even if they absorb uniformly in the visible spectrum, they frequently absorb the ultraviolet and the infrared selectively. For much sensitometric work, it is possible to use wedges made by suitable exposure and development of a photographic material. If such wedges are developed in a metol-hydroquinone developer, they will be very nearly neutral throughout the visible spectrum and the near infrared and near ultraviolet. Intensity-scale sensitometers employing these various types of step tablets or wedges are in general use for obtaining sensitometric data and for controlling photographic operations. However, unless these tablets are essentially non-selectively absorbing and have been carefully calibrated, they are not suitable for primary standards in a sensitometric laboratory.

In addition to the modulation of intensity by optical wedges, several systems of intensity modulation have been introduced which are based upon the principle of a diaphragmed optical system. Although there are many special forms of this system for modulating the intensity of light in a sensitometer, they are all dependent upon the simple law of optics that for a lens of given focal length the illuminance of the image is a function of the effective diameter of the lens; that is, the light is modulated in much the same way as the effective exposure of the common camera is reduced by stopping down the lens. Although satisfactory diaphragmed optical-system types of intensity-scale sensitometers have been designed[3,4] they have not been used extensively in practice because of their relative complexity as compared to instruments employing a wedge or step tablet to modulate the exposure. With a wedge in contact with the photographic material, all the intensity-scale exposures are made simultaneously, whereas with the diaphragmed optical system the exposure at each intensity level must be made independently, since the aperture must be changed to change the illuminance of the sample. On the other hand, modulating the exposure by a diaphragmed optical system does not affect the spectral composition of the radiant energy from the light source.

Development of the Sensitometric Samples

It is very difficult to develop photographic materials evenly and reproducibly because of the effect of development products on the rate of development (see Chapter 7). These products are formed most abundantly in the most exposed regions of the material, and if they are not removed by agitation or by a chemical reaction in the developer, they lead to uneven and non-reproducible results. As in all phases of sensitometry, the development must be carried out in such a manner that the results will be reproducible and will conform to those obtained in practice.

In most reactions between a photographic material and a developer, the change in specific gravity of the solution containing the reaction products is sufficient to set up convection currents. In vertical development without agitation, the reaction products, which usually have a higher specific gravity than the developing solution, drift to the bottom of the tank, and the rate of development accordingly varies from the upper part of the sample to the lower. These reaction products generally retard development, and the resulting difference in photographic density between the ends of a sample developed in a vertical tank without agitation can be as high as 10 per cent.

Many modifications of the vertical method of development have been proposed to eliminate the uneven development usually produced by this method. The object of all these modifications is to agitate the developing solution and the sample so as to remove constantly the development products from the region being developed. One of the earliest methods of insuring a flow of the developing solution over the sample during vertical development was to enclose the sample in a tube and to shake the tube by hand so that the sample moved from one end to the other. The flow of the developer over the sample was produced by the motion of the sample through the solution, and thus air could be excluded by filling the tube with the developing solution. It was found that the irregular motion produced when the tube was shaken by hand was more efficient in producing even and reproducible results than the regular motion produced when the tube was shaken by mechanical means. The British and American Standards Committees[5] adopted a similar system employing a vacuum bottle partly filled with the developer. The sample is fastened to a long, narrow strip of glass or metal attached to the stopper. Because of the vacuum jacket surrounding the tube, handling produces only a negligible temperature rise.

Harrison and Dobson[6] secured an effective flow of the developer over the sample by employing a plunger which moved up and down near the face of the sample. Many modifications of this system have been used in developing machines.

In many sensitometric laboratories, such as those operated by the motion-picture industry and the manufacturers of photographic materials, special developing machines are employed which give a very uniform image and very reproducible results. A section of a developing machine for sensitometric strips is shown in Fig. 9·8. A relatively slow, uniform circulation of the developer in the vertical direction is produced by the propeller, which forces the developer down into the well and up past the sensitometric strips as shown by the arrows. In addition to this general circulation of the developer, a much more vigorous agitation is produced by the vertical paddles, which move back and forth close to the surface of the samples. The temperature of the developing solutions is maintained constant by the thermostatically controlled water jacket.

Although developing machines are employed extensively for quantity work, there are many instances where it is desirable or necessary to carry out development in a tray. To obtain even and reproducible results with tray development, a considerable amount of developer must be used in order that the loss of the

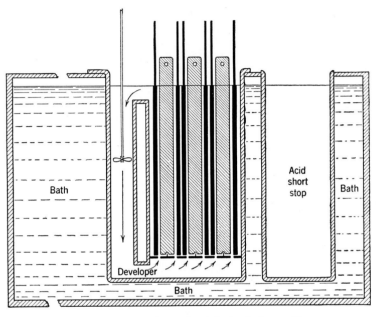

Fig. 9·8 Section of a sensitometric developing machine.

developing agent by oxidation will not be serious. During the process of development, local concentration of development products must be avoided by careful, irregular rocking of the tray. In general, uniform mechanical rocking of the tray should be avoided because it produces standing waves in the developer which result in uneven development. Although it is difficult to control the temperature of the solution during tray development, good results can be obtained by using special water-jacketed trays or by setting the tray containing the developer in a much larger tray containing water at the desired temperature.

Another method of obtaining even development is to brush the strips continuously during development with a soft, flat, long-haired brush. Clark[7] studied this method of development at length and found that brush development gives a very uniform image and that the right type of brush does not damage the emulsion. However, it is very difficult to obtain reproducible results with the brush development technique because the rate of development depends upon the rate at which the development products are removed by brushing.

Developers for Sensitometric Work

If the purpose of a sensitometric procedure is to determine the properties of the material used in practical photography, the developers and development conditions should conform as nearly as possible to those used in practice. On the other hand, developers used for scientific investigations of the principles of photography should be reproducible to specification and should be stable with respect to time and usage. Many of the developers used in practice in the past have not met these requirements, but the present metol-hydroquinone (M-Q) developers are reproducible to specification and are sufficiently stable with respect to time and usage for sensitometric work. Two such formulas (one for amateur roll films and one for miniature-camera films) have been adopted for determining speed by the American standard (ASA) method.[8]

REFERENCES

General

Mees, *The Theory of the Photographic Process,* revised edition, Macmillan, New York, 1954, Chapter 19.

Jones, *Photographic Sensitometry,* Eastman Kodak Co., Rochester, New York, 1935.

Specific

1. Jones, *J. Franklin Inst.,* **189**, 303 (1920).
2. Jones, *J. Soc. Motion Picture Engrs.,* **17**, 536 (1931).
3. Jones and Morrison, *J. Franklin Inst.,* **228**, 445 (1939).
4. Bornemann and Tuttle, *J. Optical Soc. Am.,* **32**, 224 (1942).
5. *Phot. J.,* **80**, 341 (1940).
6. Harrison and Dobson, *Nature,* **114**, 752 (1924).
7. Clark, *Phot. J.,* **65**, 76 (1925).
8. American Standards Association, *American Standard PH2.5-1954.*

Sensitometry II, Density and Its Measurement

The amount of photographic image produced by the exposure and development of a light-sensitive material can be measured either in terms of the mass of silver per unit of projection area in the photographic deposit or the amount of light stopped by the image. Hurter and Driffield[1] in their classical work on sensitometry reported that the optical density of a silver deposit in a photographic image was directly proportional to the mass of silver per unit of projection area. Although this conclusion was confirmed by some subsequent workers, later investigations have shown considerable departures from this linear relation. Since the purpose of the photographic image is to modulate the light passed through or reflected from the deposit, the most significant practical property of the image is its light-stopping power. Consequently, the concept of optical density as developed in the following sections will be based entirely upon the optical properties of the photographic image. The relation between the optical properties of the image and the mass of silver per unit of projection area has been discussed in Chapters 1 and 7.

Optical Density

When radiant energy falls on the photographic image; some is reflected backward, some is absorbed, some is scattered, and some is transmitted through undeviated, as illustrated in Fig. 10·1. The flux of radiant energy P_o is incident on the deposit A, where some is reflected backward and some is passed through.

The transmitted flux of radiant energy P_t has the distribution indicated by the envelope surrounding P_t. The exact spatial distribution of the transmitted light depends upon the light-scattering properties of the individual deposit.*

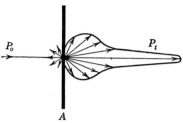

Fig. 10·1   Distribution of light reflected and transmitted by a photographic image.

The light-stopping power of the deposit is measured in terms of its *optical density D,* which is defined by

$$D = \log_{10} \frac{P_o}{P_t} \qquad (10 \cdot 1)$$

The ratio P_o/P_t is known as the *opacity O,* and the ratio P_t/P_o is known as the *transmittance T.* Equation 10·1 may now be rewritten

$$D = \log_{10} O = -\log_{10} T \qquad (10 \cdot 2)$$

This concept of density is often applied not only to photographic deposits but also to other materials, such as light filters and colored glass.

Types of Density

A number of different numerical values of density can be obtained for the same deposit, depending upon the geometry of the optics used to measure P_o and P_t. *Diffuse density* is given by equation 10·1 when the radiant flux is incident normally on the

---

*P_o and P_t are in power units such as ergs per second or watts. In deriving the general concept of density, this more precise physical quantity is employed in place of the usual quantity which, in photographic literature, is used in a loose sense as being measured in either visual units, such as meter-candles, or physical units, such as ergs per square centimeter per second.

sample and all the transmitted flux is measured, or in accordance with the optical reversibility principle, when the incident radiant flux is perfectly diffuse and only the specularly transmitted component is measured. These two methods of measuring diffuse density are illustrated in Figs. $10 \cdot 2(a)$ and $10 \cdot 2(b)$. *Specular density* is given when the radiant flux is incident normally on the sample and only the normal component of the transmitted flux is measured, as shown in Fig. $10 \cdot 2(c)$. *Doubly diffuse density* is given when the radiant flux incident on the sample is completely diffuse and all the transmitted flux is measured, as shown in Fig. $10 \cdot 2(d)$.

For a given sample, specular density is higher than doubly diffuse density, which in turn is higher than diffuse density.

It is very important to note that, although P_o is customarily defined as the flux of radiant energy incident on the sample and P_t as the flux of radiant energy transmitted by the sample, in practice *P_o is the flux of radiant energy measured by the photometer when the sample is not in place, and P_t is the flux of radiant energy measured by the same photometer when the sample is in place.* For example, when P_o is measured as shown in Fig. $10 \cdot 2(b)$, the flux measured is not the total flux from the diffuse radiant flux incident on the sample, but only that specular component of the diffuse flux which is measured by the photometer when no sample is in place.

The effect of scattered light upon the relative values of specular or diffuse density was a source of disagreement between Hurter and Driffield and their critics. Hurter and Driffield measured approximately specular densities and Abney measured approximately diffuse densities. Abney correctly ascribed the difference between the values he obtained and those obtained by Hurter and Driffield to the light-scattering property of the silver deposit, but Hurter and Driffield thought that it was due to interreflections between Abney's diffusing medium and the negative. In 1898 Chapman Jones confirmed Abney's idea that the loss of light by scattering gave a higher value for specular density than that for diffuse density.

In 1909 Callier made a large number of measurements to determine the relation between specular density $D\|$ and diffuse density $D\|$. He designated the ratio of $D\|$ to $D\|$ as Q, and this ratio is commonly referred to as the *Callier Q factor*. According to Callier's measurements Q is a constant at all values of density for a given material. Bloch and Renwick[2] later showed that Q is not constant for all values of density, but can be expressed as a logarithmic function of density. They found that when the logarithm of diffuse density is plotted against the logarithm of specular density, straight lines are obtained. Tuttle[3] verified the findings of Bloch and Renwick with experiments performed many years later.

The value of Q varies not only with density but also with gamma. In Fig. 10·3 the values of Q for the densities on five

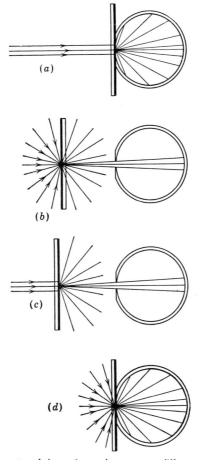

Fig. 10·2   Geometry of the optics used to measure different types of density.

sensitometric strips of motion-picture positive film which were developed to different gammas are plotted against diffuse densities. It is evident that for a given density the value of Q depends upon the gamma to which the strip was developed. In the same strip, the value of Q increases rapidly with density up to densities of about 0.3 and then decreases somewhat. The Q factors used in this figure were calculated from densities of the silver plus base. The Q factor for silver plus base is important in some operations, such as sound recording, whereas the Q factor of the silver deposit alone is important in other operations, such as granularity measurements. Usually the effect of the base may be neglected but, if the film has a gray base, the values of the

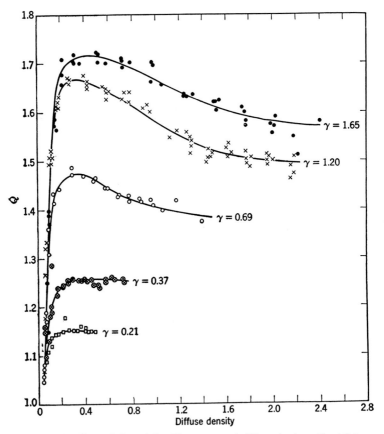

Fig. 10·3 The variation of Q with gamma and diffuse density. (Sandvik.)

Q factor for the silver deposit and the base together will be appreciably lower than those for the silver deposit alone. For low densities, where the density of the silver deposit is of the same order of magnitude as the density of the base, measurements of the Q factor without corrections for the density of the base will always lead to a value which approaches unity.

The density of a photographic deposit which is spectrally selective in its absorption depends upon the spectral characteristics of the incident radiant energy and the spectral sensitivity of the device employed to measure the transmitted or reflected flux. The density for any given wavelength of radiant energy is of interest and can be measured. Spectrophotometer traces showing the densities of two different photographic deposits at different wavelengths are shown in Fig. 10·4. Curve A in this figure is representative of many photographic deposits, since they are fairly non-selective. Some developers, like pyrogallol, produce yellowish deposits, and many will do so when development is stopped far short of completion. Spectrophotometric curves for emulsions developed in such developers resemble curve B. Very fine-grain materials also show selective absorption as a result of selective scattering of the light. A broad classification of density according to its spectral selectivity follows:

a. At any wavelength c. Printing

b. Visual d. Photoelectric

This classification applies to all three main types of density: diffuse, specular, and doubly diffuse. The classification of each of

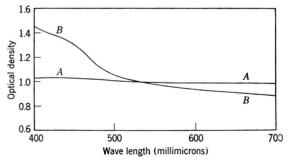

Fig. 10·4   Spectrophotometer traces for a photographic material developed in *(A)* a non-staining and *(B)* a staining developer.

these three types of density depends upon the spectral quality of the light source and the spectral response of the receiver employed to measure P_o and P_t.

Density at any wavelength is usually measured by illuminating the sample with nearly monochromatic radiant energy and measuring the quantities P_o and P_t with any receiver which has sufficient sensitivity. The other classes of density are measured by illuminating the sample with a light source having the spectral quality of a tungsten radiator at 3000°K and measuring the quantities P_o and P_t with a receiver having the required spectral sensitivity. In the determination of visual density the spectral sensitivity of the element used to measure the light flux is that of the normal photopic eye, whereas for printing density it is the blue-green sensitivity of the common photographic papers. These required spectral sensitivities can be obtained by the proper combination of a photoelectric tube and filter. The spectral sensitivity of the receiver employed to measure photoelectric density is that of the surfaces used in commercial photoelectric tubes.

This broad classification of density on the basis of spectral selectivity can in turn be subdivided into several different types based upon other light sources and other light-measuring devices.

Two of the most important spectral types of density are *visual* and *printing*. With a deposit which is spectrally non-selective, these two types of density are of course identical. However, in general, colored images give characteristic curves having different gammas according to whether visual or printing density is measured. Two such curves are shown in Fig. 10·5. These curves are representative of those most commonly obtained in practice in that they have nearly the same inertia point, with the result that there is a nearly constant ratio between the values of printing and visual density as measured on a single photographic deposit. Jones and Wilsey[4] examined the spectral selectivity of photographic images in detail. The *color coefficient* χ was defined by these men as the ratio between the printing gamma and the visual gamma $(\chi = \gamma_{printing}/\gamma_{visual})$.

For negatives developed with non-staining developers, such as ferrous oxalate and hydroquinone, the value of χ is low, usually below 1.1. With developers containing pyrogallol and very little sulfite, the value of χ may be as high as 2.75 because of the high printing density of the yellow stain image produced under such conditions and the relatively low density of this image as measured visually. It has been shown that the yellow image produced by pyrogallol is a non-silver image consisting of yellow oxidation products. Frayne[5] has shown that the color of fine-grain images is a function of density. At least part of the color of these fine-grain images must therefore be attributed to the light scattered by the grains.

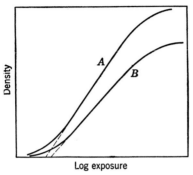

Fig. 10·5   Characteristic curves for a colored photographic image. Curve A is for printing density, and curve B is for visual density.

The density in a developed photographic image which is not the result of exposure to light is known as *fog*. A density as normally measured includes both that produced by fog and that produced by exposure to light. Although the printing characteristics of a negative are related to the total densities in the negative regardless of whether these densities are the result of fog or exposure to light, it is nevertheless sometimes desirable to be able to correct the density readings for fog. As a first approximation, it is satisfactory to subtract the fog density in the unexposed region from all densities. However, this correction is only a first approximation, since the fog density is higher for the unexposed areas on the plate than it is for the areas that received relatively heavy exposures. The exact correction for the contribution of fog to a given density is assumed to be proportional to the number of silver halide grains *not* developed, since some of the grains which would produce fog in an unexposed region are exposed in the area producing the image density. Formulas to be used in making exact fog corrections have been suggested by Meidinger,[6] Wilsey,[7] and Nietz.[8]

Densitometers

Instruments used to measure optical density are called *densitometers*. Although they are essentially photometers, they measure merely the ratio between two beams and not an absolute amount of light flux.

Many of the early densitometers were simply modified forms of bench photometer. In such an instrument, two light sources are used and an intensity balance is made with the sources unscreened and with one source screened by the sample to be measured. The photometer head, in which the intensity balance is made, may be any one of the several used in photometric work, such as the Bunsen grease spot or the Lummer-Brodhun cube. Although the density of the sample can be computed from the transmittance values thus obtained, such instruments are clumsy to use and the light sources must be maintained constant. Densitometers of the bench type have been replaced very largely by instruments which compare two beams of light from a single source. The best known and the most widely used instrument for the matching of the two beams is the Martens photometer.

Many of the densitometers used in photographic work are merely instruments which are used to compare the density to be measured with the density of a calibrated wedge or series of wedges. These instruments have the advantage that they are relatively simple to make and easy to use. A simple form of comparator that is widely used was designed by Capstaff and Purdy; it is sketched in Fig. 10·6. Light from the source *A* passes through the circular photographic wedge *W* and onto the opal glass *H*. The sample is placed in contact with this opal glass, and the observer, on looking through the eyepiece *J*, sees a circular spot of light illuminated by the opal glass. The light passing through the sample is modulated by *both* the sample and the wedge. Light from the source *A* also enters the eyepiece *J* by the path *B*, *C*, *D*, *E*, *F*, and *G*. The opal glass *C* and the ground glass *E* are placed in the comparison beam, as shown, to insure that the illumination of this beam is uniform. The comparison beam is reflected by the semi-transparent mirror *F* onto mirror *G*, which has a small area in the middle from which the silver has been removed. On looking through the eyepiece, therefore, the observer sees a field illuminated by the comparison beam, in the middle of which is a small spot illuminated by light that has passed through the sample and the wedge. The area illuminated by the comparison beam remains of a fixed brightness, and the density of the wedge in the beam passing through the sample is then adjusted until the small central spot disappears and the entire field appears uniform. Since this requires that the sum of the densities of the sample and the wedge should be constant, the density of the sample can be me ·ured in terms of the density of the wedge. It should be noted that the accuracy of this instrument depends not only upon the ability of the operator to obtain a match, but also upon the accuracy of the calibration of the photographic wedge.

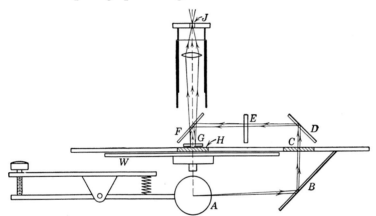

Fig. 10 · 6   Schematic diagram of the Capstaff-Purdy densitometer.

A type of modulating device that is now frequently used is a variable aperture or stop in the illuminating system. A theoretical calibration, based on the geometrical size of the stop, is not strictly valid unless the optical system is free from aberrations, but with a well-corrected system, it is found in practice that such a calibration is adequate for a density range of 2.0. The range can be extended with neutral filters, and if there is doubt as to the validity of the geometrical calibration, an empirical calibration can be made. This type of modulator is used in some commercial instruments.

Many densitometers have been made in which radiation-sensitive electrical devices replace the human eye. These instruments have the advantage that they eliminate visual fatigue, frequently attain higher precision, and increase the reading speed. The precision of visual readings cannot exceed about 0.008 in density because of the inherent characteristics of the eye, and even experts can make only five or six readings a minute and then only for a limited period. Physical densitometers have been built which will read densities with a precision of 0.0004, and some will make as many as 120 readings a minute.

The earliest physical densitometers, which were designed by astronomers and spectroscopists, incorporated a thermopile and a galvanometer. Transmittance was computed from the galvanometer readings with and without the sample in place. Thermoelectric instruments have little advantage in speed over visual instruments. They are affected by temperature variations, are of low sensitivity, and most of their response is in the extremely long wavelength region of the spectrum. These instruments are of little value in the measurement of materials which are spectrally selective.

Photoelectric tubes are free from many of the shortcomings of the thermal devices because they respond instantly and, with the proper tube-filter combinations, their response can be made to match quite closely that of the human eye or the printing medium. However, the output of ordinary phototubes must be amplified, with the result that for many years such equipment was less stable than thermal devices. This instability limited the use of phototubes in densitometers until the multiplier phototube was developed. This type of phototube is now widely used, specifically in microdensitometers.[9,10] However, stable amplifiers for ordinary phototubes have since been developed and are used in some commercial densitometers.

Photoresistive cells, of which the selenium type is best known, have been used for densitometers because of the greater current available as compared to the photoemissive cells. With these cells a much less sensitive indicating instrument can be employed. Unfortunately, they are inherently less stable and considerably slower to respond than the photoemissive types. No photoresistive cell instrument has been an unqualified success.

The barrier-layer, self-generating photoelectric cell is stable and simple, gives a high current, and has a spectral response that lies almost entirely in the visible spectrum. It is almost universally used in exposure meters and is used in many physical densitometers.

Since all the radiation-sensitive devices used in physical densitometers have a response which is approximately a linear function of the illuminance, such instruments have non-linear scales unless they are especially designed. Their precision, therefore, decreases rapidly as density increases, and they are not satisfactory for measuring densities above about 1.3. This defect has been partially overcome by galvanometers having an expanded scale at the low deflection end. Some of these non-linear instruments used in commercial densitometers are calibrated to a density of 3.0 or higher. Logarithmic amplifiers have been used with ordinary phototubes, but it has been difficult to make them with adequate sensitivity, range, and linearity (in density).

The entire electrical problem can be sidestepped by making the radiation-sensitive device move a logarithmic neutral wedge to balance the light passing through the sample against a standard beam. With the advent of the multiplier phototube, such expedients were rendered unnecessary because the cathode potential that is required to maintain the anode current constant has an almost perfect logarithmic relation to the light flux incident on the cathode. A circuit based on this principle has been described by Gunderson.[11] The advantage of such an arrangement is that it is not necessary to balance two beams if the light source and power supply are adequately stable, and therefore the instrument can be made direct reading or direct recording.

It is much harder to measure accurately the density of microscopic areas, as is required in studying the structure of the developed image (Chapter 13), than it is to measure the density of large areas. One difficulty is that stray light in the instrument adds significantly to the light that should be measured and thus lowers the reading. Formerly it was also difficult to measure high densities with the small amount of light flux available, but with the multiplier phototube, instruments have been devised that will measure to a density of 3.0 with a resolving power of 800 lines/mm.[9]

Color Densitometry

The use of optical densities to describe color images is more complicated than the use of densities to describe silver images. The concepts of color densities are more complex, and density measurement is more difficult.

The silver images of black-and-white photography differ among themselves principally in that they transmit different amounts of light. The *kind* of light transmitted varies hardly at all from one image to another; therefore, it usually matters little what kind of light is used for the density measurement. On the other hand, the essential quality of a color image is that it is spectrally selective; great care must therefore be taken to measure with the proper kind of light.

In black-and-white sensitometry the object of density measurement is almost always to predict the action of the image, as a whole, in reducing the response of a light-sensitive receiver. For example, the assumed receiver for negative materials is the printing paper or positive film, and the density measurement predicts the extent to which the measured image decreases the printing exposure of that positive material.

In color sensitometry *printing densities* are also measured. But in most color-printing processes the print material itself is a color film or paper and therefore has not one response but three —namely, that of its red-sensitive layer, its green-sensitive layer, and its blue-sensitive layer. Every single image of a color negative, therefore, has three printing densities—a red-printing density, a green-printing density, and a blue-printing density. For the red-printing density, the absorption of only red light by the negative is important, and similarly for the green and blue densities.

More than that, exactly the correct kind of red, green, and blue light must be used for the density measurement. To obtain the red-printing density, the product of the spectral-energy curve of the light in the densitometer and the spectral sensitivity of the phototube must be proportional, wavelength by wavelength, to the product of the curve of the light in the printer and the spectral sensitivity of the red-sensitive layer in the print material. Then the densitometer gives an accurate indication of the response of the red-sensitive layer of the print material to a color negative. Similar conditions must be met to obtain accurate measurements of the green- and the blue-printing densities.

Densitometers are made to approximate the requirements for such exact measurement by use of specially designed red, green, and blue color filters. It is generally impossible to construct a perfect filter, and for the most exacting applications of printing densities, the errors due to imperfect filters must be eliminated. Fortunately, the error of an approximate red-printing density, for example, can be predicted by a linear combination of the approximate red-printing density itself, the approximate green-printing density, and the approximate blue-printing density. Similarly, the error of an approximate green-printing density or blue-printing density can be predicted from a knowledge of all three approximate printing densities. Therefore, accurate values of true printing density can be obtained by linear transformations of approximate printing densities.

Printing densities are one kind of a general class of color-image densities called integral densities. The term *integral density* means simply that the density describes something about the whole, or integral, image. Another, and simple, kind of integral density is *spectral integral density,* which is the density of the whole color image to light of a single wavelength.

Another kind, analogous to printing densities but sometimes used to describe images in positive transparencies, is *colorimetric density.* In the science of colorimetry, the color response of the eye is generally divided into a red sensitivity, a green sensitivity, and a blue sensitivity. If a densitometer is constructed in accordance with the spectral distributions of these sensitivities rather than those of a color-print material, the resulting measurements are called colorimetric densities. Complete sets of colorimetric densities are rarely used, but extensive use is made of the one corresponding to the sensitivity of the eye, which is predominantly to green light. In the present standard method of colorimetry, the wavelength distribution of this sensitivity, which is called the Y-stimulus function, is the same as the wavelength distribution of the brightness response of the eye. Therefore, if one wishes to determine the relative brightness of images of different colors, the data are obtained by measuring the Y-function colorimetric density, usually called *visual density.*

The densities used in black-and-white sensitometry are usually either printing densities or visual densities. Just as these densities are used to construct D-log E curves in black-and-white sensitometry, printing or visual densities can be similarly used in color sensitometry. A single graded set of images in color sensitometry will, however, result in three related printing-density

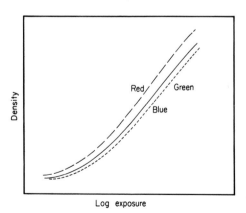

Fig. 10·7   Illustrative curves of printing density for a color negative.

curves or three related colorimetric-density curves. Fig. $10 \cdot 7$ illustrates a set of printing-density curves drawn from measurements of images in a color negative.

In many kinds of color sensitometry, it is not sufficient to know the functional characteristics of the integral image; one needs to know the composition of the image, that is, the amount of cyan dye, yellow dye, and magenta dye that it contains. An optical density is used for the specification of the amount of each dye, since it is the optical effect of the dye absorption that is important in sensitometry. This kind of color density is called *analytical density* because it serves to analyze the color image into its component dye deposits.

Several kinds of analytical density exist, but the most important is *equivalent neutral density*. If a color image happens to be a gray with a density of 1.0, it is obvious that each of the dye deposits is sufficient to join with the others in making a gray image of density 1.0. The cyan dye absorbs enough red light, the magenta enough green light, and the yellow enough blue light to do this. Now if there were less cyan dye present, the image would be reddish instead of gray. This cyan dye would not be enough to form a gray density of 1.0, but would be enough to form a gray of some lower density. The equivalent neutral density of a dye deposit is the density of the gray image which it is capable of forming in combination with the just-required amounts of the other dyes of the process.

The value of such a density description will be apparent by reference to Fig. $10 \cdot 8$, which is the set of D-log E curves in equivalent neutral density resulting from exposing a color film to a series of intensities of white light. Suppose that it is the purpose of this color process to form a series of gray images from such a graded series of white-light exposures. The description of dye deposits in terms of equivalent neutral densities, as indicated by the figure, shows that two things are wrong with the color process. In the first place, although the magenta-forming emulsion matches the cyan-forming emulsion in contrast, as it should, its sensitivity is too high. In the second place, although the yellow-forming emulsion matches the cyan-forming emulsion in sensitivity, its contrast is too low. This form of presentation is an efficient way for the sensitometrist to present to the process chemist information useful in correcting the color process.

One can measure equivalent neutral densities by the use of wedges made of the dyes used in the color process, or compute

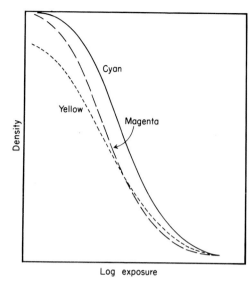

Fig. 10·8 Illustrative curves of equivalent neutral density for a color positive.

them by a mathematical transformation from measurements of red, green, and blue spectral integral densities.

Two types of wedge densitometer are used. In one the color film is placed in one of two identical optical beams, and in the other beam is placed a set of cyan, magenta, and yellow dye-wedges made of the color-process dyes. To make a measurement, all three of the wedges are adjusted until the color of the sample beam is matched by the color of the beam containing the wedges. The wedges may be calibrated by performing this adjustment for a series of gray images, Such images form a convenient calibration standard, because for gray images all three equivalent neutral densities are equal to the visual density, which is easily measured.
measured.

In the other type of wedge densitometer, the color film and the wedges are placed in the same beam, along with a non-selective wedge. A gray comparison beam of constant luminance is provided. With no sample in the reading beam, the beams can be balanced to give the zero settings of the wedges. When a color-film sample is placed in the proper beam, a balance can be re-established by moving the wedges. It is convenient to use only one or two of the color wedges to supply whatever dye densities the film sample needs to become gray, and then by moving the non-selective wedge to take from the beam a density equal to that amount of gray density. From the wedge calibrations, all three equivalent neutral densities are thus determined. In this densitometer, also, gray samples can provide the means of calibration.

Accurate wedge-type analytical densitometers are difficult to make, operate, and maintain. Much analytical densitometry is therefore done by the mathematical transformation of spectral integral densities. Any integral density of a three-dye subtractive color-film image is the sum of density contributions from all three dyes. For example, although the magenta dye is primarily responsible for absorbing the green light, the other color-film dyes also absorb some green light. If the density is a spectral density, determined with light of a single wavelength, the total density will be the simple arithmetic sum of the three density contributions. Therefore, if one measures a red, a green, and a blue spectral integral density, one has three values, each of which is the sum of spectral densities of the cyan, magenta, and yellow dye deposits.

One can determine, for the three spectral-density wavelengths being used, that for the cyan dye of the color film being measured, fixed ratios exist among the spectral densities to red, green, and blue light. These ratios will not change with the concentration of the dye. Other fixed ratios exist for the magenta dye and for the yellow dye. A knowledge of these fixed ratios enables one to write the relationships between the spectral integral densities and the amounts of cyan, magenta, and yellow dye in the measured image as a set of three simultaneous equations in three variables. The set of equations below is such a set, simplified by defining the unit amount of cyan dye as the amount that has unit density to the red light being used, and similarly defining unit amounts of magenta and yellow dye.

$$D_R = C + a_{11}M + a_{12}Y$$
$$D_G = a_{21}C + M + a_{22}Y$$
$$D_B = a_{31}C + a_{32}M + Y$$

Solving these three simultaneous equations yields the following set of three equations in which the amounts of dye are expressed in terms of the red, green, and blue spectral integral densities:

$$C = b_{11}D_R + b_{12}D_G + b_{13}D_B$$
$$M = b_{21}D_R + b_{22}D_G + b_{23}D_l$$
$$Y = b_{31}D_R + b_{32}D_G + b_{33}D_B$$

The coefficients b are invariable for a particular dye set. If one uses for R, G, and B the spectral integral density values obtained from measuring a color-film image, the resulting quantities C, M, and Y are the analytical densities of that image in a unit called *spectral analytical density*. The value of C, for example, gives directly the density of the cyan deposit to the red light being used for measurement.

By determining these values for a few gray images of the color film, one can determine that a nearly fixed ratio exists between spectral analytical density and equivalent neutral density for a given dye. If one then multiplies the three coefficients b of each of the foregoing equations by the ratio appropriate to the dye involved, a new set of equations results which gives C, M, and Y directly in equivalent neutral density. In laboratories where much of this work is done, the spectral integral densities are transformed to equivalent neutral densities by means of automatic or semi-automatic computers.

The Measurement of Density by Reflection

For many purposes, such as a print on paper, it is necessary to measure the optical properties of the image by reflected light. The relationship between the transmission of a photographic image and the light reflected from it when it is placed in contact with an opaque support has been the subject of many investigations. If R represents the ratio of the light reflected by the image to the light reflected by the base, the *reflection density* D_r is defined by the following formula:

$$D_r = \log \frac{1}{R} \qquad (10 \cdot 3)$$

This definition of reflection density is analogous to that for transmission density. According to Jones, Nutting, and Mees,[12] the relation between the transmittance of a silver deposit and its reflection density is given by the equation

$$D_r = \log \frac{1}{(1 - C)T^2 + C} \qquad (10 \cdot 4)$$

C being a constant. It is clear that reflection density is not exactly equal to twice the transmission density. The exact relation between transmission and reflection density depends upon the diffusing properties of the photographic deposit and the base, and upon the nature of the illumination.

As with transmission density, the numerical value of reflection density depends upon the character of the optical system. The distribution of the reflected light is one of the most important optical factors that influence the measured value of reflection density.

The reflected light from a photographic print has both a specular and a diffuse component. The reflection density values obtained with a given densitometer depend upon the relative amounts of each of these two components accepted by the light-measuring element of the instrument. For viewing a photographic print, it is desirable to arrange the lighting and viewing conditions in such a manner that the amount of the specularly reflected light reaching the observer's eye is a minimum; if these viewing conditions are not fulfilled, the image of the light source as seen on the picture will produce an unpleasant glare. In photographic paper sensitometry, the illumination and the angle of acceptance of the measuring element of the densitometer are arranged to eliminate the principal specular component and to measure the diffusely reflected light. A satisfactory way to fulfill these conditions is to illuminate the sample with light that is incident on the paper at an angle of 45° and to measure the light that is reflected normally from the surface. The various forms of densitometers discussed previously can be adapted to read reflection density. However, when densitometers using polarized light are employed, precautions must be taken to insure that the measuring beam has not been polarized by reflection.

The microdensitometry of papers is more difficult than the microdensitometry of negative materials because the image is visible only by light diffused from it, and some non-image-forming light finds its way to the phototube and reduces the maximum density that can be measured accurately. Nevertheless, by exercising extreme care, it is possible to make an instrument that will measure even color densities up to 2.2 with a 2-μ slit through the filters that are necessary for color materials.[10]

REFERENCES

General

Mees, *The Theory of the Photographic Process,* revised edition, Macmillan, New York, 1954, Chapter 20.
Jones, *Photographic Sensitometry,* Eastman Kodak Co., 1935.

Specific

1. Hurter and Driffield, *J. Soc. Chem. Ind.,* **9**, 455 (1890).
2. Bloch and Renwick, *Phot. J.,* **56**, 49 (1916).
3. Tuttle, *J. Optical Soc. Am.,* **12**, 559 (1926).

4. Jones and Wilsey, *J. Franklin Inst.*, **185**, 231 (1918).
5. Frayne, *J. Soc. Motion Picture Engrs.*, **36**, 622 (1941).
6. Meidinger, *Z. physik. Chem.*, **114**, 89 (1924).
7. Wilsey, *Phot. J.*, **65**, 454 (1925).
8. Nietz, *Theory of Development*, Eastman Kodak Co., 1922.
9. Altman and Stultz, *Rev. Sci. Inst.*, **27**, 1033 (1956).
10. *Ibid.*, *Phot. Sci. and Tech.*, **4**, 10 (1957).
11. Gunderson, U. S. Patent 2,454,871 (1948).
12. Jones, Nutting, and Mees, *Phot. J.*, **38**, 342 (1914).

11.

Sensitometry III, Interpretation of Sensitometric Data

Sensitometric data are usually expressed in graphic form, and the numerical constants derived from the curves are used to express the characteristics of the photographic materials. One of the most useful curves is that obtained by plotting the optical densities of the deposits against the logarithms of the exposures as shown in Fig. 11·1 (also see Chapter 1). This curve, which is correctly called the *characteristic curve* or the *D-log E* curve, is popularly known as the H & D curve because it was first plotted by Hurter and Driffield in 1890. The characteristic curve is sometimes described as being S-shaped, but actually a considerable portion is usually a straight line within the limits of experimental error.

The Characteristic Curve

For a given density interval ΔD there is a corresponding log E interval, Δ log E, and the ratio $\Delta D/\Delta$ log E of these intervals is known as the *gradient G*. Except for the straight portion of the curve, the gradient is not constant. For the straight portion the gradient is equal to the tangent of the angle α formed between the straight portion of the curve and the log E axis. This tangent is commonly called *gamma*. It should be noted that gamma gives information pertaining only to the slope of this straight portion of the curve and tells nothing about the other portions.

The projection of the straight portion of the characteristic curve on the log E axis (MN) determines the log exposure range over which direct proportionality exists between D and log E.

This log E interval is called *exposure latitude* and is expressed in exposure units, either on a natural or a logarithmic scale. Although density is directly proportional to the logarithm of exposure only throughout the straight portion of this curve, nevertheless exposure differences in the range represented by the curved portions of the curve are reproduced as density differences. The portion C to A, in which the gradient increases from

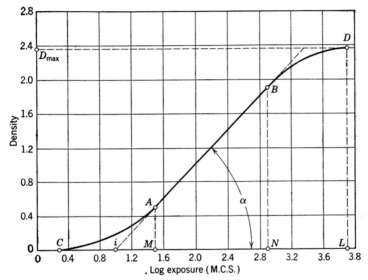

Fig 11·1   Characteristic curve.

zero to that representing the straight portion, is known as the *toe* of the curve. The portion B to D, in which the gradient decreases to zero from that of the straight portion, is known as the *shoulder* of the curve. The value of density corresponding to point D is D_{max}, the maximum density obtainable with this material under the conditions of exposure and development used to obtain these sensitometric data.

The term "exposure latitude," as defined above, should not be confused with the *total scale* (CL, Fig. 11·1), which is the exposure range within which the material is capable of rendering differences in object luminance* by density differences. The total scale of most negative materials is considerably larger than the

* See Table II in the Appendix.

luminance range in the majority of scenes. The total scale of a given material is not a constant because its value depends upon the extent to which development is carried (γ) and, to a lesser extent, upon the processing factors and exposure conditions.

When the straight portion of the characteristic curve is extended to cut the log E axis, the value of log E at the point of intersection is called *inertia i* (i, Fig. $11 \cdot 1$). The equation of this straight portion is

$$D = \gamma(\log E - \log i) \qquad (11 \cdot 1)$$

The Determination of Sensitivity

The effective sensitivity of a photographic material depends upon the results desired and upon the exact way in which the material is used. In astronomical photography, exposures of minutes and hours are common. Ordinary camera exposures are of the order of fractions of a second, whereas with modern speed lamps and in sound recording, exposures are of the order of milliseconds. The relative sensitivity of photographic materials is of course not constant over this very large range of exposure times and intensity levels.

One of the earliest methods used for measuring sensitivity was to determine the minimum exposure that would produce a just-perceptible image after development. This threshold method was used by the Warnerke, the Scheiner, and the Eder-Hecht sensitometers. The difficulty of determining what constitutes a just-perceptible image led to measuring sensitivity in terms of the exposure necessary to produce a given density. The DIN system adopted by the Deutscher Normenausschuss[1] in 1931 and still followed in the 1957 revision derives film speed from the exposure required to give a density of 0.1 above the fog level.

Hurter and Driffield specified speed by the quantity $34/i$, where i is inertia. This adoption of inertia speed was based upon the assumption that, for the correct reproduction of tones in the final positive, the scale of luminance in the object must be represented by exposures on the straight portion of the characteristic curve of the negative. It has been shown recently that this assumption is unwarranted. Another reason for using·inertia speed was that the combinations of photographic emulsions and developers available in Hurter and Driffield's time gave characteristic curves in which the extensions of the straight portions intersected the exposure axis at a fixed point regardless of gamma as development proceeded. In other words, inertia speed was independent of development time. This is so far from being true for materials that are available nowadays (see Chapter 7 and Fig. 7·3) that inertia speeds may vary as much as 500 per cent with increasing gamma. Moreover, the curve of an occasional material will exhibit merely a point of inflection rather than a straight portion of significant length. Nowadays inertia speed is used only for special purposes, and the Ninth International Congress of Photography in 1935 unanimously rejected the inertia method of measuring speed for a standard, as it also did the threshold method described in the preceding paragraph.

The normal function of a photographic material is to reproduce as density differences the luminance differences in the object being photographed. The minimum useful exposure, therefore, is that required to reproduce the luminance differences in the shadows of the object by some minimum density difference. For exact proportional rendering in the *negative* of the various object luminances, the minimum exposure would be that which would place the exposures representing the shadow regions of the object just at the beginning of the straight portion of the characteristic curve. On the other hand, it should be noted that the density differences in the *print,* and not those in the negative, are of practical importance. Consequently it is necesssary to consider the properties of the printing medium as well as those of the negative.

Since the minimum useful exposure is that which will reproduce detail in the shadows with some minimum contrast in the print, it seemed logical to assume that satisfactory prints might be obtained from *negatives* exposed in such a manner that shadow detail was recorded by some minimum gradient in the toe of the characteristic curve. This idea was first discussed by Luther and was further expanded by Jones and Russell. Although experiments have shown that these assumptions are valid, they have also shown that it is difficult to determine the value to be taken as representing the minimum useful gradient.

L. A. Jones[2] proposed that negative film speeds be evaluated in terms of the minimum exposure required to give a negative from which a print of excellent quality can be made. He conducted a statistical examination of prints made from a series of negatives in which the exposure was increased progressively from very low to very high values. This investigation indicated that the "first excellent prints" were obtained from negatives so

Fig. 11·2 *(a, b c)* Prints made from negatives in which the exposure was increased progressively.

exposed that the deepest shadows were reproduced at a point on the toe of the D-log E curve where the minimum gradient was about 0.3 of the average gradient over a log exposure range of 1.5. A series of "excellent" prints is shown in Fig. $11 \cdot 2$ (a, b, c). The characteristic curve for the negative material is shown in Fig. $11 \cdot 2$ (d) together with the exposure range covered by each negative. Figure $11 \cdot 2$ (a) represents the "first excellent print" and corresponds to section A of the characteristic curve.

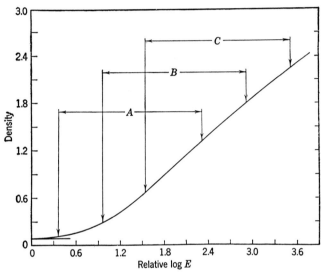

Fig. $11 \cdot 2$ (d)   Characteristic curve for the negative material, together with the exposure range covered by the negatives used in making the prints shown in Figs. $11 \cdot 2$ (a, b, c).

This method has been adopted by the American Standards Association[3] for determining the speed of black-and-white negative materials designed for landscape and pictorial photography. It has also been recommended for international adoption by the International Standards Organization. According to this method, the photographic speed of a material is given by the relation $1/E$, where E is the exposure value at the fractional-gradient point C as shown in Fig. $11 \cdot 3(a)$. In this figure, the difference in log exposure between B and C is 1.5. The lower point C is the point on the curve for which the gradient $dD/d \log E = \tan a$ is equal to 0.3 times the average gradient $\overline{G} = \tan b$ between

B and *C.* If, for example, the value of *E*, the abscissa of *C*, is 0.0025 meter-candle-second, then $1/E = 400$. If, in addition, all the requirements for determining speed according to the

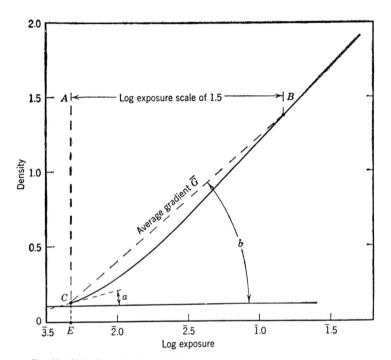

Fig. 11 · 3(a) Determination of film speed by the fractional-gradient method.

standard method have been fulfilled, the speed is specified as ASA 0400.

The average gradient $\overline{G}$ is called β in the American Standard. It is more representative of the gradient over the entire density range of a print than is γ, since the latter is the gradient of only a portion of the *D*-log *E* curve. It has therefore been found suitable for use as an index of the extent to which development is carried, and the American Standard specifies that β shall have a value of at least 0.50.

The values of speed determined as just described are numerically about four times as great as the speed indices that have been used by makers of exposure meters, and therefore a standard exposure index that is equal to the speed value divided by 4 has been adopted. Thus the material just cited as an example would have an American Standard Exposure Index of 100.

An index that led to the minimum exposure for an excellent print would leave no tolerance for underexposure arising from errors in the meter, lens, or shutter, and therefore it had become conventional for meter manufacturers to assign exposure indices that were lower than the index required for the first excellent print by about 2.5 times; the American Standard Exposure Index thus implicitly incorporates this safety factor. Experience, how-ever, showed that the fear of underexposure was not well found-ed. Moreover, the small negatives that are increasingly common are almost invariably enlarged, and a high negative density leads to an inconveniently long printing time and excessive heating of the negative, which tends to make the negative go out of focus. Graininess also increases with density, especially when the nega-tive is developed to a high contrast. There is, therefore, an in-creasing tendency to recommend exposure indices that are about 2.5 times as great as the American Standard Exposure Index so that the resulting exposure is the minimum that will give an excellent print. When an unfamiliar material is used, or when emulsions are being compared for speed, it is essential to note whether the safety factor has been included in the computation of exposure index. This safety factor, of course, enters only into the assignment of the index and not into the determination of speed.

It is important to note that speed values and exposure indices may be designated "ASA" or "American Standard" only when the materials are those to which the American Standard speci-fication applies and then only when they are processed in the standard manner. The specification does not apply to color and reversal materials, but manufacturers assign indices to such ma-terials that are suitable for use with meters calibrated for ASA indices. Color films, however, are not given safety factors because overexposure is almost as harmful as underexposure.

With the DIN and the ASA exposure indices both in common use and adopted as standards in different parts of the world, it is convenient to be able to convert from one to the other. It was not possible to convert an ASA measure to the DIN measure as the latter was originally specified because the DIN development procedure consisted in developing until the speed value attained a maximum, while the ASA procedure involves a fixed development time. In 1954 the DIN development procedure was changed to agree with the ASA procedure, and now a sufficiently good logarithmic relationship exists between the ASA and the DIN speeds.[4] This relation is

$$\log_{10} (\text{ASA Exposure Index}) = \tfrac{1}{10} (\text{DIN speed} - 1.0) \quad (11 \cdot 2)$$

For example, an American Standard Exposure Index of 100 is equivalent to a DIN speed of 21°, and an index of ASA 10 is equivalent to 11° DIN. Adding 10° to the DIN speed is equivalent to multiplying the American Standard Exposure Index (and therefore dividing the expo   re) by 10.

The strict method of determining fractional-gradient speed described on page 213 is difficult to apply in practice because the defining points on the characteristic curve must be determined from two interrelated gradients, and therefore an attempt has been made[5] to derive a simpler procedure for determining the same speed value within tolerances that are close enough for practical purposes. In Fig. $11 \cdot 3(b)$ let P be the point on the characteristic curve where the density is 0.1 above the base and fog density. Let the horizontal distance to the point on the curve where the gradient is $0.3\overline{G}$ as defined by the fractional-gradient method be ΔX. This point, often called the *speed point*, corresponds to point C in Fig. $11 \cdot 3(a)$. Then measure from P a distance $\Delta \log E = 1.30$ to the right and let the corresponding density increment of the curve be ΔD. The question is now, is there a relation between the distance ΔX and the density increment ΔD? Many landscape and portrait emulsions produced by manufacturers all over the world and developed in different

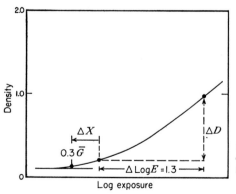

Fig. $11 \cdot 3(b)$ Determination of film speed by the simplified method.

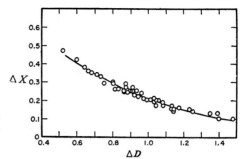

Fig. 11·3(c) Relation of ΔX to ΔD for some landscape and portrait films.

ways were studied, and a few of the results are shown by the small circles in Fig. $11 \cdot 3(c)$. The curve shown in the figure is the least-squares parabolic fit to the data, and it is evident that, with errors which are unimportant in practice, the curve represents all the materials and all the developing conditions. For example, if $\Delta D = 0.8$, $\Delta X = 0.29$. Since P and ΔD are easily obtained, the distance ΔX from P to the speed point is readily found from this curve. This procedure is to be used as the new American standard method of determinating speed, and since it incorporates the fixed-density feature of the DIN method of speed measurement, there is a possibility that it will be adopted internationally.

In applying this procedure, a series of identically exposed sensitometric strips are developed for closely-spaced time intervals and the resulting D-log E curves are plotted. These curves are then tested in turn to find the one for which $\Delta D = 0.80 \pm 0.05$ when the point P from which it is measured represents $D = 0.1$ above base and fog density. For this standard development condition, ΔX is essentially constant and a very good correlation exists between the fractional-gradient speeds and the fixed-density speeds of the various films. The new American standard speed is equal to $0.8/E_p$, where E_p is the exposure in meter-candle-seconds required to obtain a density of 0.1 above base and fog density. This ASA speed replaces both the former ASA Exposure Index and the former ASA speed. The new value is intended to be used directly with existing exposure meters. It is twice as large as the former ASA Exposure Index, so that the safety factor is in effect reduced from 2.50 to 1.25. This makes the ASA Indices for black-and-white materials consistent with the indices that are customarily given for color materials.

A method of determining exposure that is becoming widely used is the *exposure value* system. It is based upon solving the equation

$$\text{Film sensitivity} \times \text{Illuminance} = \text{Aperture} \times \text{Exposure Time} \tag{11·3}$$

Since addition is easier than multiplication, these quantities are expressed in terms of their logarithms to the base 2, starting from a suitable value for each quantity, and thus a difference of unity in any logarithmic value corresponds to a doubling or a halving of the corresponding quantity itself. Then equation 11·3 becomes equivalent to

$$\begin{aligned} \text{Exposure Value} &= \text{Film Value} + \text{Brightness Value} \\ &= \text{Aperture Value} + \text{Time Value} \end{aligned} \tag{11·3'}$$

or $$Ev = Sv + Bv = Av + Tv \tag{11·3''}$$

These values are given in Table III of the Appendix. For example, a film having an American Standard Exposure Index of 100 has a film value Sv of 5, and if the average luminance of the scene to be photographed is 500 foot-lamberts, which is common in bright sunshine, the brightness value Bv is 9 and the resulting exposure value Ev is therefore 14. The time value Tv corresponding to an exposure time of $\frac{1}{60}$ sec. is 6, and therefore the required aperture value Av is 8, which corresponds to $f/16$. If the diaphragm scale and the time scale of the shutter are both graduated in power-of-two steps, they can be locked together in a relation that depends upon the required exposure value. Then the diaphragm can be set to give a suitable depth of field, for example, and the exposure time is automatically adjusted. It is becoming a frequent practice to graduate exposure meters, especially those that are built into cameras, so that the film value can be set when the camera is loaded, and then the exposure value is given directly by the meter, or the diaphragm is even adjusted automatically for the predetermined exposure time.

It appears that after further investigations speed values based upon a fractional-gradient criterion for the determination of the minimum useful exposure will be employed for an ever wider range of photographic materials. However, there are special applications of the photographic process, such as in spectroscopy, astronomy, and photoengraving processes, where special methods of measuring speed appear to be desirable. In many applications of photography to spectroscopy and astronomy, the photographic material is employed to determine the position and magnitude of the light in an optical image. According to Dunham,[6] adequate detection and measurement of weak absorption lines require both sufficient contrast and a minimum density of about 0.6. On the basis of Dunham's criterion, the speed of spectroscopic and astronomical materials is frequently expressed in terms of the reciprocal of the exposure, expressed in meter-candle-seconds, which will produce a density of 0.6 when developed to a given gamma. Speed values determined in this manner depend upon the order of the exposure times for which they are computed. The speed of a material when used with spectroscopic exposures of the order of 1 second may be as much as ten times as great as it is when it is used with astronomical exposures of the order of hours.

In making line and halftone negatives for photoengraving, the ideal process negative consists of clear glass alternating with opaque deposits. There is no graduated scale of density in the ideal negative, since the gradations are rendered by various dot sizes and not by various densities. The highest speed material is therefore that which will produce the necessary opacity with the minimum exposure. For example, if two materials have the same inertia speed, but if one can be developed to a higher gamma than the other, the material with the higher gamma will be the faster for photoengraving processes because it will produce a given opacity with less exposure.

Vector Parameters

Photographic emulsions are frequently compared in terms of their sensitometric parameters, such as speed, contrast, and fog. These parameters are usually measured from the D-log E curve by graphical methods, but means have been devised to make such comparisons by parameters computed directly from the density data without plotting a curve at all. An illustrative method is that of vector parameters, which was designed to compare emulsions directly with a selected reference in terms of speed, contrast, and fog, all specially defined for the purpose.[7]

Operating with the density data themselves, rather than with curves derived from them, has obvious advantages where a great many such comparisons must be made and where electronic computers are available for the work. It also has the advantage, even in small-scale operations, of avoiding the personal judgment which enters into graphical work. Two different operators using graphical methods on the same set of data may obtain quite different results, but a reliable computing machine always gets the same answer from the same data.

Although curves are not used in the vector-parameter system, the system can best be explained by reference to such curves. The general principle involved is that the differences between two D-log E curves can be described by describing the changes that must be made in one of them to make it congruent with the other. In Fig. 11·4, let a sample curve be represented by the broken curve X and let R be the curve of a reference film. Now if R is to be altered to match curve X, it will obviously have to be·reduced in contrast. Let this be done by multiplying all the densities above fog in curve R by a constant — the same constant for all densities — such that a new curve, R_2, is formed which matches X as well as possible in its distribution of gradients. Now R_2 needs to be slid sideways to approach better congruence with X. This shifted curve, R_3, is the curve which would be obtained with an emulsion like that giving R_2, changed only in sensitivity. Therefore, the amount of required shift Δt is defined in this system as the change in emulsion sensitivity

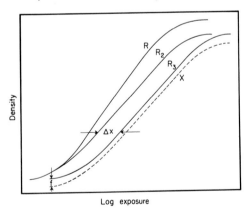

Fig. 11·4   Method of matching a reference curve R to a sample curve X by vector parameters.

or speed. A third change is also advisable, shifting the curve R_3 vertically by subtracting a fixed amount from each of its densities. The amount of this shift compares the two emulsions in terms of the amount of useless density which accompanies those densities forming useful gradients in the D-log E function. This change in useless density is, for convenience, referred to as the change in fog.

Each of the changes of curve R which have been roughly described can be accomplished by adding to the densities of curve R the required amount of a density function defined in terms of R itself. Such a function of densities may be termed a vector, hence the name, *vector parameter*.

The contrast vector V_1 that is added to R to change the contrast of R is a fraction of the density D of R itself at each point; that is, $V_1 = AR$. In case curves R and X differ only in contrast, a curve Q, congruent with X, can be drawn by making the density at each point

$$D_Q = D + AD = (1 + A) D$$

or, if $C = 1 + A$,

$$D_Q = CD$$

The quantity C is *vector contrast*.

The speed vector, V_2, must be a set of density differences which has the effect of moving a curve sideways. The general expression for such a density set is given by Taylor's series, but for cases where the required sidewise shift is small, it is sufficient to note that if one adds to a curve at every point an amount proportional to the slope of the curve at that point, the result is a duplicate of the curve laterally shifted. In fact, if one adds to the curve an amount Δx times the slope of the curve, the curve will be shifted by the amount Δx. One can then, for this simple case, write the speed vector as $V_2 = dD/dx$, where D is density and x is log exposure, and one effects a speed shift Δx by adding to curve R densities equal to $\Delta x(dD/dx)$. The quantity Δx is *vector speed*.

The fog vector, V_3, is simply a constant and, conveniently, is 1.0. Then one effects a fog shift by adding to curve R this vector times an amount f, where f is the fog shift required. Then f is *vector fog*.

The sensitometrist's problem is now to determine, for a given curve X and its reference curve R, the amounts of the three vectors V_1, V_2, and V_3 which should be added to R to produce the best congruence with X. By applying the method of least squares to this problem, one constructs formulas which express the optimum amounts as simple functions of the density values taken from the test of emulsion X. In each case, one simply multiplies each density value by a prescribed constant and adds the products; the sum is directly the value C for the contrast of X relative to that of R, or the value Δx for the speed of X relative to R, or f for the fog of X relative to R.

As used in sensitometric practice, the vector-parameter system provides for comparing emulsions that differ in speed more than is allowable with the simplifying assumption made here and also provides for specifying quantitatively certain differences in curve shapes. This latter provision is made by specifying for each kind of curve shape of interest a density function that is to be added to curve R in the same manner as the density functions defined as contrast, speed, and fog. In order that the addition of the new vector shall not affect the measurement of C, Δx, and f, instead of adding the new vector directly, only the part which is orthogonal to the vectors 1.0, R, and dD/dx is added. In this manner, the sensitometrist may appraise his progress toward accomplishing a desired change in curve shape even though his experimental steps may at the same time produce differences in speed, contrast, and fog.

Principal Components

A method of growing importance for sensitometrically comparing related emulsions is to describe the differences among a set of curves by the *principal components* of the *variability* of the set —a concept taken from the field of statistics.[8]

Suppose the difference between only two D-log E curves is to be exactly specified. An obvious way is to take the differences between their densities at various log E values and plot these differences as a function of the log E values themselves. The result would be a D-log E difference function which would exactly explain the differences between the two original curves. Suppose now that the D-log E curve of a third emulsion of the same type as the first two is to be studied. Even though it differs from the first two, it is quite possible that the D-log$E$ difference function derived from the first two would do a fair job of describing the difference between the third curve and, say, the average of the first two; this is because differences among emulsions of a given type are apt to be largely of a single kind. The principal-component method is a means of finding, for a whole set of curves, just such a D-log E difference function. It finds the exact and unique function which, used in various amounts, will best describe the differences among the set. By adding this difference function in various amounts to the average curve of the set, one can get a fair approximation to each individual curve.

Each approximation, however, will have errors. If, now, these errors are plotted as new D-log E curves, these new curves may also be found to differ in a systematic way, which the same principal-component treatment will discover and describe. Better approximations to each curve can now be had by adding to the average curve the required amounts of *both* basic differences. The residual errors can again be examined for the principal component, and the process repeated as often as necessary. Usually three principal components do an excellent job of describing all differences.

In mathematical language, the principal components are eigenfunctions of the exposure variable, or eigenvectors of the density space, and the latter term is frequently used; the description of each curve then is by the *scalar multiples* of the eigenvectors needed to explain the difference between the curve and the mean or other reference curve. An electronic computing machine will in a few minutes find both the eigenvectors of a large set of curves and the scalar multiples of them which describe each individual curve. The ability of eigenvectors to describe a curve completely by two, three, or four numbers makes them an important tool in sensitometric research.[9]

Development Constants

The rate of development of a photographic material has been discussed in Chapter 7. In practice, the development characteristics of a photographic material are determined from a family of characteristic curves obtained by developing the material for various times. A typical family of such curves is shown in Fig. $11 \cdot 5(a)$. The time-gamma curve shown in Fig. $11 \cdot 5(b)$ is then obtained from these sensitometric data. This curve may be represented approximately by the exponential equation

$$\gamma = \gamma_\infty (1 - e^{-kt}) \qquad (11 \cdot 4)$$

where γ_∞ is the value which γ approaches as a maximum on prolonged development, fog excluded, and k is the velocity constant of development. The values of γ_∞ and k can be determined by solving the simultaneous equations obtained when the values of gamma for times t and $2t$ are substituted in equation $11 \cdot 4$. However, equation 11·4 rarely represents the actual time-gamma curve with sufficient accuracy to be employed in sensitometric calculations (see Chapter 7).

For practical purposes the sensitometric data concerning the rate of development can usually be obtained best from curves

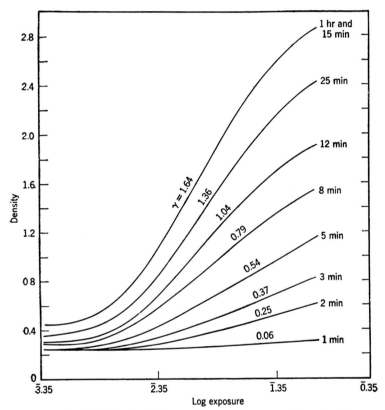

Fig. 11 · 5 *(a)* Family of characteristic curves for a negative material.

similar to those shown in Figs. 11·5(*a*) and 11·5(*b*). To obtain a negative having a given gamma, it is only necessary to refer to the time-gamma curve [Fig. 11·5(*b*)] for the required time of development.

Sensitometric Constants of Photographic Printing Paper

The sensitometric properties of photographic printing papers are described by a series of numerical constants which are de-

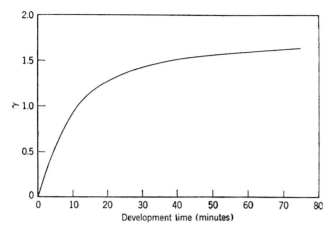

Fig. 11 · 5 (b)   Time-gamma curve for the material whose characteristic curves are shown in Fig. 11 ·5 (a).

rived from the characteristic curves for the papers. The characteristic curve is obtained by plotting reflection density against the logarithm of exposure.

A typical characteristic curve for a photographic paper is shown in Fig. 11 · 6. The limiting exposure E_s in the high-density region corresponds to the point S on the shoulder of this curve where the gradient is equal to the average gradient $\overline{G}$, and the limiting exposure E_h in the low-density region corresponds to the point h on the toe at which the gradient is equal to $0.1\overline{G}$, where $\overline{G}$ is the average gradient of the curve between these two limiting exposures (see Fig. 11·6). The difference between the limiting exposures E_s and E_h is the *exposure scale ES* of the paper. Therefore

$$\log\ ES = \log E_s - \log E_h \qquad (11\cdot5)$$

The *density scale DS* is the difference between the ordinate values corresponding to the limiting exposures, and the *useful maximum density* is the ordinate value corresponding to the limiting exposure E_s. The speed of the photographic paper is given by the expression

$$\text{Paper speed} = \frac{10^4}{E_s} \qquad (11\cdot6)$$

Although this speed value is based on a fractional gradient criterion, as is the speed value for negatives, it should be noted that

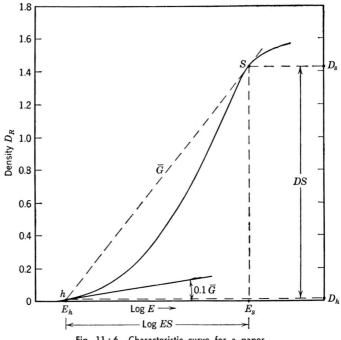

Fig. 11·6 Characteristic curve for a paper.

the speed point is now taken in the shoulder region rather than in the toe region, as for negative materials. The constants for printing papers as defined above are in agreement with those adopted by the American Standards Association.[10]

In addition to those constants set up by the American Standards Association, it has been common practice to refer to the *contrast of the printing paper*. Contrast is a very complex matter involving both psychological and physical quantities. It has been expressed[11] as

$$\Omega = \frac{(DS) \cdot \overline{G}(D)}{(l\Delta D)^2} \qquad (11 \cdot 7)$$

where DS is the density scale, $\overline{G}(D)$ is the average gradient computed in terms of equal density increments, and $l\Delta D$ is the smallest density difference which can be distinguished by the eye. Since the denominator is a constant it can be neglected in the calculation of relative contrast. In computing $\overline{G}(D)$, the characteristic curve is divided into segments of equal density increment. The gradient of the curve is measured at each division point. The average of these gradient values is $\bar{G}(D)$. When the characteristic curve has a long straight portion, the average gradient is approximately equal to the gamma to which the paper is developed. It should be noted that when the contrasts of papers with essentially equal density scales are compared, the relative contrasts are equal to the relative average gradients. Contrast may be referred to as the product between a *rate* or *gradient* factor and the *extent* or *density scale* factor.

Effect of Development on the Sensitometric Characteristics of Photographic Paper

The velocity of development of chloride and chlorobromide paper is very high, gamma infinity is reached very rapidly, and the only effect of prolonged development, after the initial stages, is an increase in the speed of the paper, as shown in Fig. 11·7. With bromide papers, on the other hand, prolonged development increases the average gradient and the speed simultaneously, as shown in Fig. 11 · 8.

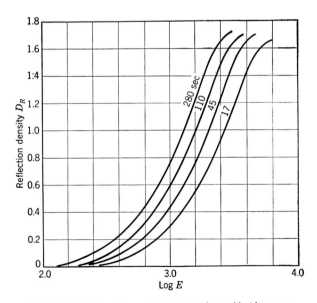

Fig. 11 · 7   Family of characteristic curves for a chloride paper.

Spectral Sensitivity

In using photographic materials it is important to know the way in which the sensitivity is distributed throughout the spectrum, in both the ultraviolet and the infrared as well as in the visible. All methods of measuring spectral sensitivity involve the isolation of sections of the spectrum and the observation of the response produced when the materials are exposed to these spectral bands and then developed. A wide variety of devices, monochromatic sensitometers, spectrographs, tricolor tablets, color charts, and filter assemblies, have been used in connection with making these exposures. The more refined methods, which involve the dispersion of the radiation with prisms or diffraction gratings, may be divided into two general classes: first, the spectrographs, in which the material is exposed to the entire spectrum at the same time; and, second, the monochromatic sensitometers, in which the material is exposed to a single narrow band of practically homogeneous radiation.

Monochromatic Sensitometers

Monochromatic sensitometers for the ultraviolet regions of the spectrum have been made which consist of two quartz mono-

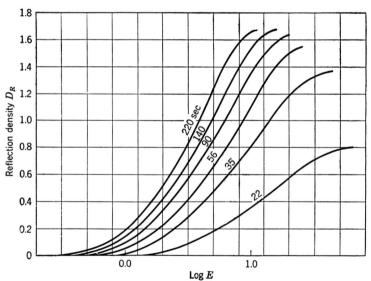

Fig. 11 · 8   Family of characteristic curves for a bromide paper.

chromatic illuminators. The radiation emerging from the exit slit of the first illuminator passes into the second. In this manner most of the stray radiation is eliminated, and the radiation emerging from the second illuminator is of high purity. For longer wavelengths it is desirable to disperse the radiation by means of diffraction gratings because of the low dispersion of the quartz illuminators. A prime requisite for this work is high spectral purity in the isolated band. High spectral purity is particularly necessary for those regions where the relative amount of energy from the light source or the sensitivity of the material is low compared to that in other spectral regions. The samples are exposed to the homogeneous radiation, and the time of exposure is modulated by any of the methods discussed previously (see Chapter 9).

Exposure is normally expressed in terms of visual meter-candle seconds. However, in monochromatic sensitometry, exposure must be expressed in terms of suitable energy units, such as ergs per unit area. One of the most difficult steps in monochromatic sensitometry is the determination of these energy values with sufficient precision. A common procedure is to use a thermopile-galvanometer combination of high sensitivity.

Spectral sensitivity can be expressed in many ways, and the particular method employed must be chosen to fit the problem in hand. For theoretical purposes, it is often desirable to express spectral sensitivity in terms of the reciprocal of the energy required to give a density of unity when development for each wavelength is carried to a gamma of unity. On the other hand, for practical purposes spectral sensitivity is often expressed in terms of the reciprocal of the energy required to produce a density of unity for a fixed time of development. The time of development is usually that which, for a white light exposure, will give a gamma approximately equal to that used with the material in practice. The spectral sensitivity curves obtained by the above methods are modified somewhat if a different value of density is chosen for these measurements. Spectral sensitivity can also be expressed in terms of reciprocal inertia values (equation $11 \cdot 2$).

The relative values of spectral sensitivity for various wave lengths depend markedly upon the method employed for expressing spectral sensitivity. The curves for a panchromatic film as measured by several methods are shown in Fig. $11 \cdot 9$. In curve

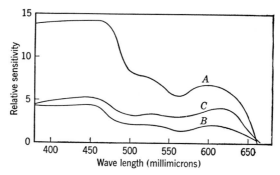

Fig. 11·9 Spectral sensitivity curves for a panchromatic film as expressed by different methods: *(A)* reciprocal inertia, *(B)* reciprocal energy for density of unity and gamma of unity, *(C)* reciprocal energy for density of unity and fixed development time.

A the reciprocal inertia value is plotted against wavelength. In curve *B* the reciprocal of the energy required to give a density of unity when development for each wavelength is carried to a gamma of unity is plotted against wave length. In curve *C* the reciprocal of the energy required to produce a density of unity for a fixed development time is plotted against wavelength, the development time being that required to give a gamma of unity for white light exposures.

Spectral sensitivity curves such as those shown in Fig. 11·9 represent the characteristic of the photographic material itself

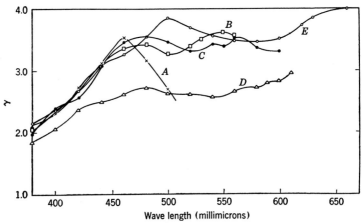

Fig. 11·10 Variation of gamma with wavelength for an emulsion *(A)* unsensitized, *(B)* sensitized with a pseudocyanine, *(C)* sensitized with a merocyanine, *(D)* sensitized with a thiacarbocyanine, and *(E)* sensitized with a dibenzothiacarbocyanine.

and do not take into consideration the energy distribution of the light sources with which they are commonly exposed. These curves show the relative response of the material only when it is used with a light source which is emitting equal amounts of energy at all wavelengths. The light sources ordinarily used for photography depart greatly from this condition of equal energy radiation. The spectral response curve of a material to any light source can be obtained by multiplying, wavelength by wavelength, the ordinates of the sensitivity curve of the material on an equal energy basis by the ordinates of the energy distribution curve for the light source (see page 175 and Fig. 9 · 3).

The relation of gamma to wavelength follows no general rule. However, gamma often increases as the wavelength of the light employed to expose the material increases. The variation of gamma with wave length depends upon the emulsion and is complicated by reciprocity law failure, particularly in optically sensitized emulsions. Typical curves for the variation of gamma with wavelength are shown in Fig. 11 · 10.

Spectrographs

In a spectrograph, the radiation from the source is dispersed by means of a prism or a diffraction grating, and the sample is exposed to the entire spectrum at the same time. When a neutral gray wedge is placed directly over the slit in such a manner as

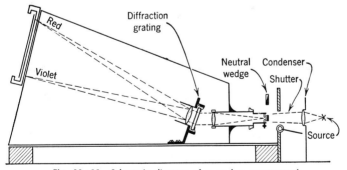

Fig. 11 · 11 Schematic diagram of a wedge spectrograph.

to modulate the light along a spectrum line of a given wave length, the spectrograph may be made to give directly a graphic representation of the effective spectral response curve of a photographic material and light source combination. Such an instrument is usually referred to as a wedge spectrograph, and the photographic record is called a *wedge spectrogram*. The schematic diagram of a typical wedge spectrograph is shown in Fig. 11 · 11, and three wedge spectrograms of the type obtained with this instrument are shown in Fig. 11 · 12. An inspection of wedge spectrograms may yield considerable information about the distribution of sensitivity and some qualitative information concerning the variation of gamma with wavelength. The wedge spectrograph has the advantage of simplicity and rapidity. However, it cannot be considered to be as satisfactory for precise determinations as the monochromatic sensitometer.

Specifications of Color Sensitivity

It is often desirable to obtain a simple specification of color sensitivity in terms of a few numerical constants; such a system

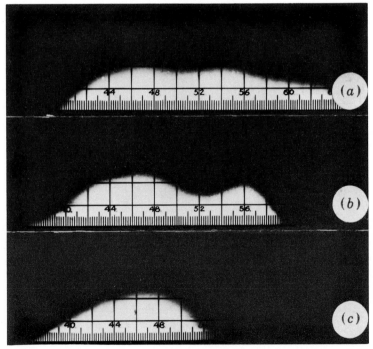

Fig. 11 · 12   Wedge spectrograms of (a) panchromatic, (b) orthochromatic, and (c) unsensitized materials

has been adopted by the American Standards Association.[9] The method consists in dividing the spectrum into three parts and determining the relative response of the photographic material in each of these regions. These regions are blue, green, and red. Since it is difficult to obtain sharp-cutting filters which will isolate each of these spectral regions individually, the relative responses are determined by exposing the material with no filter, through a yellow filter, such as Wratten No. 12, and through a red filter, such as Wratten No. 25. The yellow filter transmits in the green and red regions of the spectrum, but is opaque in the blue. The response to blue light is therefore obtained as the difference between the responses to exposure without a filter and to exposure through the yellow filter. The response to green light is obtained as the difference between the responses to exposure through the yellow filter and through the red filter. The response to red light is determined merely by the exposure through the red filter. The percentage contribution of each of these regions to the total response is taken as the *spectral sensitivity index*. In practice the degree of differentiation given by these index values is frequently greater than that required for many purposes, such as computing exposures. Photographic materials with similar properties of spectral response are therefore classified into groups in terms of *spectral group numbers*. Materials in a given group show similar color responses in photographing colored objects and require similar filter factors when used with the common filters. The spectral group numbers are based upon the relative responses of the material when exposed through a yellow filter such as the Wratten No. 12 and a red filter such as the Wratten No. 25. The two parameters of the grouping system are the sum of the red and green percentage contributions, and the ratio of the red and green percentage contributions. The spectral group number is determined from an appropriate table, such as that adopted by the American Standards Association.[12]

REFERENCES

General

Mees, *The Theory of the Photographic Process*, revised edition, Macmillan, New York, 1954, Chapters 21, 22.

Jones, *Photographic Sensitometry*, Eastman Kodak Co., 1935.

Specific

1. Deutscher Normenausschuss, *DIN 4512*, 1957 revision. [Changed but slightly from revision described in *Phot. Korr.*, **90**, 127 (1954)].

2. Jones, *J. Franklin Inst.*, **227**, 297, 497 (1939).
3. Amercan Standards Association, *American Standard PH2.5-1954.*
4. Simonds, *Phot. Sci. and Eng.*, **2**, 162 (1958).
5. Nelson and Simonds, *J. Optical Soc. Am.*, **46**, 324 (1956).
6. Dunham, *Ber. VIII intern. Kongr. Phot., Dresden*, 287 (1931).
7. Bayer, Simonds, and Williams, to be published.
8. Hotelling, *Educ. Psychol.*, **24**, 417 (1933).
9. Simonds, *Phot. Sci. and Eng.*, **2**, 205 (1958).
10. American Standards Association, *American Standard PH2.2-1953.*
11. Jones, *J. Franklin Inst.*, **203**, 11 (1927).
12. American Standards Association, *American Standard PH2.6-1954.*

12.

The Theory of Tone Reproduction

One of the basic relations in photographic theory is that which exists between the *luminance** and *luminance differences* in the original scene and the *density* and *density differences* in the photographic reproduction of the scene. The fundamental work on this relationship by Hurter and Driffield, Renwick, Jones, and others has established a series of principles known as *the theory of tone reproduction.*

Introduction

The tone reproduction problem has two major aspects: the objective and the subjective or psychological. In a study of the objective phase, the *luminance* and *luminance differences* in the object being photographed may be considered the starting point. A lens forms an image of the object on the light-sensitive material. When this image has been allowed to act for a sufficient time, a latent image is formed which is then converted into a real image by development and fixation to produce a negative. An image of this negative is now formed on the positive material by means of an enlarger or contact printer, and after sufficient exposure time a latent image is created that is then developed into a real image, and the positive photographic reproduction is obtained. The *density* and *density differences* of this positive are now compared with the log *luminance* and log *luminance differences* of those in the original object. This comparison provides direct information about the perfection with which the photographic process has met the requirements for exact objective tone reproduction.

---

* See Table II in the Appendix.

A study of the subjective phase of tone reproduction involves the comparison of the sensations and the mental impressions produced by the luminances in the various areas of the scene with those produced by the same areas in the illuminated reproduction. The magnitude attribute of the visual sensation produced by light is termed *brightness.*† These subjective comparisons are difficult to evaluate in precise terms since brightness, being a sensation, cannot be measured directly and recourse must be made to indirect methods. In making these comparisons, it is important to consider the illumination on both the positive and the original scene and the nature of the surrounding areas. The white border on a print, for example, affects its appearance because it reduces the ability of the visual system to see brightness differences and makes the shadow detail in the print more difficult to see. In addition, there are the adaptations which take place in the eye or brain. Psychologists refer to these phenomena as brightness constancy and simultaneous contrast.

The foregoing discussion of the tone reproduction problem is entirely qualitative. The quantitative solution of this problem will be discussed in detail in the following sections.

A Graphic Solution of the Objective Phase of Tone Reproduction

The faithfulness of the objective tone reproduction obtained in a negative-positive photographic process depends upon the following factors:

1. Luminance scale of the scene.
2. Optical and physical characteristics of the camera.
3. Negative material and its treatment.
    a. Exposure.
    b. Spectral sensitivity.
    c. Development.
    d. Shape of the D-log E curve.
4. Characteristics of printing system.
5. Positive material and its treatment.
    a. Exposure.
    b. Development.
    c. Shape of the D-log E curve.
6. Method of measuring the densities in the photographic reproduction.

---

† See Table II in the Appendix.

Luminance Scale of Scenes

The *luminance scale* of a scene is defined as the ratio of the maximum to the minimum luminance in the scene. Since the best reflectors reflect only about 98 per cent of the incident light, whereas the best absorbers reflect as much as 1 or 2 per cent, the maximum luminance scale that can be realized, if all objects are illuminated uniformly, is in the order of 90 to 95 per cent. On the other hand, all the objects in a scene seldom receive the same illumination. Thus, objects in the shadows receive much less illumination than those in direct sunlight, and the luminance scale may be much higher than that for uniform illumination.

For many years it was thought that the luminance scale of an average outdoor scene was approximately 30:1. This is a log luminance scale of 1.5. Since the density scale of photographic papers is often 1.5 or more, the luminance range in such a scene should be reproducible on photographic paper. However, in 1940 Jones and Condit[1] published data for 126 exterior scenes showing that the average log luminance scale for these scenes was 2.2, the shortest being 1.45 and the longest 2.8. In terms of arithmetic units this corresponds to a scale of 160:1 for an average scene, with 27:1 and 760:1 as the scales of the scenes having the shortest and longest scales, respectively. Later measurements showed that some scenes have scales exceeding 1000:1. Obviously, a faithful reproduction of the latter scenes would require a positive material having a density scale of more than 3.0. Such a scale can be obtained in a transparency, but if a reflection print is desired, some compression of the tonal scale must be accepted. The photographer usually has his choice of taking the compression uniformly throughout the tonal scale, all in the shadows, all in the highlights, or part in the shadows and part in the highlights. Much of the research in tone reproduction deals with determining which of the possible reproductions are the most pleasing and seeking rules for obtaining such reproductions by control methods.

The measurements of Jones and Condit were made with a portable luminance photometer of the telescopic type in which precautions were taken to reduce flare light to a minimum. A reproduction of one of the scenes in which the luminance distribution was analyzed is shown in Fig. 12·1. The small lettered circles indicate the points at which luminance measurements

Fig. 12·1   Scene for which the luminance measurements in Table 12·1 were made.

were made, and in Table $12 \cdot 1$ are shown the luminance values expressed in foot-lamberts corresponding to these points. The maximum luminance in this scene was 4990 ft-L and the minimum 10.7 ft-L, the luminance scale being 466:1.

TABLE $12 \cdot 1$

LUMINANCE VALUES OF SEVERAL AREAS IN AN EXTERIOR SCENE

Area	Foot-Lamberts
a	4990
b	1500
c	890
d	475
e	165
f	10.7

Flare Light in the Camera

The camera image is not an exact luminous reproduction of the scene being photographed. The illuminance on the photographic material consists of two parts: one, the image-forming light, and the other, the non-image-forming or flare light. If I_i is the total image illuminance, if I_{io} is the illuminance resulting from the image-forming light, and if I_{if} is the illuminance resulting from flare light alone,

$$I_i = I_{io} + I_{if} \tag{12 \cdot 1}$$

The non-image-forming flare light I_{if} arises from several sources. Light is scattered or reflected by the glass-air surfaces of the lens system, by flaws in the glass, and by dust or fingerprints on the surfaces. Additional flare light may be introduced by reflections from the lens mount, the diaphragm, and the shutter blades.

One of the most important sources of flare light is the multiple reflections from the glass-air surfaces of the lens system. Part of the light passing through the lens is reflected back toward the object at the first surface and therefore need not be considered further. However, part of the light reflected at the second surface is returned toward the image by reflection from the first surface. These reflected beams form an image for each reflection at a glass-air surface, as shown for a simple meniscus lens system in Fig. $12 \cdot 2$. The image at *a*, which is produced by a single reflection, can be neglected, but the image at *b*, which is produced by double reflection, represents a serious source of flare light. Every pair of glass-air surfaces in a lens represents a system which is sending flare light in the direction of the image plane. The number of flare-producing images formed by a lens system equals $N(N-1)/2$, where N represents the number of glass-air surfaces. The light reflected from a cemented surface is small and can be neglected. These images are usually formed near the lens, and the flare light on reaching the photographic material is spread out over the entire film or plate. Frequently, however, this light falling on the plate is not spread uniformly over the surface, and a flare spot or ghost is produced.

Flare light introduced by reflections from the glass-air surfaces can be reduced by applying one or more layers of the proper transparent material to the surface of the glass. Usually only a

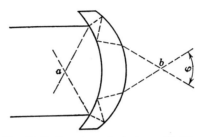

Fig. 12·2   Flare in a simple lens.   (Goldberg.)

single layer is used, and it should have an index of refraction equal to the square root of the index of refraction of the glass; its optical thickness should be equal to one-quarter the wave length of green light. Such a layer will reduce the reflectivity for green light falling normal to the surface to nearly zero and will reduce the average reflectivity for all colors to about ½ per cent. Coating a four-element lens should increase its total transmittance by about 50 per cent. This large an increase in transmittance is not realized in practice, and the flare light is not reduced by the theoretical amount because of the flare introduced by the other elements of the camera, such as the bellows and the diaphragm blades.

Flare light compresses the tonal scale considerably because it has a much greater effect on the shadow tones than it has on the highlights. For example, the addition of 1 unit of flare light to 100 units of image-forming light in the highlight region increases the illuminance only 1 per cent, whereas the addition of 1 unit of flare light to 1 unit of image-forming light in the shadows increases the illuminance 100 per cent.

Jones and Condit[1] found that the magnitude of flare depended not only on the type of camera and lens, but also upon the type of scene. They defined *flare factor* as the ratio of the luminance scale of the scene to the illuminance scale of the camera image. Using a camera with appreciably less flare than an average camera, they found that for 126 different scenes the flare factor varied from 1.15 to 9.50. The average flare factor with this camera was 2.35. The flare factor for a typical amateur camera and an average scene is in the order of 3 to 5. Since most high-quality negative emulsions have an exposure scale of several hundred, it is clear that the flare factor reduces the luminance scale of most scenes to a camera image illuminance scale which can easily be accommodated by the negative material.

The Flare Curve

The method employed in the graphic solution of the complete tone reproduction problem as described in this and the following sections was first suggested by L. A. Jones.[2] The first step in the solution of the objective phase of the problem is to determine the *flare curve* as shown in Fig. 12·3. The log luminance of different points in the scene, log B_o, is plotted against the log luminance of the corresponding points in the camera image, log I. If the

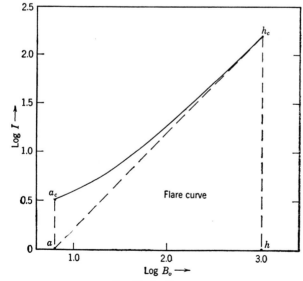

Fig. 12·3   Flare curve

image were an exact luminance reproduction of the scene, the data in this graph would fit a straight line having a slope of unity. In practice flare light usually has little effect on the gradients in the highlight region. On the other hand, flare light frequently lowers the gradient in the middle tones to 0.7 and those in the shadows to as low as 0.3.

In determining the gradient characteristics of the camera image it is also necessary to consider the optical properties of the lens, since the image-forming component I_{io} of the total image-forming light from a uniformly luminous object is not distributed uniformly over the image. If the luminance, B_o, of an object area is known, the value of I_{io} for a corresponding point in the image formed on the photographic material can be computed by the formula

$$I_{io} = B_o \frac{f^2}{4V^2F^2} \cos^4 \theta \cdot H \cdot T_g \qquad (12 \cdot 2)$$

where I_{io} = image illuminance (foot-candles)
B_o = object luminance (foot-lamberts)
f = focal length
V = image distance
d = diameter of stop
$F = f/d$, aperture ratio
θ = angle of image point off axis
T_g = transmission factor due to reflection and absorption by glass
H = transmission factor at points off axis due to vignetting by the lens barrel.

If the object lies on the axis of the lens, the $\cos^4\theta$ and H terms in this equation may be ignored, and if the object is at infinity the equation simplifies to

$$I_{io} = B_o \frac{1}{4F^2} T_g \qquad (12 \cdot 3)$$

On the average, however, objects are not at infinity, and a correction should be made for the difference in the relationship between I_{io} and B_o as given by equations $12 \cdot 2$ and $12 \cdot 3$.

In a practical formula, account should also be taken of the loss due to vignetting and the optical loss from the angle subtended by off-axis objects. The weighted average displacement from the optical axis of important objects may be taken as 15°. The loss from vignetting by the barrel of the lens depends upon the design of the lens and the aperture, but for a point 15° off axis this loss may be represented by an average of 25 per cent. Light is lost by reflection at the glass-air surfaces of the lens and by absorption within the glass. On the average, modern lenses, which frequently have six or eight glass-air surfaces, do not transmit more than 70 per cent of the incident light.* These various factors, which must be considered in the determination of a probable average value of the relation between I_{io} and B_o, may therefore be taken as

$$\theta = 15°$$
$$\cos^4 \theta = 0.866$$
$$T_g = 0.70$$
$$H = 0.75$$

and for a finite object distance,

$$\frac{f^2}{V^2} = 0.90$$

When these four values are inserted in formula 12·2 the result becomes

$$I_{io} = B_o \frac{0.409}{4F^2} \qquad (12 \cdot 4)$$

In the solution of the tone reproduction problem the gradient curve for the camera image (Fig. 12·3) is usually determined for points near the axis. It should be noted that this curve applies *only* to objects near the axis and that a different camera image curve would apply to objects at some distance from the axis. However, if the focal length of the lens is equal to or greater than the diagonal of the negative in the camera, errors introduced in the calculations by disregarding the non-uniformity of the image-forming light I_{io} are small and are usually disregarded.

The Negative Material

The shape of the D-log E characteristic curve of negative materials and their available exposure and density scales is of particular importance in the solution of tone reproduction prob-

---

*This example has been carried directly from the first edition. Now all but the cheapest singlet camera lenses are coated so that the transmittance of even the most complicated ones is of the order of 90 per cent.

lems. Since densities represented by the shoulder of the characteristic curve are seldom used in practice, the important characteristics of the material are the lengths of the toe and the straight portions of the characteristic curve. Some materials show long sweeping toes covering a relatively long exposure range; in their curve the straight portion does not begin until fairly high density values are reached. On the other hand, materials of the short-toe type give straight lines beginning at relatively low density values, and the exposure scale covered by the toe regions is quite short.

For many years it was believed that the negative exposure should always be such that the scene was reproduced entirely on the straight portion of the characteristic curve. Recent work has shown, however, that a considerable portion of the toe can be, and frequently is, used with some gain in print quality. The American Standard criterion of negative film speed is, in fact, based on the measurement of a *minimum useful gradient* on the toe as discussed in Chapter 11. The gradient or gamma of the straight portion is usually kept within the limits of 0.7 and 0.9 by controlling the extent of development. If these gamma limits are not exceeded, satisfactory tone reproduction in the final print can ordinarily be achieved even when the negative exposure varies widely.

On the other hand, negative materials are sometimes developed to give a gamma of 0.9 to 1.2 when used in specialized fields such as press photography. Such negatives must be given a carefully controlled camera exposure because the high gamma decreases the camera exposure latitude. Any exposure which is great enough to place the scene on the straight portion of a high gamma curve produces so contrasty a negative that it cannot be printed successfully even on the softest available printing paper. The resulting tone reproduction is poor, and the print is displeasing. The exposures must then be limited to the toe of the negative where the contrast or gradient is sufficiently low for satisfactory printing. This difficulty is avoided when gamma values of 0.7 to 0.9 are used.

For correct objective tone reproduction of the colored objects in the scene, the spectral sensitivity of the negative material should be equal to that of the human eye. Generally, this factor is not critical, although distinctly better tone reproduction is obtained with panchromatic and orthochromatic negative materials than with materials which are sensitive only to blue light.

The second step in the graphic analysis of the tone reproduction cycle combines the flare curve, Fig. 12·3, with the characteristic curve for the negative material. The two curves are combined as shown in Fig. 12·4, where the log I scale of the flare curve has been transferred to the log E axis of the char-

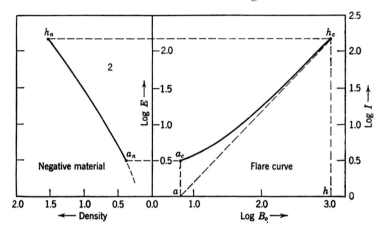

Fig. 12·4   Combined flare and negative characteristic curve.

acteristic curve for the negative material. From these combined curves it is now possible to determine the density produced in the negative by an exposure to any part of the scene having a known luminance value. The characteristic curve employed in this analysis must be obtained by employing a light source, a time of exposure, and development conditions which are in agreement with those used in obtaining the negative.

Characteristics of Printing System

When a negative is printed onto a positive material, in either a contact or a projection printer, the effective densities in the negative depend upon the geometric distribution or degree of diffusion of the light falling on the negative and the fraction of the transmitted light which is collected by the positive. The type of density which is effective when using a given printer must be determined experimentally; it may be diffuse, doubly diffuse, specular, or some intermediate type. This experimentally determined effective density must be the type employed in determining the sensitometric properties of the negative material for the graphic analysis of tone reproduction (Fig. 12·4).

If the negative is stained by development or is spectrally selective for any reason, the spectral quality of the light used in printing and the spectral sensitivity of the positive material should be taken into account; that is, the effective negative densities should be determined for the particular spectral conditions involved (see Chapter 10).

Projection printers also contribute flare light to the projected image. This flare light has the same origin as flare in camera systems but, in general, the amount in projection printers is very much less than that in the negative-making operation. As a rule, the only illuminated area presented to the objective of the projection printer is the negative itself, the surrounding areas being dark. However, particularly for negatives having large density scales, the amount of flare light may be sufficient to produce a very definite distortion in the distribution of illumination on the positive material. If the amount of flare light is sufficient, the effective enlarger illumination must be determined in the manner employed to determine the flare curve (Fig. 12·3). For a given level of illumination on the negative, each density corresponds to a value of log luminance, and this value of log luminance is plotted against the log illuminance of the corresponding point in the enlarger image.

Positive Material

Modern printing papers fall into three general categories: chloride, bromide, and chlorobromide. The first group is characterized by high development rates; in a few seconds the curve shape has attained equilibrium. With extended development, the curve merely moves parallel to itself along the log exposure axis. Bromide papers develop somewhat more slowly and there-

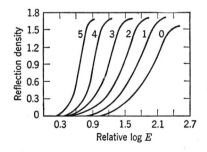

Fig. 12·5 Characteristic curves for six grades of printing paper.

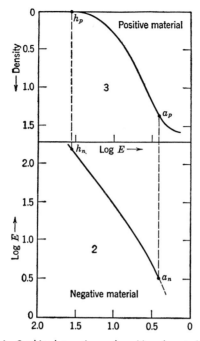

Fig. 12·6 Combined negative and positive characteristic curves.

fore afford a greater control of gradient. The chlorobromide group lies intermediate between the first two but resembles the chloride papers more closely.

In practice, the development of negatives is carried to a fixed extent; therefore, if the scenes vary appreciably in luminance scale, the resultant negatives have a rather wide variation in density scale. To print these various negatives satisfactorily, different grades of printing paper must be used. In Fig. 12·5 are shown the characteristic curves for six grades of a developing-out paper. It is seen that they have approximately the same value of maximum density. The available exposure scale, however, varies from approximately 1.5 in log E units for the No. 0 grade to approximately 0.5 for the No. 5 grade. These materials, as well as practically all commercially available developing-out papers of the chloride type, are characterized by long sweeping toes, straight portions which, if existent, are very short (with respect to exposure scale), and shoulders which break sharply at relatively high densities and become parallel to the log E axis.

The maximum densities obtainable on printing papers depend upon their surface characteristics. With high-gloss surfaces the maximum density obtained is about 1.7, whereas for semi-matte surfaces it is about 1.55, and for dead-matte surfaces it is about 1.3. It is obvious that there are many luminance scales of natural scenes which cannot be reproduced by an exact objective tone reproduction, since the average log luminance scale of the exterior scenes discussed previously is 2.2. This limitation can only be overcome by the use of positive materials having a higher maximum density, such as transparencies which have maximum densities of 3 or 4.

The third step in the graphic analysis of the objective phase of the tone reproduction problem is the combination of the characteristic curve for the positive material with the characteristic curve for the negative material. These curves are combined as shown in Fig. 12·6 where the density scale of the negative has been plotted as the log E scale for the positive. The exact value of log E depends upon the level of illumination of the negative. As pointed out previously, the type of density measured in the negative must be that which applies under the printing conditions employed and, if necessary, a curve similar to Fig. 12·3 must be introduced to correct for flare in the printing system.

Viewing Conditions

In the graphic analysis of tone reproduction, it is important that the measured densities of the positive actually represent the relative log luminances in the areas of the photograph as viewed by the observer. As pointed out previously (Chapter 10), the values of reflection density depend very markedly upon the manner in which they are measured. It is clear that the measurement of the reflection densities used in any tone reproduction analysis must be made consistent with the viewing conditions. On the other hand, if the positive is a transparency and is viewed by projection, the flare light and the specularity of the projector must be considered part of the viewing conditions. These effects are particularly important in the projection of motion-picture positives because, in addition to the above factors, degradation of the image contrast by general illumination in the room or theater must be taken into consideration. These corrections are made by performing a graphical analysis similar to that discussed in connection with the flare curve shown in Fig. 12·3.

The Objective Tone Reproduction Curve

The complete graphic solution of the objective phase of the tone reproduction curve is obtained by combining the separate curves for flare, the negative material, and the positive material

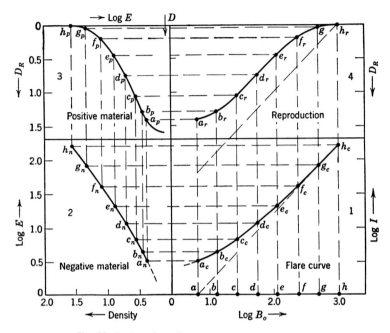

Fig. 12 · 7   Complete objective tone reproduction curve.

to give the objective tone reproduction curve as shown in the fourth† quadrant of Fig. 12 · 7. The abscissa of the reproduction curve is the log luminance scale of the original scene, and the ordinate scale is the density scale of the positive photographic reproduction. The reproduction curve is obtained by first constructing perpendicular lines from selected object luminances a to h on the abscissa scale of the flare curve. The intersections of these lines with the camera image curve locate points a_c to h_c. Horizontal lines through these points locate points a_n to h_n on the negative characteristic curve. Vertical lines through these

---

†Following the precedent of L. A. Jones, the quadrants of the tone reproduction diagram are numbered in clockwise order, beginning with the lower right-hand quadrant.

points establish points a_p to h_p on the positive characteristic curve, and horizontal lines through these points determine the densities with which luminances a to h in the original object are reproduced in the reproduction. The vertical lines through a to h intersect the horizontal lines through a_p to h_p at points a_r to h_r, and the curve through these points is the desired objective tone reproduction curve because it affords a graphic comparison between the log luminances in the original scene and the densities by which they are reproduced in the photographic reproduction.

For exact objective tone reproduction, the reproduction curve must be a straight line at an angle of 45° to the horizontal axis, and it must pass through the origin. If the gradients at any point a to h on the four curves, 1, 2, 3, and 4, in the tone reproduction diagram, Fig. 12·7, are designated G_c, G_n, G_p, and G_r, respectively, these four gradients satisfy the condition that

$$G_r = G_c G_n G_p \qquad (12 \cdot 5)$$

That is, the gradient of the reproduction curve G_r at any point is equal to the product of the gradients at the corresponding points on the other curves, G_c, G_n, and G_p. For perfect objective tone reproduction, therefore, the product of these three gradients must equal unity. If two of the three gradients are known, the value of the third can be computed. It is often stated that for the straight portion of the characteristic and flare curves this relationship becomes

$$\gamma_r = \gamma_c \gamma_n \gamma_p \qquad (12 \cdot 6)$$

However, this condition is seldom met in practice because the corresponding points would have to be on the straight portion of every curve; points a to h in Fig. 12·7, for example, would all have to be on the straight portion of each curve. Points G_c and G_n are on the straight portions of their respective curves, but point G_p definitely is not. Perfect objective tone reproduction must therefore satisfy equation 12·5, but it need not satisfy equation 12·6.

A tone reproduction diagram of the type shown in Fig. 12·7 can be used to illustrate some interesting relationships concerning the required shapes for the negative and the positive characteristic curves which are required for correct tone reproduction.

The negative characteristic curve shown in the second quadrant of Fig. 12·4 is combined with the flare curve shown in the first quadrant to obtain the curve shown by A in Fig. 12·8. The

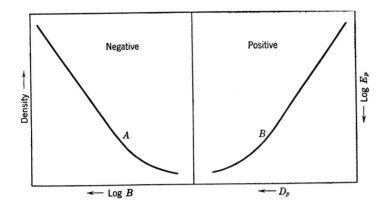

Fig. 12·8   Mirror-image curves.

curve obtained by this combination represents the relation between the log brightness of the scene, log B, and the densities by which these brightnesses are represented on the negative. If this composite curve has the shape shown by A in Fig. 12·8, then for perfect objective tone reproduction the positive characteristic curve must have the shape shown by B. It is evident that these curves are mirror images of each other. This relation is commonly referred to as the *mirror-image law*. It should be noted that curve B includes the effect of any flare light in the printing system. If this flare light is appreciable, the required positive characteristic curve as determined sensitometrically is obtained by combining curve B with the flare curve for the printer. The negative and the positive characteristic curves as obtained by sensitometric procedures remain the important properties of these photographic materials irrespective of the flare conditions in the camera or printer, but these curves must be adjusted to take flare into consideration when such operations as the mirror-image law are applied. In the general solution of the objective tone reproduction problem as shown in Fig. 12·7, the correction for camera flare is introduced automatically by the operation shown in Fig. 12·4.

For a given negative material, the effect of variations in the camera flare curve can frequently be compensated for by using positive materials having different characteristic curves. A practical example of this compensation is shown in Fig. 12·9. The flare curves for two different flare conditions, such as different

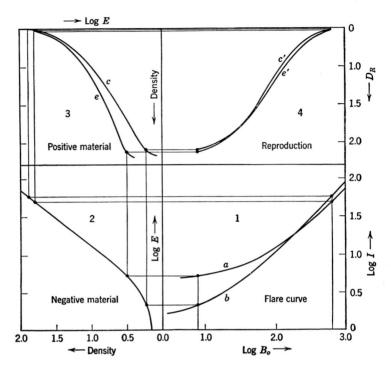

Fig. 12·9 Compensation for flare with different printing materials.

lenses, on a single scene are shown at *a* and *b* in the first quadrant, and the reproduction curves obtained when a single negative material but two different positive materials are used are shown at *c'* and *e'* in the fourth quadrant. By the use of positive materials having the characteristics shown at *c* and at *e*, respectively, in the third quadrant, it was possible to obtain these very similar reproduction curves.

The Subjective Phase of Tone Reproduction

If a photograph is a perfect tone reproduction of the original scene from a subjective standpoint, the impression given by it when viewed must be identical with that received when the original scene was viewed. The graphic solution of the tone reproduction problem by the method illustrated in Fig. 12·7 refers to the objective phase. This objective solution is identical with the subjective solution only when the observer viewing the

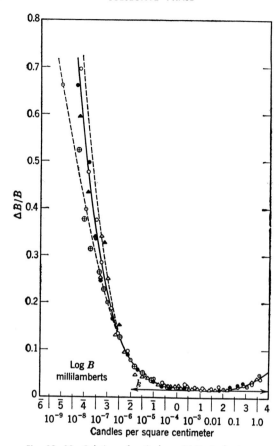

Fig. 12·10   Relation of retinal sensitivity to luminance.

photograph gets the same sensation from the density differences at all parts of the photograph as he does when viewing the corresponding luminance differences in the original scene. Since the photograph and the original scene are usually viewed under radically different conditions, the response of the eye to luminance differences at various luminance levels and other viewing conditions must be known before the faithfulness of the subjective reproduction can be appraised. What is needed is a "characteristic curve" of the eye relating response or sensation to luminance or stimulus.

It has often been questioned whether sensations can be measured, but if they are measurable, the evaluation must be done indirectly. The customary procedure is to measure the just noticeable difference in luminance ΔB as a function of the level of luminance B itself. The just noticeable fractional change $\Delta B/B$, known as the *Fechner fraction,* varies as shown in Fig. $12 \cdot 10$. Although it drops very rapidly at first as the luminance increases from zero, it attains a practically constant value at about one millilambert (~ 1 ft-L), and it maintains this value over the luminance range that is representative of everyday conditions. This means that for practical purposes we may consider $\Delta B/B$ to be constant.

The classical assumption at this point in the argument is that a constant fractional change $\Delta B/B$ in the stimulus results in a constant just noticeable change ΔS in the resulting sensation, regardless of the value of luminance level B, and hence regardless of the sensation level itself. Simple integration then shows that, on this assumption, the sensation S should be proportional to the logarithm of the luminance B except for a constant of integration. This constant can usually be neglected because it does not affect the relative values of S as B is changed.

This logarithmic relationship has been under criticism since its inception a century ago, and recent psychological studies have given definiteness to these criticisms. The assumption that $\Delta S = K \Delta B/B$ implies that the just noticeable increase in sensation is a constant amount ΔS regardless of the value of the sensation S itself. If, on the other hand, the just noticeable increase in sensation is taken to be *proportional* to the sensation,[3] we have $\Delta S/S = K \Delta B/B$, and when this equation is integrated, the result is

$$\ln S = K \cdot \ln B + \ln C \qquad (12 \cdot 7)$$

where C is the constant of integration. This relationship can be written

$$S = C \cdot B^K \qquad (12 \cdot 8)$$

To solve an actual problem, the response function of the eye must be known, and it is not certain whether this relation or some other is correct. But, despite our uncertainty in this respect, the procedure can be illustrated by simply assuming that a curve expressing the correct relation *can* be plotted. In general, a different part of the curve will be used when the photograph is viewed than when the original scene is viewed, because of the difference in luminance if nothing else. In Fig. $12 \cdot 11$ the two parts of the curve that are applicable to the example are

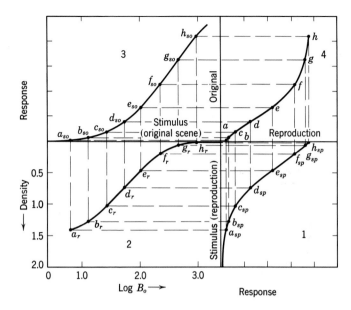

Fig. 12 · 11   Subjective tone reproduction curve.

drawn in the first and the third quadrants. The curve of the photographic print, taken from the fourth quadrant of Fig. 12 · 7, is redrawn in the second quadrant. The vertical scale of this curve represents the stimulus to the observer's eye when the photograph is viewed, and therefore the assumed response curve of the eye has been plotted on a logarithmic scale. Because of the uncertainty in the nature of the visual response, this curve must be regarded as hypothetical. The curve in the third quadrant, also hypothetical, is a similar curve for the eye under the conditions obtaining when the original scene was viewed. When the points $a_r, b_r, \ldots h_r$ are carried around the chart in two directions as described in connection with Fig. 12 · 7, the resulting curve $a, b, \ldots h$ in the fourth quadrant represents a comparison between the original scene and the photograph as seen by the observer. If this curve is straight, the photograph should look exactly like the original scene from the standpoint of tone reproduction.

Whether or not a linear reproduction curve really signifies faithful reproduction in terms of sensation depends upon whether or not the visual response curve that is used in Fig. 12 · 11 is applicable to the problem. It is a far cry from detecting a liminal luminance difference in a small spot, as is done in most studies of visual sensitivity, to evaluating a scene covering a large field and including a wide range of luminances. In color photography it is known that certain familiar colors have to be slightly falsified if they are to seem natural in a photograph, but no comparable studies seem to have been made in black-and-white photography.

If data on the sensitivity of the eye are to be used to construct the response curves showing the subjective relationship between brightness and luminance, it is necessary to know what value of field luminance determines the sensitivity. Although it has usually been assumed that the sensitivity of the eye is controlled by the average field luminance, data by Lowry[4] and the work reported by Pitt[5] indicate that this assumption is not strictly correct. They report that when the scene is one in which the luminance varies over an appreciable range, the sensitivity of the eye varies with the portion of the scene being viewed. This effect can be explained, at least in part, by reference to Fig. 12·10. The ordinates are inversely proportional to the sensitivity of the eye, and the abscissas represent the luminance of the sensitizing field. If the sensitivity of the eye is controlled by a small field element, such as one subtending 2° at the eye, then the sensitivity of the eye will vary with the luminance of the portion of the scene which is being viewed. For the range of luminance indicated by K in Fig. 12·10 the sensitivity of the eye *as measured in this specific manner* will not vary with the luminance of the sensitizing field, but for all other ranges the sensitivity will be expected to change as reported by Lowry and Pitt. The range of illuminance indicated by K is realized in practice only if the print is examined under relatively high values of illuminance, in the order of 100 ft-c. Even for the range of illuminance indicated by K, it is not certain that sensitivity remains constant; the eye moves constantly, and hence it is continually subjected to different levels of illuminance rather than to any single general level B, as it is in obtaining the data for Fig. 12·10. It should also be noted that if both the scene and the print are examined at the same level of illuminance, the changes in sensitivity with the area being viewed will tend to be the same except for differences in the angles subtended by the same areas in the scene and in the print.

Some studies have been made on the effect of uneven illumination.[6] It has been found that, in an unevenly illuminated scene, such as one having part of a wall in direct sunlight and part in shadow, the average observer will realize that the part in the light and the part in the shadow have the same reflectance, although they differ in luminance. But it is only through the knowledge that part of the wall is in shadow that the observer can reach this conclusion. When viewing a photograph, therefore, the observer must also be aware of the existence of the uneven illumination or he will mistakenly interpret the higher density of the shadow region to be a result of a difference in reflectance rather than of a difference in illumination. Effects of this type can be reduced by a flat lighting of the scene, which also has the beneficial effect of decreasing the luminance scale and thus reducing the magnitude of the task that the photographic process is called upon to perform.

The brightness contrast of a photograph is affected by its sharpness even when the luminance contrast or gradient of the reproduction is held constant. When the sharpness of the details is perceptibly increased, even when the maximum difference in density between large areas is held constant, the photograph appears "snappier," and this increased sharpness may be mistakenly interpreted as an increase in luminance contrast.

Instead of trying to analyze the phenomena involved in satisfactory reproduction from the standpoint of sensation, it is possible to submit prints of diverse tone characteristics to a jury of observers and correlate their collective evaluations with the reproduction curves. Two such prints from the same negative but on different grades of paper are shown, together with their objective reproduction curves, in Fig. 12·12. The print shown in (b) was judged the best print which could be obtained from this negative, and the print shown in (a) was judged definitely inferior to the first-choice print. It has been found that in general the most pleasing prints are those whose objective tone reproduction curves have a relatively straight portion making an angle of 45° with the axis. Investigations of this nature have enabled manufacturers to improve the characteristics of the negative and positive materials in a manner that leads to improved subjective tone reproduction.

Tone Reproduction as Applied to Photographic Printing

Experimental studies in tone reproduction have led to useful rules and procedures for obtaining high-quality photographic

Fig. 12·12 Prints from the same negative on two grades of paper together with the

objective tone reproduction curves.

prints. Since the properties of the negative and the positive materials have been controlled by the manufacturer to yield the highest number of first-quality prints under normal conditions, research on photographic printing is directed toward the choice of the optimum grade of paper and printing exposure.

Trial-and-error methods are commonly used in making prints. The operator examines the negative visually and estimates the grade of paper and the exposure which in his opinion will give a pleasing print. If the contrast of the print is too high or too low, or if the exposure was incorrect, he makes another print, using a different grade of paper or a different exposure. This process of trial and error is repeated until a satisfactory print is obtained. This method can yield results of very high quality and, if the operator has experience and skill, the time and materials consumed are not excessive. Some skilled operators will make a high percentage of good prints on the first trial.

There has long been both a need and a desire for methods of making prints automatically or by instrumental control based upon physical measurements made on the negative and the printing papers. The investigations of Tuttle showed that the integrated density of the negative as a whole could be used successfully as a criterion of printing exposure for any given grade of paper. Accordingly, he designed an automatic printer based on this principle. He used a medium grade of paper and found that the majority of negatives were properly printed with respect to both the grade of paper and the exposure. Tuttle discovered that the minimum density of the negative could also be used as a criterion of printing exposure. However, the minimum density criterion of exposure was not used in an automatic printer because of the difficulties involved in measuring this property of a negative automatically as compared with its integrated density. Tuttle reported that the maximum density of the negative was a poor criterion of printing exposure.

Jones and Nelson[7] and their co-workers made a very comprehensive investigation of the control of photographic printing by measuring the characteristics of the negative. They found, like Tuttle, that the minimum density of the negative when used as a criterion of printing exposure gave a very high percentage of properly exposed prints. Furthermore, they found that the difference between the maximum and the minimum densities in the negative, that is, the *density scale* of the negative, could be used satisfactorily as a criterion for choosing the grade of paper. The following sections describe the research of Jones and Nelson in greater detail.

Selecting the Grade of Paper from the Density Scale of the Negative

One method of approaching the problem would have been to assume that exact tone reproduction was desired in the final print and then to work out the theoretical relations between the properties of the negative and the positives which would gave this assumed tone reproduction. However, such a solution would be based on the assumption that exact tone reproduction, either subjective or objective, would give the most pleasing prints. As pointed out previously, it is very difficult, if not impossible, to obtain the exact solution of the subjective phase of the tone reproduction problem. In addition, because of the limited density scale of photographic papers it is sometimes impossible to obtain an exact objective tone reproduction of the entire tonal scale of natural scenes. To solve the problem by theoretical considerations, it would therefore be necessary to make assumptions concerning the necessary compromises in the tone reproduction solutions which would be least detrimental to the print quality. There is no way of determining in advance the compromises which would furnish the optimum quality prints.

Consequently, the problem was approached by the more laborious method of making a number of prints which differed in tone reproduction and then judging the prints to determine which ones were the most pleasing to most people. The negatives represented about 165 different exterior scenes and a few interior scenes. Five prints, differing progressively in exposure, were made from each negative on each of three, and sometimes four, different grades of paper. Each set of prints was judged by a number of people to determine which print they considered best. The judges did not have an intimate knowledge of the technical details involved, and each judge worked separately to avoid being influenced by other judgments.

Density measurements were made on the negatives and on the selected prints, and a correlation was sought between the density scales of the negatives and the log exposure scales of the papers. A correlation was found to exist, but it was far from perfect. The minimum or shadow densities in the negatives were found to print at very nearly a fixed point on the shoulder of the

D-log E curve of the paper, but the maximum or highlight densities of the negatives were found to print at widely different points of the D-log E curve of the paper, depending upon the type of scene. In fact, the extreme highlights in many of the best prints were completely off the toe of the paper curve, that is, at zero reflection density and zero gradient. One set of such data is shown graphically in Fig. 12·13. Each horizontal line represents a first-choice print. The extremities of these lines represent the minimum and the maximum densities in each print, and the small circles on the lines represent the average density of the print.

The relation between the density scale of the negative and the sensitometric log exposure scale of the paper was found to be a complex one. For soft grades of paper, the density scale of the negative usually *exceeded* the log exposure scale of the paper. For the hard grades, the density scale of the negative usually was *less than* the log exposure scale of the paper.

The sensitometric *log exposure scale* of each paper was determined by taking the difference between the log exposure corresponding to a point on the shoulder of the curve where the

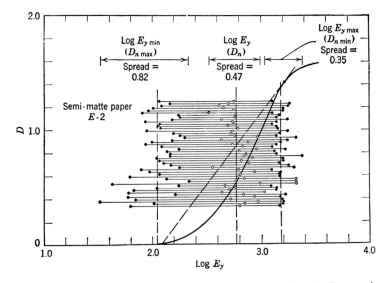

Fig. 12·13 Density scales of negatives from which "first-choice prints" were obtained, together with the characteristic curve for the positive material on which the prints were made.

gradient was equal to $1.0\overline{G}$ and the log exposure corresponding
to a point on the toe of the curve where the gradient was equal
to $0.1\overline{G}$, $\overline{G}$ being the average gradient between the two points
on the curve. This fractional gradient method was chosen be-
cause it gave values of the log exposure scale which were in
closest agreement with the average of the density scales of the
negatives which gave first-choice prints on each paper. No sensitometric criterion for log exposure scale was found which
would give perfect agreement. The discrepancies were not due
to experimental errors, but appeared to be related to variations
in the distribution of luminance in different types of scenes.

From the experimental data, Jones and Nelson worked out an
empirical conversion chart relating the sensitometric log exposure
scales of papers, ES_y, to the density scales of negatives, DS_n. The
construction of the conversion chart as shown in Fig. $12 \cdot 14$ is
described by the authors[7] as follows: "Assume a set of four
photographic papers differing in contrast grade whose log exposure scales have been found to be 0.60, 1.00, 1.20, and 1.50,
respectively. These are then plotted as the points 1, 2, 3, 4, on
the log ES_y scale. The DS_n scale is numerically equal to the log
ES_y scale, but it is displaced downward by a convenient distance d. From the 1.2 point on the log ES_y scale a vertical line
is erected having a height equal to $4d$. The point P at the top of
this line serves as a pivot for a straight edge which is made to
pass through P and the midpoint between any two adjacent
papers on the log ES_y scales. The straight edge (lines PA, PB,
or PC) intersects the DS_n scale at the proper points A, B, C between the papers. The shaded triangles are then constructed using the points 1, 2, 3, 4, and A, B, C. The base of each shaded
triangle embraces the negatives which should be printed on the
paper found at the apex of the triangle. It can be readily seen
that these triangles are not all isosceles and that they lean toward
the center of the diagram. This is a graphic representation of
the fact that for contrasty negatives the density scale of the
negative tends to exceed the log exposure scale of the paper
and for flat negatives the density scale of the negative tends to
be less than the log exposure scale of the paper." It should be
noted that the authors point out that this method does not always
give the best possible print, but rather that, on the average, a
higher percentage of best quality prints will be obtained by this
procedure than by using any other known method of predicting

the contrast grade of printing paper to be used in printing a given negative. These results were found to apply to enlarging as well as to contact printing.

Determining the Printing Exposure

In the research described in the previous section, a record was kept of the illuminance on the negatives and the exposure times used in making all prints. Thus, the printing exposures were known for the prints which were found to be the most pleasing to the majority of observers, and an excellent correlation was found between the optimum printing exposure and the minimum density in the negative. Although the integrated density of the negative as a whole was a good guide to printing exposure, as

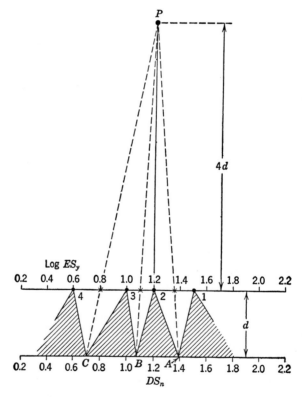

Fig. 12·14 Conversion chart relating sensitometric log exposure scales of papers to density scales of negatives.

reported by Tuttle, it was found to be inferior to the minimum density criterion as given by the formula

Log printing exposure

$$= \text{minimum density of negative} - \log \frac{\text{speed of paper}}{K}$$

where K is an arbitrary constant used in expressing the speed of the paper as discussed in Chapter 10.

This mechanical method for selecting the printing exposure and the method described in the preceding section for selecting the grade of paper will usually yield a good print the first time, but they fail for unusual scenes. Consider, for example, a brightly lighted human subject in dark surroundings. If the printing exposure is determined on the basis of integrated density, it will be too low for the face, which may not be reproduced above the fog level in the print and will thus be devoid of detail. Commercial printing machines with automatic exposure selectors are equipped with manual controls by which the operator can modify the exposure to suit such unusual subjects. Another procedure, made possible by the practically instantaneous response of a cathode-ray tube to changes in the flux on an associated phototube, is to do the printing by a flying-spot scanner and to modify the intensity of the electron beam in accordance with the density of the negative at each point.

A certain degree of judgment is also sometimes required in selecting the paper. For example, the maximum density may be represented by a very small and unimportant highlight, or the minimum density by a small and unimportant bit of shadow. Such inconsequential areas should be disregarded, or the paper that is selected will be too soft to give the best reproduction of the scene as a whole. This procedure is analogous to disregarding the sky in taking a reading with an exposure meter preparatory to photographing a landscape.

REFERENCES

General

Mees, *The Theory of the Photographic Process,* revised edition, Macmillan, New York, 1954, Chapter 23.

Specific

1. Jones and Condit, *J. Optical Soc. Am.,* **31**, 651 (1941).
2. Jones, *J. Franklin Inst.,* **190**, 39 (1920).
3. Stevens, *Psychol. Rev.,* **64**, 153 (1957), p. 172.
4. Lowry, *J. Optical Soc. Am.,* **18**, 29 (1929).
5. Pitt, *Proc. Physical Soc.,* **51**, 817 (1939).
6. Evans, *J. Optical Soc. Am.,* **33**, 579 (1943); **34**, 533 (1944).
7. Jones and Nelson, *J. Optical Soc. Am.,* **32**, 558 (1942).

The Structure of the Developed
Photographic Image

The process by which the exposed silver halide grains are transformed into silver has been discussed in Chapter 5. In examining the structure of the resulting image, it is necessary first to understand the relation between the silver grains in the image and the silver halide grains from which the image was formed.

The Structure and Distribution of the Silver Grains

Photomicrographs of developed and undeveloped grains are shown in Fig. 1·1. The developed silver grains shown in this photomicrograph occupy *approximately* the same positions as the undeveloped silver halide grains. In general, however, the shape and position of the developed grains are only roughly related to the shape and position of the silver halide grains. Whereas the undeveloped grains have definite geometrical shapes, the developed grains are generally quite irregular in shape and tend to form clumps. Although it is generally assumed that developability is not transferred from one grain to another, there is conclusive evidence that this assumption is not always valid (see Chapter 5).

With the advent of the electron microscope, it has been possible to examine the developed silver image in greater detail. From electron micrographs such as those shown in Figs. 5·2 and 5·5 it is seen that at least some of the silver exists in the form of filaments. The filamentary structure is very apparent in silver grains obtained by the development of silver halide grains which had first been removed from the emulsion, and thus were not subjected to the confining action of the gelatin during reduction. Grains which have been fully developed in their normal surrounding of the emulsion show evidence of a filamentary structure around the edges, but in the center they usually appear opaque to the electron beam. If the centers of these grains have a filamentary structure, as they probably have, the electron microscope does not resolve this structure.

The distribution of the image in the depth of the emulsion is shown in Fig. 13·1. Each photomicrograph shows a cross section of a different density, the difference in density being obtained by constant development and variable exposure. Although a small part of the increase in density is produced by a higher concentration of developed grains near the surface, the larger part of the increase in density results from an increase in the concentration of the grains throughout the emulsion. On the other hand, when

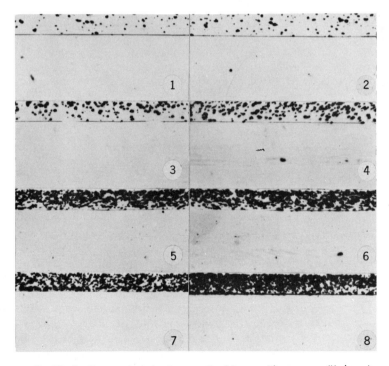

Fig. 13 · 1   Cross sections showing growth of image with exposure. (Hodgson.)

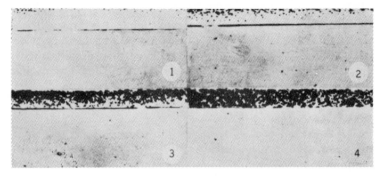

Fig. 13·2 Cross sections showing growth of image with development. (Hodgson.)

an increase in density is obtained by increasing the development and holding the exposure constant, there is a steady growth of the image toward the bottom of the emulsion. The extent of this effect varies appreciably with the nature of the developer. As shown by the photomicrographs in Fig. 13·2, the image starts at the surface and penetrates downward as development increases. The depth of the image also depends very markedly upon the wavelength of the radiation to which the material is exposed because of the absorption of the radiation by the emulsion. With ultraviolet light, the image is confined to the surface, whereas with x-rays the image is distributed throughout the emulsion.

Graininess and Granularity

Most photographic images appear to be homogeneous when viewed without magnification. When magnified, however, these images are seen to be inhomogeneous arrangements of silver grains in gelatin. It should be noted that this structure is the result not only of the distribution of the individual grains and clumps of grains in a plane parallel to the surface, but also of the patterns produced by the overlapping of the grains in a plane perpendicular to the surface as shown in Fig. 13·3.

One of the important aspects of this inhomogeneous structure of the image is that which is apparent when the enlarged image is examined visually. The impression or sensation of non-uniformity in the image, produced on the consciousness of the observer when such an image is viewed, is termed *graininess*. The term *granularity* is used to designate the objective aspect of these inhomogeneities in terms of spatial variations in the transmitting or reflecting properties of the developed photographic image. In the literature the term graininess has frequently been used for both graininess and granularity. Both of these properties of the photographic image are important, but they are not identical, and the two terms should not be used interchangeably.

The graininess of different materials can be compared by examining them side by side at a constant magnification. It should be noted that this method is purely subjective because it does not measure but rather compares the graininess of the materials. One method of assigning a value of graininess to photographic materials would be to make a series of enlargements at different magnifications and then to observe them from a constant distance to determine the maximum magnification at which graininess is not objectionable. Although this procedure is a reasonable one, it is very difficult to employ in practice because of the difficulty encountered in making the several en-

Fig. 13·3 Photomicrographs of a cross section (top) and horizontal plan (bottom) of a photographic image.

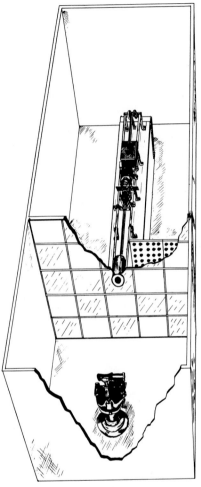

Fig. 13·4 Apparatus for evaluating graininess visually. The projector at the top forms an image of the sample on the circular test field at a variable magnification. This field is viewed by the observer in the chair at the bottom of the figure.

largements identical from the standpoint of tone reproduction. A similar procedure that requires fewer enlargements is to make one enlargement from each negative at a high magnification and then determine the minimum viewing distance at which graininess is just perceptible.

Many instruments based on both the blending-distance and the blending-magnification methods have been described, but in most of them incidental conditions, such as the size of the test field, also varied with the magnification or the viewing distance and vitiated the results. A very elaborate apparatus[1] in which such conditions were maintained constant is shown in Fig. 13·4. The observer viewed a circular test field set in a wall, and on this field an image of the sample was projected from the opposite side of the wall. The projector ran along rails to vary the projection distance and hence the magnification, while the position of the sample was simultaneously varied by means of a cam to keep the image in focus on the test field. The luminance of the test field could be changed at will, and, once set, it remained constant automatically by changing the size of the diaphragm in the projector as the magnification was varied. The test field was surrounded by an annular border whose luminance could be varied independently, and the entire side of the room consisted of translucent panels whose luminance could also be varied independently. The observer could cause the projector to move so as to vary the magnification until graininess just appeared or disappeared. Alternatively, when the magnification was preset by the experimenter, the observer could record "yes" or "no" according to whether the field appeared grainy or not. When the magnification was preset, an occulting shutter blurred the image while the projector was moving to the new position.

The flexibility of the apparatus was such that the effect of varying the viewing conditions could be readily determined.[2] It was thus found that the blending-magnification and the blending-distance methods do not give a linear correlation. Also, when the angular subtense of the test field was varied from a very small size, the graininess increased rapidly until the field subtended about 2°, after which the graininess was substantially constant. When the luminance of the annular border was held constant, the graininess was greater if the wall of the room was dark than if it was illuminated. The difference between the two conditions became more pronounced as the density of the sample increased and hence the luminance of the test field diminished. A variation in the luminance of the annular border also caused the graininess readings to vary, and when it was too high, readings at high sample densities became impossible. It was found best to allow the observer to match the luminance of the annular border to the integrated luminance of the test field. Considerable latitude in making this match was permissible, and indeed the observers usually preferred to have the annular border slightly darker than the test field. The standard conditions that were finally adopted for observation were as follows:

Viewing distance, 2 meters;

Angular subtense of test field, 2°;

Angular subtense of annular border, 6°;

Luminance of test field, no sample, 50-ft-L;

Luminance of annular border, same as test field
for each sample or slightly lower;

Luminance of wall surrounding annular border, 2 ft-L.

Graininess was expressed quantitatively as 1000 times the reciprocal of the blending magnification when the latter was determined under these standard conditions. The variation of graininess for a typical landscape material under these conditions is given by curve D in Fig. 13·5. The other curves show the variation when the luminance of the test field was different from the standard value of 50 foot-lamberts. The reliability of the readings can be estimated from the fit of the observed points to the smooth curves.

It will be noticed that the graininess has a maximum value somewhere around a density of 0.3. The existence of this maximum has been known ever since quantitative evaluations of graininess were first made. At this density, approximately half of the field is occupied by opaque silver grains and half is clear, so the existence of a graininess maximum for such a density is intuitively to be expected. A good share of the decrease at higher densities is to be explained on the basis of the reduced acuity of the eye at low values of field luminance.

A different method of evaluating graininess that has been used somewhat is to place the sample in a microscope and com-

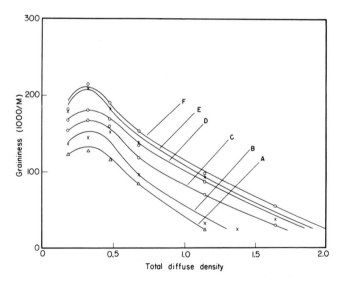

Fig. 13·5 Graininess-density functions for a certain sample for six values of the luminance of the test field with no sample in place. These values of luminance were as follows: A, 8; B, 12; C, 30; D, 50; E, 65; F, 100 ft-L.

pare it with a series of standards. The magnification is usually of the order of 75×, and thus the granular pattern is clearly evident, so that the problem is reduced to comparing the type of pattern in the sample with the types represented by the standards. One disadvantage of this method is that it does not give a numerical measure; its results are expressible only in terms of the order in which the standards are arranged by visual estimation. A more serious fault is that the appearance of the grain pattern under a high magnification does not necessarily bear a close relation to the blending magnification of the sample or the relative order of the samples as determined from practical picture tests.

The ultimate measure of graininess is of course the values obtained from picture tests, and the practical photographer is usually interested in the maximum enlargement that he can make from a negative without having graininess become obtrusive. For this reason, the blending-magnification method is probably the most indicative and is the one with which any objective measure of granularity should probably be correlated. It should be noted that graininess measurements are psychophysical in that they evaluate a purely physical stimulus (the spatial inhomogeneity of the developed silver image) in terms of the subjective response. Such methods are thoroughly inconvenient for routine measurements, and therefore many attempts have been made to measure the objective quantity *granularity* in terms that will correlate with the subjective sensation of *graininess*.

One method that has been proposed is based on the light-diffusing properties of the silver deposit. Since these properties can be indicated by the Callier Q factor (Chapter 10), the proposal was to evaluate granularity as $100 \log Q$. This has had a measure of success with negative materials, but not with prints. In the case of prints, it evaluates only the positive stock; the granular pattern of the negative as printed on the positive is not taken into account, since it does not influence the Q factor of the latter.

A more fundamental method is to scan the deposit with a microdensitometer. When a sample of a uniformly exposed and developed photographic image is scanned, as indicated in Fig. 13·6, the resulting trace has the form shown superposed on the track of the scanning aperture in the figure. To evaluate such a trace, statistical methods are obviously indicated, and these are

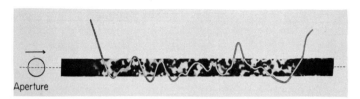

Fig. 13·6 Photomicrograph showing the track of a microdensitometer aperture over a developed photographic emulsion. The resulting trace is superposed on the track to show the correspondence.

very easily applied if the distribution of the deviations from the mean follows the normal or Gaussian curve of error. An actual census of these deviations shows indeed that they usually follow such a curve to a fair approximation, and thus the relationships that have been derived for the normal curve of error also apply to the curve relating the number of deviations having a magnitude ΔD against the magnitude ΔD itself.

One important relation involves aperture size. As the size increases, all the deviations diminish in magnitude because a large aperture exerts an averaging effect. If some parameter associated with the magnitude or number of the deviations is to be taken as a measure of granularity, it must be independent of aperture

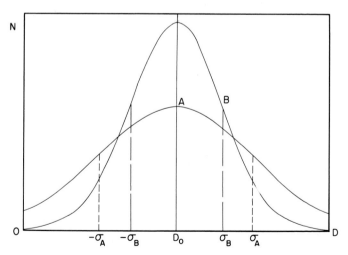

Fig. 13·7 Two normal or Gaussian distribution curves having the same mean value D_O but different values of standard deviation σ_A and σ_B.

size. On the basis of a normal distribution, the number N of deviations that represent a density D is

$$N = \frac{\exp\left[-(D-D_o)^2/2\sigma^2\right]}{(2\pi)^{1/2}\sigma} \qquad (13 \cdot 1)$$

where D_o is the mean value and σ is a parameter. As can be seen from the two normal curves A and B in Fig. 13·7, the parameter σ indicates the spread of the individual values of D. Mathematically, it is the abscissa value of the inflection point, and 68 per cent of the values lie between $-\sigma$ and $+\sigma$. This quantity σ is called *standard deviation*. It is obviously the parameter that must be related to granularity, but it is related to the scanning aperture as well because increasing the aperture must diminish it; if the aperture is large enough, there is no deviation from the mean whatever. From considerations involving the probability of finding a grain within an area of given size a, it is possible[3] to deduce the relation

$$\sigma = G/a^{1/2} \qquad (13 \cdot 2)$$

where G is a granularity constant that is independent of the scanning aperture.

The theory just described is susceptible to direct experimental proof because it means that the product of the standard deviation of the microdensitometer deflections and the diameter of the scanning aperture should give rise to a horizontal line when plotted against the diameter itself. Nevertheless, for many years experimenters were unable to verify this relation because the curves usually showed a persistent tendency to rise when the apertures became very large, as shown[4] by Fig. 13·8. Moreover, any such tendency was difficult to measure with certainty because the density differences and hence the microdensitometer deviations were so small.

Another way of expressing the relation of granularity to the size of the scanning spot is to plot log σ against log diameter d of the scanning spot, in which case the principle stated in the preceding paragraph would call for a straight line having a slope of minus unity. When this was done, the experimental curves usually curled slightly upwards from a straight line at the lower end, representing the smaller values of σ and the larger apertures.

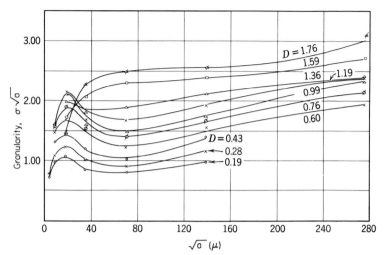

Fig. 13·8 Variation of granularity with the square root of the scanning area for routinely prepared samples.

This apparent failure of the theoretical granularity relation led to an extensive study of the way in which the human eye scans an inhomogeneous field like a photographic sample and gives rise to an impression of graininess in the brain. Out of this study came a method of evaluating granularity that was based, not on the standard deviation σ from the mean, but on the average density difference between two minute neighboring areas of the same size. This type of density difference was called *syzygetic density difference* and was designated $S\Delta D$. Just as standard deviation σ depends on the size of the scanning spot, so does average syzygetic density difference $\overline{S\Delta D}$. It has been found that, for each density (the sample illumination being constant), there exists a certain value of $\overline{S\Delta D}$ for which the aperture bears a one-to-one relation to the blending magnification that would be read in the graininess instrument described earlier if the sample was observed visually. This aperture is then a measure of the granularity of the sample in terms that will correlate with graininess. This system has been successfully used for the routine measurement of uniformly exposed and developed samples. On the other hand, it has not been found satisfactory for prints nor for color materials.

Meanwhile, the mathematicians had been making theoretical studies based on the principles of statistics,[6] and they came to the conclusion that the standard deviation in density $\sigma(D)$ should be proportional to the average syzygetic density difference $\overline{S\Delta D}$ if the sample did not have blemishes or large-scale variations in density. Microdensitometers were also improved so that they would give more precise readings for large apertures and so that their readings would indicate the standard deviation without requiring lengthy calculations. When samples were measured with this improved equipment, the curves of log standard deviation $\sigma(D)$ against log aperture diameter d on logarithmic scales very definitely had the shape shown by the broken curve G' in Fig. 13·9. The samples had been prepared with considerable care and were free from obvious blemishes, but a careful examination showed long-period variations in density of very small magnitude and in particular a steady drift in density from one side to the other. When new samples were prepared with extreme care to avoid such large-scale density differences, the curves became practically straight, parallel lines of slope minus unity, as shown by curves A to G in the figure. This can be readily shown to confirm the theoretical conclusion that the product of the standard deviation and the diameter of the scan-

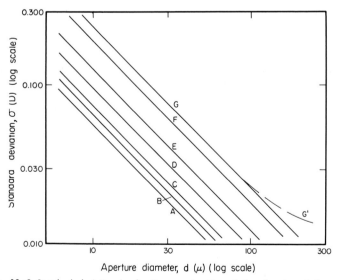

Fig. 13·9 Standard deviation in density as a function of the diameter of the scanning aperture for seven uniformly exposed and developed photographic materials A-G. Curve G' is for a sample of material G varying slightly in density over the region scanned.

ning aperture is a constant that is characteristic for a given emulsion. Moreover, this characteristic granularity constant has been shown to correlate with visual graininess judgments, as it should if it also correlates with the syzygetic-density-difference method, which in turn correlates with visual graininess.

In making routine granularity measurements, it is not always possible to attain the extreme cleanliness that characterized the strips used in the research just described. To be sure, the rise at large apertures can be eliminated by a high-pass electrical filter in the microdensitometer, but there is always the possibility of removing part of the proper granularity response as well. The syzygetic-density-difference method, which is practically immune to large-scale variations, is superior from this standpoint. On the other hand, this method is for the same reason not applicable to prints, which exhibit a large-scale mottle in addition to the small-scale or short-period pattern of what might be called "primary" grain and which contributes to the standard deviation of that type of sample.

The variation of standard deviation with aperture diameter for prints is typified[7] by Fig. 13·10. Here curves *A* and *B* are

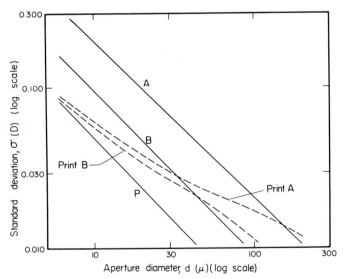

Fig. 13 · 10   Granularity curves for two negative materials, A and B, one positive material, P, and for prints of A and B, respectively, on P.

granularity curves for two different negative emulsions when uniformly exposed and developed. They are practically straight lines of slope minus unity. Curve P is for an emulsion designed to make positive transparencies, also uniformly exposed and developed; it is practically parallel to curves A and B. The broken curves represent prints made from the negatives A and B, respectively, on the positive material represented by curve P. The significant feature of these curves (and this behavior has been observed with other materials) is that, at small apertures, the granularity of the print is characteristic of the *positive* material, while at large apertures the granularity of the print is characteristic of the *negative* material.

To see what this situation means visually, the eye must be regarded as a kind of microdensitometer. When readings are made visually in an instrument like the graininess instrument described previously, the grain pattern is imaged on the retina. It is just as true to say that the retina is imaged on the sample, and each sensitive retinal element (a cone or group of cones) may be regarded as the scanning spot of a microdensitometer. It has been proved beyond doubt that the eye is constantly executing rapid "saccadic" movements, and each retinal element is subjected to a varying stimulus as it scans the non-uniform sample. The size of the sample area that is included within the image of a single retinal element clearly depends upon the magnification of the sample on the projection screen in the visual graininess instrument. Varying this magnification is thus entirely analogous to varying the size of the aperture of a microdensitometer in which the granularity of the sample might be measured. Applying this principle to Fig. 13 · 10, the scale of aperture diameters may be interpreted as an inverse scale of magnification in the visual graininess instrument or alternatively as a direct scale of distance when comparable enlargements are viewed.

Since the granularity curves for prints are not mutually parallel, they may intersect under some conditions. If this had happened for the print curves in Fig. 13 · 10, for example, it would have meant that, for long viewing distances, print A would look grainier than print B when both are made at the same magnification, while print A would look *less* grainy than print B for short viewing distances. In other words, a graininess ranking of prints is meaningless unless the distance from which they are to be viewed is also stated. From a practical standpoint, the blending distance is perhaps the most significant; nobody would make an enlargement at such a high magnification that the grain pattern would be excessively pronounced from the intended viewing position.

Turbidity and Sharpness

When a photographic emulsion is exposed to light while partially shielded by a knife edge in contact with the emulsion, the developed image does not end abruptly at the knife edge, but encroaches into the shielded area. The formation of an image in the area shielded by the knife edge results from the radiant energy reaching this area within the emulsion by reason of refraction, reflection, diffraction, and scattering at the silver halide grains. The property of a material by which light is diffused into the region receiving no direct illumination is *optical turbidity.*

According to the indications of experiments with filtered light, diffraction and Rayleigh fourth-power scattering should be responsible for most of the diffusion of light in fine-grain emulsions, and reflection and refraction should be the predominant causes of diffusion in coarse-grain emulsions. Microscopic examinations of images on fine-grain emulsions show that diffusion increases from the front to the back of the emulsion as required by diffraction and fourth-power scattering, whereas with coarse-grain emulsions diffusion is almost independent of depth as required by reflection and refraction.

When an emulsion is exposed through a slit bounded by parallel knife edges that are in contact with the emulsion, the image obtained after development rarely has the same width as the slit. The greater the exposure, the wider the image. A set of such images made through an optical wedge which modulates the light logarithmically is shown in Fig. 13·11. This increase in the width of the image depends not only upon the optical turbidity but also upon the opacity of the emulsion. If the opacity of the emulsion is high for actinic light, the light diffused sidewise is rapidly absorbed and the image is kept within narrow bounds. Since the turbidity of an emulsion is normally measured in terms of the diffusion of the *image,* it should be noted that this photographic turbidity may differ appreciably from optical turbidity. Emulsions can be made which have both a high optical turbidity and a high opacity for actinic light. This high opacity limits the diffusion of the image, and therefore the photographic turbidity is low although the optical turbidity is high. In photography, the term turbidity is generally used to mean photographic turbidity.

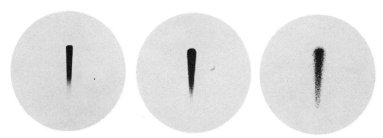

Fig. 13·11 Photomicrographs (25×) of the image of a slit covered by an optical wedge: (a) microfilm, (b) process film, and (c) portrait film.

Several investigations have been made to determine the effective absorption laws for the undeveloped silver halide emulsion. If Beer's law held, as it does for homogeneous materials, the density of the silver halide layer would be

$$D = aW^1 \qquad (13·3)$$

where a is a constant and W is the concentration of the silver halide. Bloch and Renwick found, however, that for white light the value of the exponent was not unity but 0.64. Calculations from equation 13·3 employing Bloch and Renwick's values of 0.66 for a and 0.64 for the exponent give the curves shown in Fig. 13·12, where lines A to N represent equiluminous surfaces in an emulsion, and the dotted line II' represents the geometrical boundary of the illuminated area. These surfaces, each of which represents an additional 10 per cent absorption, are not equidistant as they would be if the absorption obeyed Beer's law.

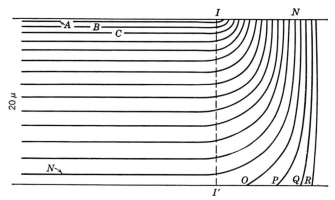

Fig. 13·12 Equiluminous surfaces at the edge of an image on an emulsion, according to Bloch and Renwick.

One of the first investigations of the turbidity of photographic emulsions was that of Mees, who employed a technique which gave "tadpole" images similar to those shown in Fig. 13·11. Goldberg[8] was one of the earliest to make a quantitative investigation of turbidity. A photographic emulsion was exposed through a diaphragm consisting of three fine holes which were placed in contact with the material. A series of exposures was then given to the material, and turbidity was expressed as the amount of spreading per unit increase in the logarithm of the exposure, $dx/(d \log E)$. Turbidity measured in this way usually increases with increasing exposure. Wildt, however, found a strictly linear relationship between image diameter and the logarithm of exposure when these exposures were made with monochromatic light. He employed four wavelengths and three diameters of diaphragm. Turbidity was found to be independent of the diameter of the diaphragm for any given wavelength, but it was found to increase with wavelength for measurements with a single diaphragm. On the other hand, Wildt found that this linear relation between image diameter and the logarithm of exposure no longer held when he made his exposures with a mixture of red and blue light of low intensity.

Various methods have been proposed for expressing turbidity numerically. One of the most convenient of these methods is Ross's quantity Δ, which is the increase in the width of the image when exposure is doubled. This is equal to Goldberg's ratio $dx/(d \log E)$ when $\log E = 0.3$.

Many experimental difficulties are encountered in making turbidity measurements. The first of these is the problem of

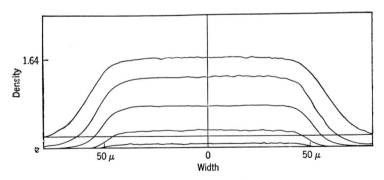

Fig. 13·13   Microdensitometer traces across the image of a slit.

impressing an image of a small spot or narrow slit on the material. Usually less difficulty is encountered in making the exposures through small holes which are placed in contact with the emulsion. However, it is then very difficult to determine accurately the size of the image obtained after development. The simplest procedure for obtaining narrow line images is to photograph a large single-line test object on a microscopic scale. The objective used in making this reduction must be the best available since the sharpness of the edge of the optical image is reduced by lens aberrations and diffraction.

The next experimental difficulty encountered is the problem of measuring the width of the image. The width of a line image can be determined by scanning this image with a microdensitometer whose slit is parallel to the edge of the image. A set of microdensitometer traces showing the variation in density across the image of a slit 100μ wide is shown in Fig. 13 · 13. Each curve represents a different exposure, the exposure time for each curve being twice that of the one directly below. While the point where the density of the image equals fog density might be considered the edge of the image, it is clear from the traces shown in Fig. 13 · 13 that it would be a difficult point to determine accurately. It is more convenient to define the edge of the image as that point where density has reached some set fraction of the maximum density. If the edge of the image is taken as the point where the density is equal to one-half of the maximum density, the width of the images represented by the traces in Fig. 13 · 13 can then be plotted as a function of log E, as shown in Fig. 13 · 14. The slope of this line is Goldberg's ratio $dx/(d \log E)$.

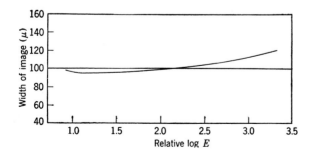

Fig. 13 · 14   Width of the images in Fig. 13 · 13 as a function of log E.

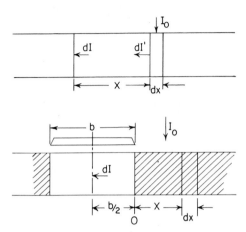

Fig. 13 · 15   Cross sections of emulsion layer showing sidewise diffusion of light.

More recently, Frieser[9] has described a practical method of evaluating turbidity. In the upper part of Fig. 13 · 15, let I_o be the illumination on the surface of an emulsion that is inhomogeneous and therefore diffuses light. The flux diffused sidewise by a vertical slice of thickness dx is then proportional to I_o and to dx, or

$$dI' = KI_o dx \qquad (13 \cdot 4)$$

If this flux is assumed to be attenuated with distance in accordance with Bouguer's law, which may not hold in this case although it holds strictly for absorbing media, the flux passing through a plane normal to the drawing at a distance x from dI_o can be expressed as

$$dI = 10^{-2x/k}\, dI' = KI_o \cdot 10^{-2x/k}\, dx \qquad (13 \cdot 5)$$

where k is an absorption coefficient.

It is first necessary to evaluate the constant K. This can be done by considering that, if the emulsion is uniformly illuminated over an essentially infinite area, as much flux is lost from each elementary slice as is gained from the adjacent slices so that the flux within the emulsion is uniform and equal to the incident flux, or

$$I_o = KI_o \cdot 2 \int_0^\infty 10^{-2x/k}\, dx \qquad (13 \cdot 6)$$

This integrates to

$$I_o = \frac{-KkI_o}{2.3 \cdot 10^{2x/k}} \Big|_0^\infty \qquad (13 \cdot 7)$$

At infinity this quantity equals zero and at zero it equals $KkI_o/2.3$, whence

$$K = 2.3/k \qquad (13 \cdot 8)$$

and equation 13.5 can be written

$$dI = \frac{2.3}{k} I_o \cdot 10^{-2x/k} \, dx \qquad (13 \cdot 9)$$

The way this equation is applied in practice depends on the shape of the test object. The simplest procedure, all things considered, is to place a double knife edge on the emulsion, as shown in the lower part of the figure, and expose the emulsion uniformly. If the knife edge has a width b, the amount of flux in the center of the shadow coming from a slice of thickness dx at a distance x from the knife edge is

$$dI = 2 \frac{2.3}{k} I \cdot 10^{-2(b/2 + x)/k} \, dx \qquad (13 \cdot 10)$$

the factor 2 being introduced because the shadow receives light from both sides of the knife edge. The total amount of flux in the center of the shadow from the entire surrounding region is then

$$I = 2 \frac{2.3}{k} I_o \cdot 10^{-b/k} \int_0^\infty 10^{-2x/k} \, dx \qquad (13 \cdot 11)$$

$$= 10^{-b/k} I_o$$

Frieser evaluates the constant k by placing an opaque bar 15 μ wide across each step of a step tablet and printing the combination on the sample. The processed sample is scanned in a microdensitometer to give a curve like the one shown at the left in Fig. 13 · 16. The characteristic curve of the material can be plotted as shown at the right, and the difference in height between the line and the surrounding part of each step can be projected on the characteristic curve to give the corresponding value of $\Delta \log I$. It is easy to show from equation 13·11 that

$$\Delta \log I = - b/k \qquad (13 \cdot 12)$$

Since b is known, the value of k can be readily computed. Its unit is length and its value ranges from about 15 to 40 μ. It represents the distance at which the flux is attenuated to 1/10 of its original value. Obviously it is affected by adjacency effects, and an unequivocal result can be obtained only when these effects are absent. Sometimes it is given the name "contour sharpness." More accurately, it is a measure of turbidity, and although emul-

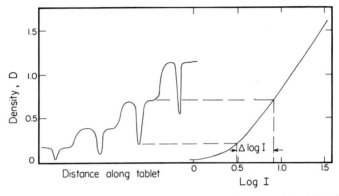

Fig. 13 · 16   Trace of image of opaque lines superposed on step tablet (left) related to illuminance of emulsion under each line through the characteristic curve (right).

sions that give sharp images also have low values of k, they give sharp images because of other characteristics that are associated with a low value of k.

The concept of sharpness as usually understood can be explained with the aid of Fig. 13·17. Let a beam of light be incident on a film that is partly shielded by a knife edge in accurate contact in the manner sketched at the top of the figure. As pointed out at the beginning of this section, the developed image will not be perfectly sharp, and its sharpness depends upon its density gradient at the edge.

This density gradient can be plotted by means of a microdensitometer whose scanning slit is parallel to the edge. The result is a trace looking somewhat like curve D in Fig. 13·17 that shows density as a function of the distance along the sample normal to the edge.

The difficulty in evaluating edge traces is that the gradient constantly changes and it is not at once evident what criterion the eye applies in appraising the sensation of sharpness. One possible criterion is the slope $\Delta D/\Delta x$ at the inflection point C where the slope has its maximum, but experiment shows that this is not the criterion that is applied by the eye. Another possibility is the mean gradient between some point A in the toe and a point B in the shoulder, but experiment also shows that this is not the proper criterion. Such a result is not surprising. The straight line E and the curve F whose curvature has a constant sign both have the same mean gradient as curve D, but their shapes are different, and it might be expected that they would

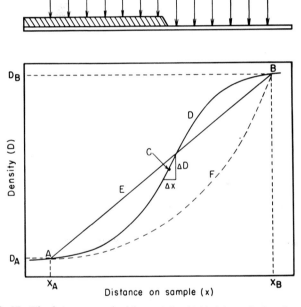

Fig. 13 · 17   Film being exposed while partially shielded by a knife edge (above). Certain possible resulting edge traces D, E, F having the same average gradient $(D_B - D_A)/(x_B - x_A)$ between A and B (below).

give rise to different sensations of sharpness. What is needed is a criterion that takes the form of the curve into account.

Such a criterion has been found.[10] Consider equal increments Δx between x_A and x_B. Determine the density increment ΔD corresponding to each increment Δx, square it, add all the squares together to get $\Sigma(\Delta D/\Delta x)^2$ and divide by the number N of increments between A and B to obtain the quantity

$$\overline{G_x^2} = \frac{\Sigma(\Delta D/\Delta x)^2}{N} \qquad (13 \cdot 13)$$

The value of this quantity is profoundly affected by the amount of the toe and shoulder that is included in the evaluation, and therefore points A and B must be selected with care. It was found that A and B should be the points where the gradient $\Delta D/\Delta x$ is approximately 0.005 when x is measured in microns and a 4$\times$ enlargement is to be made from the negative.

It is also probable that the density difference $D_B - D_A$ affects one's impression of sharpness. Systematic studies have not been made, but there are theoretical reasons for believing that, for a given value of $\overline{G_x^2}$, the edge appears sharper as the density scale becomes smaller. Over the density range embraced by ordinary continuous-tone pictures, this relation can be taken as a simple reciprocal, and some experiments tend to substantiate this assumption.

In the older literature, the term "sharpness" was used indiscriminately to signify the impression received by the observer and the physical characteristics of the photograph itself. To avoid confusion, it is now customary to restrict the term to the former meaning. A new term was therefore needed to denote the objective correlate, and the word *acutance* was coined for this purpose. Accordingly, we may say

$$\text{Acutance} = \overline{G_x^2}/(D_B - D_A) \qquad (13 \cdot 14)$$

Acutance should increase with the opacity of the emulsion because the rate of diminution of light flux with distance sidewise in the emulsion increases with opacity. A yellow dye will produce such an increase in opacity, and it has been found that acutance for white light can be increased greatly with a yellow dye at the expense of speed. Many years ago, Ross found that the sharpness of an emulsion (which he measured as the slope of the steepest part of the edge trace) was increased by such a dye when the exposure was made to blue light but not when it was made to red light, which a yellow dye does not absorb. Sandvik showed that the sharpness of a typical emulsion (likewise in terms of the steepest slope of the trace) was greatest in the violet end of the visible spectrum, where the opacity was greatest.

Development Phenomena and the Interaction between
Adjacent Photographic Images

The manifold forms of development phenomena have been instrumental in introducing several names for the same effect. It is customary to use descriptive terms such as "Eberhard effects"

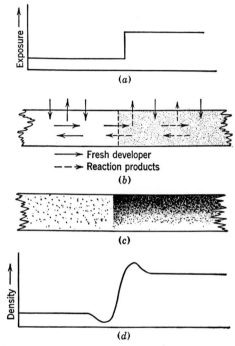

Fig. 13 · 18   Pictorial diagrams describing development phenomena.

to describe the manifestations of these phenomena, and they can all be described by the generic term "adjacency effects."

The development phenomena can best be explained by reference to a set of pictorial diagrams such as those shown in Fig. 13 · 18. The essential condition for obtaining an adjacency effect is a relatively sharp boundary between two areas having a large difference in density such as would result from an exposure similar to that shown in Fig. 13 · 18 (*a*). During the process of development the developer has relatively little silver halide to reduce to silver in the lightly exposed region while it is being exhausted

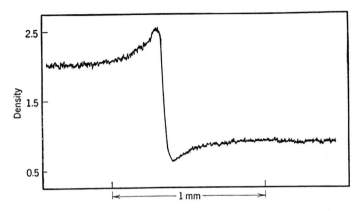

Fig. 13·19 Microdensitometer trace across boundary between exposed and unexposed areas on developed emulsion.

by the reduction taking place in the heavily exposed region. As shown in Fig. 13·8 (*b*), the fresh developer and the reaction products pass back and forth across this boundary between the heavily exposed and lightly exposed areas. The influx of the relatively fresh developer into the heavily exposed region from the lightly exposed area accelerates the growth of density in the heavily exposed region, and thus the image near the boundary of this region is more dense than elsewhere. Likewise, the diffusion of the reaction products, largely bromides, from the heavily exposed region into the lightly exposed area, retards development in this area, with the result that density near the boundary is reduced below the level of the surrounding low density. A cross section of the emulsion at the boundary would appear similar to Fig. 13·18 (*c*), and the variation of density across this boundary would be similar to that shown by the curve in Fig. 13·18 (*d*).

The presence of a faint dark line just within the high-density side of a boundary between a lightly exposed and heavily exposed region on a developed emulsion is known as the *border effect*. The presence of the corresponding faint light line just within the low-density side of the margin is referred to as the *fringe effect*. These lines have been called *Mackie lines*. The microdensitometer trace shown in Fig. 13·19 represents the variation in density across the border between a lightly exposed and a heavily exposed area on an emulsion which was developed without agitation. The border effect is shown by the rise in density at the high-density edge of the border, and the fringe effect is shown by the depression in density at the low-density edge of the border. These two effects are commonly called the *edge effect.*

Development phenomena may also produce bromide and developer streaks in the developed image. The *bromide streaks* are light areas which are produced by the flow of reaction products, and the developer streaks are the dark areas which are produced by the flow of fresh developer. The flow of the solutions may be the result of either convection currents or unsatisfactory types of agitation. Streaks are most pronounced when the emulsion is suspended vertically and development is carried out without agitation. Under these conditions the light bromide streaks and the darker development streaks may be as much as an inch or two in length. When the film is developed in a horizontal position, with emulsion side up, the irregular accumulation of the reaction products on the emulsion surface may give rise to a mottled appearance.

When two small areas of unequal size are given equal exposure and development, the density of the smaller area will in general be higher than that of the larger area. This dependency of the density of small areas upon the size of the area is known as the *Eberhard effect.* It is a special form of the border and fringe effects. The microdensitometer traces reproduced in Fig. $13 \cdot 20$

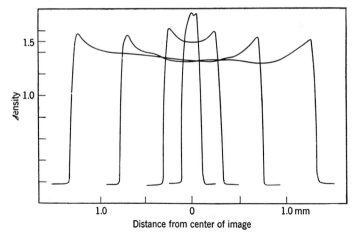

Fig. $13 \cdot 20$ Microdensitometer traces showing Eberhard effect.

show the variation in density across four small images of unequal size. Each of these images is the result of identical exposure and development. These traces show quite clearly the increase in density which accompanied the decrease in size.

The *Kostinsky effect* is another special form of the border and fringe effects in which an apparent increase in the separation of two small nearby images is produced by a shift in the geometric center of the images. This shift in the geometric center is caused by the increased concentration of the development products between the two images, which leads to an asymmetrical growth of the image.

Two other phenomena which are related to development are the *gelatin effect* and the *Ross effect*. The gelatin effect refers to the slight shrinkage of the image and its gelatin support which is produced by the tanning action of the development products on the gelatin. This tanning action introduces unequal rates of drying in the gelatin, with a consequent shift in the position of the developed silver grains. It should be noted that this effect is not present in the wet emulsion. The gelatin effect applied to two very small nearby images is known as the Ross effect. The Ross effect is a movement toward each other of two nearby images because of the interacting gelatin effects. These phenomena are of special importance in such fields as astronomy and spectroscopy.

The results of the development phenomena are reduced when development is carried on under conditions which accelerate the removal of the development products, or when development is sufficient to give a gamma approaching γ_∞. It should also be noted that turbidity tends to reduce the magnitude of the adjacency effects because it reduces the slope of the illuminance gradient between the lightly exposed and the heavily exposed areas. Under normal processing conditions these adjacency effects are usually not noticeable in general photography. However, for special types of photographic work, such as photoengraving, it is sometimes desirable to employ techniques which will produce these effects in order to increase the density of the edges of an image such as a halftone dot.

Resolving Power

The ability of a photographic emulsion to record fine details is its *resolving power*. In order to obtain a numerical value of resolving power, it becomes necessary to adopt some definite criterion as a measure of detail. Of the many types of test objects which have been used to measure photographic resolving power, the parallel-line type has probably been employed the most extensively. A very satisfactory test object is that designed by Sandvik. It consists of several sets of three parallel lines separated by spaces having a width equal to the width of the lines as shown in Fig. 13·21. Each set of lines varies from that of its

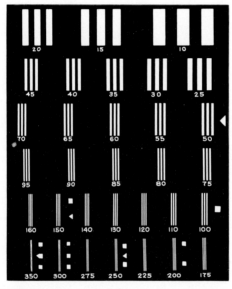

Fig. 13·21   Parallel-line type of resolving power test object. The numbers represent the number of lines per millimeter in the camera image.

neighbor by 5 or 10 lines per millimeter. As commonly used, this test object consists of clear lines on an opaque ground. The reverse, or negative, consisting of opaque lines on a clear ground, gives a much lower value of resolving power when photographed by projection because of the flare arising from the background.

The test object can be printed either by contact or by projection on the photographic material being examined. If the test object is to be printed by contact, it must have a higher resolution than that of the best material to be measured. This is difficult to attain except when measuring materials of relatively low resolving power. Furthermore, it is difficult to obtain sufficiently good contact between the test object and the sample. It should also be noted that, even when the test object is printed by contact, the distribution of the light in the image of the test object is affected by diffraction.

The more common procedure is to photograph the test object on the sample to a reduced scale. This facilitates preparing the test object because the reduction can be of the order of fifty to a hundred times, but it requires the use of a very well-corrected lens of high aperture. The image is always degraded to some extent by the lens, as shown by Fig. 13 · 22, and for a given wave

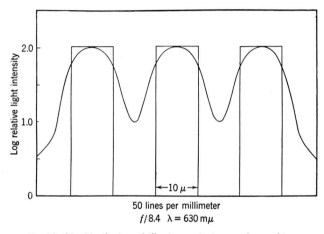

Fig. 13 · 22   Distribution of illuminance in image of test object.

length of light, the illuminance ratio between maximum and minimum diminishes in proportion as the line separation becomes less and the lens aperture becomes smaller. The lens used in the Kodak Research Laboratories for many years had a theoretical resolving power of about 300 lines/mm, and it was found to be affecting the measured value of emulsions whose resolving powers exceeded about 120 lines/mm. As a rule of thumb, the resolving power of the lens should be at least three times that of the emulsion if the maximum performance of the emulsion is to be realized. Microscope objectives used backwards are very satisfactory, but the test object should be designed to cover a small field.

After the sample is exposed and developed, it is examined in an ordinary microscope to determine the finest set of lines that can be individually distinguished. The viewing magnification is not important within wide limits, but in general it should be the lowest for which the distribution of density within the line pattern can be readily seen. The numerical value of resolving power is the number of lines per millimeter in this test chart, although it is occasionally expressed as the reciprocal, that is, the separation of homologous parts of the lines constituting this pattern. It should be noted that, contrary to the custom in television engineering, the spaces are disregarded; photographic resolution of 100 lines/mm, for instance, corresponds to television resolution of 200 lines/mm.

When emulsions are measured, it is customary to make a graded series of exposures, read the resolving power for each step,

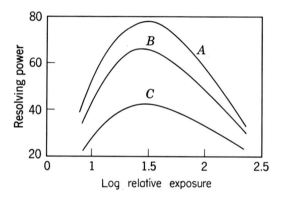

Fig. 13 · 23   Variation of resolving power with exposure.

and plot this value against the log exposure, as shown in Fig. 13 · 23. Curve A is for a test object in which the background of the lines is opaque, which for practical purposes is represented by a background density of 3.0 or more, or a luminance ratio between lines and background of 1000:1. Curves B and C are for test objects in which the density differences between lines and background are 0.9 and 0.3, respectively, corresponding to luminance ratios of 8:1 and 2:1. When resolving power is expressed by a single figure for any luminance ratio, it is ordinarily the maximum value, and when a figure is given to represent the emulsion, it is the maximum value for the opaque background.

If the maximum values are plotted against the logarithm of the luminance ratio, often termed the contrast, of the test object, a curve like the one in Fig. 13 · 24 results. This curve can be ap-

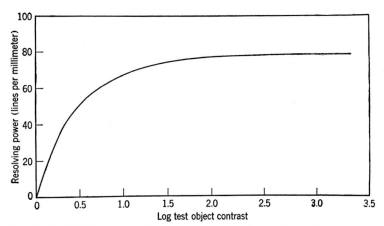

Fig. 13·24 Variation of resolving power of a certain emulsion with test object contrast.

proximately represented by the equation

$$R = R_m \left(1 - e^{-\alpha D}\right) \tag{13·15}$$

where D is the logarithm of the luminance ratio in the test object (density difference between the characters and the background), R_m is the resolving power for an infinite luminance ratio, and α is a constant that has been found to have a value of almost 2.3 for most emulsions.

The differences between emulsions can be detected most readily by converting this equation into an expression that represents a straight line. If ρ is the luminance ratio between the lines and the background (equals $\log^{-1} D$ in the preceding equation), it is not difficult to show that

$$R = R_m \left[1 - (1/\rho)^{\alpha/2.3}\right] \tag{13·16}$$

Since α was found to have a value of approximately 2.3, the exponent of $1/\rho$ is approximately unity and the equation represents a straight line when R is plotted against $1/\rho$. Such a plot for a typical emulsion is shown in Fig. 13·25. The broken line represents equation 13·16 with $\alpha = 2.3$, and it can be seen that the solid line representing the experimental points deviates from it systematically. This same type of deviation has been found for all emulsions studied, but they were all exposed in the same camera and there is always the possibility that the results might be different for a camera of different characteristics.

Resolving power has been widely used as a criterion of the performance of emulsions, and the factors that affect it have been studied intensively. The effects of exposure and of contrast in the test object have already been described. The effects of some other factors that have been studied are as follows:

1. Sandvik showed that a linear relation exists between resolving power and the logarithm of the ratio of the line-to-space width. It is customary to make this ratio equal to unity.

2. Although it is well-known that the wavelength of light affects resolving power, the exact manner in which this variation takes place is not conclusively known. However, the data indicate that, in general, resolving power increases with decreasing wavelength in the visible spectrum.

3. While some fine-grain developers improve resolving power, all such developers do not do so. The effect of the composition of the developer on resolving power is not well established.

4. Over the useful range of development times, resolving power is essentially constant.

5. Dyeing an emulsion yellow increases its resolving power very appreciably to blue light, although this increase is accompanied by a serious loss in sensitivity. The dye apparently re-

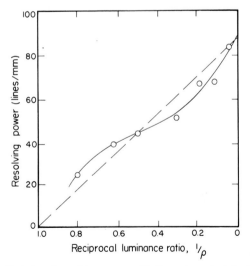

Fig. 13 · 25   Variation of resolving power with the reciprocal of the luminance ratio in the test object for a certain emulsion. A density difference between lines and background of 1.0, for instance, is equivalent to a luminance ratio of $\rho = 10$ or $1/\rho = 0.1$.

duces the effect of turbidity by increasing the absorption of diffused light, as mentioned in connection with acutance.

6. In general, resolving power increases with the contrast of the emulsion.

7. Fine grain and good resolution are usually synonymous, but there are cases where this relationship does not hold. In general, however, materials having small grain size have low turbidity and high resolving power.

The reason why resolving power has been used so long as a criterion of the quality of photographic materials is partly because it seems reasonable that fine details should be reproduced distinguishably if a photograph is to be satisfactory, and partly because of the apparent (although deceptive) ease with which resolving power can be measured. But even coarse-grained negative materials, for which such evaluations are usually made, will resolve far better than the eye except under magnifications of several times; if the eye will resolve only 10 lines/mm at the ordinary reading distance, what difference does it make whether the resolving power of the negative is 100 or 150 lines/mm? For good photographic definition, by which is meant the clarity with which details are reproduced, it is important that the emulsion be capable of reproducing large details sharply.[11] In other words, acutance is more important than resolving power under most conditions. The exact interrelationships between acutance, resolving power, graininess, and tone reproduction that lead to good or bad definition have still to be worked out.

Spread Function and Edge Trace

The concepts of turbidity, acutance, and resolving power indicate the behavior of photographic materials, but they do not analyze this behavior into its constituent elements. The newer concepts of spread function and sine-wave response not only do this, but also will eventually enable an optico-photographic system to be designed to produce a certain result. The concepts are common to the optical and the photographic parts of the system, and it will lead to clarity of presentation to consider the purely optical features first.

As is well known, when a point source is imaged by a lens, diffraction and aberrations cause the image to be not a point but an extended spot. In a sense, the image can be considered to be a mound of light, as shown at the left in Fig. $13 \cdot 26$. The

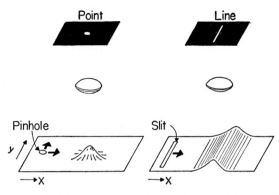

Fig. 13·26 Method of forming and scanning a point spread function (left) and a line spread function (right).

distribution of light in this image, expressed mathematically as $a(x, y)$, will be referred to as the *point spread function.* If this image is scanned by a pinhole, the resulting trace, representing the distribution of energy in one direction, would be a cross section of the light mound, as indicated in the figure. The actual shape of this cross section will of course depend upon the direction and position of the scan.

It is difficult to measure the point spread function experimentally, since the scanning spot must be small compared with the size of the image, and consequently the amount of energy available for the measurement is small. In addition, to define the point spread function completely, it is necessary to make some type of two-dimensional scan.

When a narrow, bright line is imaged by a lens, as shown at the right-hand side of this figure, the image again is a mound of light, but under these conditions it is cylindrical. When this image is scanned by a long, narrow slit parallel to the line being imaged, a cross section of the cylindrical surface will be traced out as before. This curve, which represents the distribution of light in the image of an infinitely narrow line as measured along a direction perpendicular to the line, will be referred to as the *line spread function* $A(x)$.

It is evident that a complete description of the point spread function requires two variables, taken here as x and y, while a line spread function is adequately described by a single variable, taken here as x. Mathematically, the line spread function in the

x direction is simply the point spread function integrated with respect to y, or

$$A(x) = \int_{-\infty}^{\infty} a(x,y) \, dy \qquad (13 \cdot 17)$$

If the scanning aperture is a slit, it alone will perform the integration so that the source may be either a line or a point. When the point spread function is not symmetrical, the shape of the line spread function will depend, of course, on the orientation of the slit.

The line spread function can be measured experimentally without great difficulty because both the source and the scanning slit can be long enough to supply adequate light for measurement while being very narrow in the direction of scan.

The size of the spread function sets an ultimate limit to the practical sensitivity of an emulsion.[12,13] For a final print of a given size and a lens of a given diameter, the necessary camera exposure can be made short by (a) using an emulsion of high sensitometric speed or (b) by using a small negative so that the image illuminance in the camera is high. Nevertheless, there is a limit below which the negative cannot be reduced in size, and that is set by the size of the spread function, because this size determines the greatest enlargement that is possible in printing without perceptibly degrading the definition. Moreover, the granularity must not be so great as to obscure the fine details. Because of these complications, the sensitometric speed alone of an emulsion is no criterion of what might be termed its *informational sensitivity* under the optimum conditions for obtaining a print of a given size with a lens of given linear aperture; the size of the spread function, the magnitude of the granularity fluctuations, and gamma are also involved.

The characteristics of the spread function determine the light distribution in an image. In theory, this light distribution can be computed if the geometry of the object and the spread function of the imaging system are known.[14] When the light distribution in the object is constant along one coordinate, as in the case of a series of parallel slits, the point spread function can be replaced in the computation by the line spread function. The simplest such object is a long knife edge, which mathematically is a boundary between two semi-infinite planes, one dark and one uniformly illuminated.

In Fig. 13 · 27 let the uniformly illuminated field shown at the left be bounded by a knife edge. This field can be considered to be built up of an infinitely large number of infinitely narrow, bright line sources. Four such sources numbered 1 to 4 are indicated in the figure. The distribution of illuminance in the

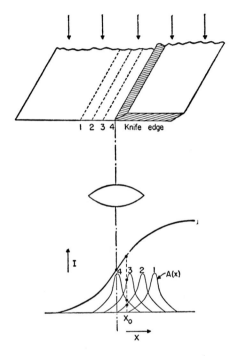

Fig. 13 · 27 Geometrical illustration of the convolution of a semi-infinite plane with the line spread function of a lens. Each linear element of the illuminated area (of which four are shown) forms its own spread function $A(x)$, and the sum of these is the image of the entire edge. The summation is indicated for x_0.

image of each of the lines can be represented by the line spread function $A(x)$ for each line, as shown at the bottom of the figure. The distribution of energy in the total image is then simply the sum of the contributions of each of the lines at each point of the image. One such point is x_0. A little reflection will show that summing the individual functions at x_0 is equivalent to integrating a single function from $-\infty$ to x_0. Thus the illuminance at the point x_0 is

$$E(x_0) = \int_{-\infty}^{x_0} A(x)\,dx \qquad (13\cdot18)$$

If this equation is differentiated with respect to x, we have

$$dE/dx = A(x) \qquad (13\cdot19)$$

This means that the *slope* of the plot of illuminance in the image of the edge at any point is equal to the value of the line spread function at that point. This plot is of course the edge trace that was discussed in connection with acutance.

These equations show immediately a method of getting the line spread function from the edge trace and vice versa. If the line spread function is known, the edge trace can be drawn by plotting the curve that represents the integral of the spread function, from minus infinity to each point x of the curve, as a function of x. Conversely, if the edge trace is known, the line spread function can be found by plotting the slope of the edge trace as a function of x.

This relation between the line spread function and the edge trace has been examined experimentally. The line spread function of a certain lens was determined as described earlier. The edge trace was then made by removing one of the jaws of the object slit and scanning the image of the other jaw as before. The measurements were purposely made at a field angle such that the lens would have an asymmetrical line spread function. The slits were oriented tangentially to the lens, since the spread function should be symmetrical when the object slit is radial.

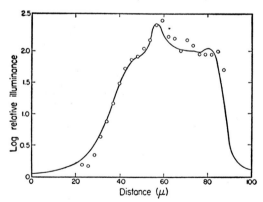

Fig. 13·28 Comparison between line spread function of a certain lens as computed from the edge trace in Fig. 13·29 (circles) and as measured (curve).

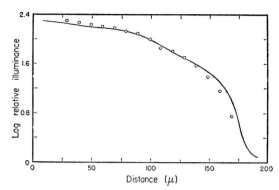

Fig. 13 · 29   Comparison between edge trace as computed from the spread function of Fig. 13 · 28 (circles) and as measured (curve).

The curve in Fig. 13 · 28 represents the line spread function $A(x)$ as measured on the lens bench. This function was introduced into equation 13 · 18 for a series of values of x_o to determine the edge trace $E(x)$, and these values are shown in Fig. 13 · 29 by circles. The curve in this figure is the edge trace as made on the lens bench, and the agreement with the computed values is seen to be excellent over most of the trace. The slope of this experimental trace was then measured at successive points and plotted as circles in Fig. 13 · 28. These circles fall close to the experimental spread function, as equation 13 · 19 says they should.

This process of adding together spread functions can be extended to any light distribution whatever in object space, whether one- or two-dimensional. The procedure is known as a *convolution* of the object function with the spread function. In like manner, the spread functions of the various components of a system can be convoluted with one another to give a composite spread function of the complete system. Thus it is the spread function which fundamentally determines the quality of the image.

Although the discussion just given was made on the basis of an optical system, it is equally valid for a photographic emulsion except that the spread function arises from turbidity instead of diffraction and aberrations. Since the light-diffusing properties of an emulsion are the same in all directions, the emulsion spread function is always symmetrical. This is far from the case with lenses, for which the spread function is rarely symmetrical except on the axis. This means that the shape of the spread function depends upon the direction of scan. In lens design, it is customary to make these directions radial and tangential with respect to a circle through the point being explored and having its center on the axis.

Sine-Wave Response

When the response of a phonograph is to be determined as a function of frequency, a record bearing pure sinusoidal waves having a graded series of frequencies is played and the output at each frequency is measured with a meter. Analogously, the spectral transmittance of a light filter is determined by measuring its transmittance at each of a series of wavelengths. In a similar way, the performance of an optical or a photographic system can be studied by impressing a sinusoidal signal and then determining the ratio of the amplitude of the emergent signal to that of the impressed signal. A graph of this amplitude as a function of frequency may be termed *sine-wave response*, although it is often called by such terms as "contrast-transmission factor" and "frequency response." As will be shown presently, it can be computed from the spread function, and under certain conditions the spread function can be computed from it.

The method of measuring sine-wave response is obvious from the definition. It is merely necessary to study the image of a line test object in which the transmittance varies sinusoidally instead of abruptly, as it does in the type shown in Fig. 13·21. The difficulty is in making a test object that varies sinusoidally in transmittance with sufficient precision. However, since the scanning slit effectively integrates in the direction of its length, a variable area pattern of the type shown in Fig. 13·30 can be used instead, and such a pattern can be made with good precision.

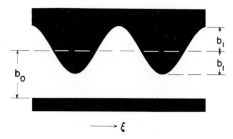

Fig. 13·30 Type of test object used for determining the sine-wave response. The mean height of the pattern is b_0 and the amplitude of the variation is b_1. Test object moves in the direction ξ.

The interrelationships between spread function and sine-wave response can be understood best by convoluting a spread function with a sinusoidal test pattern to obtain the sine-wave response theoretically.[15] Although the discussion is written in terms of a lens, it applies equally to a photographic emulsion with the important exception that the complications arising from asymmetry do not enter.

A sinusoidal test object can be represented by the equation

$$G(\xi) = b_o + b_1 \cos 2\pi\nu\xi \qquad (13 \cdot 20)$$

where ν is the spatial frequency, b_o is the mean height of the pattern, and b_1 is one-half of the total variation in height (Fig. $13 \cdot 30$). The modulation of the pattern is the ratio b_1/b_o. In practice, this ratio is made as near unity as is convenient.

When such a pattern is imaged by a lens, the image can be represented by a mathematical convolution of the test object $G(\xi)$ with the line spread function $A(\xi)$ of the lens. The convolution integral is expressed as

$$F(x) = \int_{-\infty}^{\infty} A(\xi)\, G(x-\xi)\, d\xi \qquad (13 \cdot 21)$$

When equation $13 \cdot 20$ is introduced into equation $13 \cdot 21$, it gives

$$F(x) = b_o \int_{-\infty}^{\infty} A(\xi)\,d\xi + b_1 \int_{-\infty}^{\infty} A(\xi)\, \cos 2\pi\nu(x-\xi)\, d\xi \qquad (13 \cdot 22)$$

This equation can be simplified by separating the variables x and ξ. Then, assuming that the area under the spread function, as represented by the first integral, is unity,

$$F(x) = b_o + b_1 A^{\#c} \cos 2\pi\nu x + b_1 A^{\#s} \sin 2\pi\nu x \qquad (13 \cdot 23)$$

Here ξ has been absorbed in the parameters $A^{\#c}$ and $A^{\#s}$. The first parameter is the *cosine Fourier transform*

$$A^{\#c}(\nu) = \int_{-\infty}^{\infty} A(\xi) \cos 2\pi\nu\xi\, d\xi \qquad (13 \cdot 24)$$

and the second is the *sine Fourier transform*

$$A^{\#s}(\nu) = \int_{-\infty}^{\infty} A(\xi) \sin 2\pi\nu\xi \, d\xi \qquad (13 \cdot 25)$$

of the line spread function $A(\xi)$. The # sign is used to represent a transform operation.

Since $A^{\#c}(\nu)$ and $A^{\#s}(\nu)$ are coefficients of cosine and sine functions, respectively, of a single variable ν, they can be plotted as mutually orthogonal vectors in the manner sketched in Fig. $13 \cdot 31$. The closing vector $|A^{\#}|$ forms the hypotenuse of the tri-

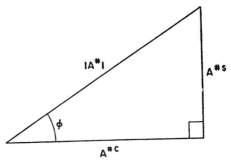

Fig. $13 \cdot 31$ Graphical combination of cosine and sine Fourier transforms $A^{\#c}$ and $A^{\#s}$ to give the sine-wave response $|A^{\#}|$.

angle and has the magnitude

$$|A^{\#}| = (A^{\#c2} + A^{\#s2})^{1/2} \qquad (13 \cdot 26)$$

By letting the angle between the hypotenuse $|A^{\#}|$ and the side $A^{\#c}$ in Fig. $13 \cdot 31$ be ϕ, the cosine and the sine Fourier transforms can be written

$$A^{\#c} = |A^{\#}| \cos \phi \qquad (13 \cdot 27)$$

and

$$A^{\#s} = |A^{\#}| \sin \phi \qquad (13 \cdot 28)$$

respectively, and the light distribution in the image represented by equation $13 \cdot 23$ becomes

$$F(x) = b_0 + b_1 |A^{\#}| \cos (2\pi\nu - \phi) \qquad (13 \cdot 29)$$

This equation is similar in form to equation $13 \cdot 20$ representing the light distribution in the test object except for two significant differences. In the first place, the modulation is $b_1|A^{\#}|/b_0$, which is $|A^{\#}|$ times as great as the modulation of the original pattern. The factor represents a degradation of amplitude in the image as compared with the amplitude in the test object and is called the *sine-wave response* of the lens. In the second place, the angle is modified by the quantity ϕ. This quantity has the mathematical form of a phase angle between the test object and its image.

If the line spread function $A(x)$ of an image-forming system is known, the sine-wave response $|A^{\#}|$ can be determined by means of equations $13 \cdot 24 - 13 \cdot 26$. Since, in general, $A(x)$ cannot be expressed analytically, this function must be considered point by point and the Fourier transform integration must be treated as a summation process. Figure $13 \cdot 32$ shows the results for a lens in one particular instance.

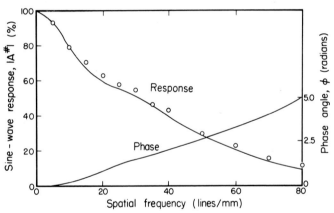

Fig. $13 \cdot 32$ Sine-wave response and phase of a certain lens deduced from its spread function. Measured values are shown by circles.

The process can be inverted to obtain the spread function from the two curves shown. This is easier for emulsions than for lenses because the spread function is always symmetrical. It can be shown that the phase angle is then zero for all frequencies and the response equals the cosine transform.

The convenience of the sine-wave response is that the curve representing the response of a combination of elements can be obtained by simply multiplying together the curves for the individual elements, so that a laborious convolution is not necessary. The process can also be reversed. In Fig. 13 · 33 the dotted curve represents the response of a certain lens as measured by scanning the aerial image of sinusoidal test objects with a narrow slit and recording the distribution of light in the image with a phototube. The broken curve was obtained by photographing the test objects and making a record of the transmittance of the resulting image patterns with a microphotometer. This curve obviously represents the response of the lens-film combination. When this curve is divided by the lens curve, ordinate by ordinate, the solid curve representing the response of the film alone is obtained. The initial rise is believed to be due to adjacency effects, which enhance the density differences in the developed image.

The curve representing the lens-film combination was plotted in terms of exposure by reference to the D-log E curve, so the curve for the film alone represents the distribution of light in the emulsion during the exposure, and hence, when adjacency effects are absent, it should be independent of development conditions. Experiment shows that such is the case and also that the sine-wave response is a very sensitive measure of adjacency effects.

The simplicity with which response curves can be combined makes them useful for determining the effect of changing some element in a system. In a cascaded series of printing operations, such as is common in the motion-picture industry, the effect of

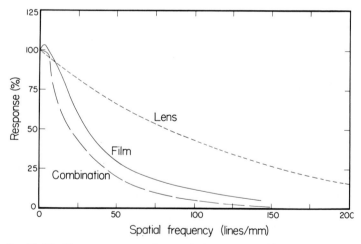

Fig. 13 · 33 Sine-wave response of a certain lens, a certain film in combination with the lens, and the film alone.

changing film stock or of substituting one printer for another can be computed if the appropriate sine-wave response curves are available. The curve for the original film stock or printer is divided into the overall response curve for the entire process, and then this quotient is multiplied by the curve for the new film stock or printer.

This simple method of combining sine-wave response curves is valid when the effect on each element of the process is linearly related to the cause. For example, when the luminance in the object being photographed is doubled, the exposure of the negative is also doubled, and the same thing is true of the exposure of the positive when the transmittance of the negative used to print on the positive is doubled. However, an analogous relation does not hold between the exposure of the negative and the transmittance of the negative; the response of the print is non-linear with respect to the exposure of the negative, and it is a general rule that a non-linear element introduces harmonic distortion. If, then, a sinusoidal test object is photographed, an analysis of the microphotometer trace of the print reveals not only the fundamental frequency of the test object but also harmonic frequencies. Fortunately it can be shown, both theoretically and experimentally, that the error from this source is not great for the usual range of γ-values if the strongly curved portions of the characteristic curve are avoided.

The concepts described in these last two sections, and some other concepts, like the correlation function, that cannot be treated here, have been applied to the photographic process only within the past few years. New applications are being constantly described in the literature, and the time may not be far distant when they will become as familiar to the practical photographer as the more directly photographic concepts like resolving power are today.

REFERENCES

General

Mees, *The Theory of the Photographic Process,* revised edition, Macmillan, New York, 1954, Chapter 24.

Ross, *Physics of the Developed Photographic Image,* Eastman Kodak Co., 1924.

Higgins and Perrin, *The Evaluation of Optical Images, Phot. Sci and Eng.,* **2,** 66 (1958).

Specific

1. Jones and Higgins, *J. Optical Soc. Am.,* **41,** 41 (1951).
2. Jones and Higgins, *J. Optical Soc. Am.,* **44,** 64 (1951).

3. Selwyn, *Phot. J.,* **75,** 571 (1935); **79,** 513 (1939).
4. Jones and Higgins, *J. Optical Soc. Am.,* **36,** 203 (1946).
5. Jones, Higgins, and Stultz, *J. Optical Soc. Am.,* **45,** 107 (1955); Jones, Higgins, Stultz, and Hoesterey, *J. Optical Soc. Am.,* **47,** 312 (1957).
6. Zweig, *J. Optical Soc. Am.,* **46,** 812 (1956).
7. Stultz and Zweig, *J. Optical Soc. Am.,* **49,** 693 (1959).
8. Goldberg, *Phot. J.,* **36,** 300 (1912).
9. Frieser, *Phot Korr,* **91,** 69 (1955).
10. Higgins and Jones, *J. Soc. Motion Picture and Television Engrs.,* **58,** 217 (1952); *PSA Jour.,* **19B,** 55 (1953).
11. Higgins and Wolfe, *J. Optical Soc. Am.,* **45,** 121 (1955).
12. Zweig, Higgins, and MacAdam, *J. Optical Soc. Am.,* **48,** 926 (1958).
13. Wolfe, *J. Optical Soc. Am.,* **49,** 172 (1959).
14. Lamberts, Higgins, and Wolfe, *J. Optical Soc. Am.,* **48,** 487 (1958).
15. Lamberts, *J. Optical Soc. Am.,* **48,** 490 (1958).

Sensitizing and Desensitizing

The spectral sensitivity of a photographic material is governed by the spectral distribution of the light which the silver halide can absorb. It is difficult to carry out quantitative measurements of the spectral range of the absorption by photographic emulsions but the measurements which have been made show good agreement between absorption and sensitivity.

Spectral Absorption of Photographic Materials

The absorption, and hence the inherent sensitivity, of plain silver halide emulsions is confined largely to the ultraviolet, the violet, and the blue regions of the spectrum. Thus, silver chloride is almost colorless and is sensitive only to violet and ultraviolet radiation. Silver bromide is pale yellow and its sensitivity extends into the blue, but the sensitivity ends at about 500 mμ for practical purposes. Silver iodobromide emulsions are sensitive to somewhat longer wavelengths, but their practical sensitivity does not extend beyond 540 mμ. The bromide and iodobromide emulsions are, however, very slightly sensitive to radiation of much longer wavelength. For example, Eggert and Biltz found that a developable image could be obtained with an iodobromide emulsion even at 700 mμ, but the exposure energy required was about ten million times that required at 400 mμ.

Silver iodobromide is remarkable in that its spectral sensitivity extends beyond that of the pure iodide itself. The longer wavelength absorption of iodobromide containing more than 1 per cent iodide is already greater than that of pure silver iodide, and it increases with increasing iodide content up to about 30 per cent. The absorption spectra of silver chloride, silver bromide,

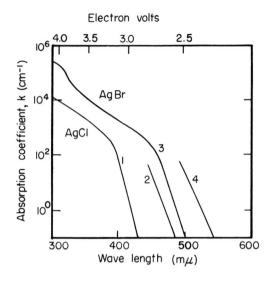

Fig. 14·1 Spectral absorption at 25°C of (1) silver chloride, (2) a mixture of 42 mole percent silver bromide and 58 percent silver chloride, (3) silver bromide, and (4) silver bromide with 3 mole percent iodide. (Based on data by Moser and Urbach).

a chlorobromide, and an iodobromide in the absence of gelatin are shown in Fig. 14·1.

The very slight inherent sensitivity which a silver bromide or iodobromide emulsion shows to light of wavelength longer than 500 - 540 mμ depends upon the gelatin and the method of preparation of the emulsion. Data obtained by Eggert and Kleinschrod[1] illustrate this dependence. Their experimental curves, in which the logarithm of the sensitivity was plotted against wavelength for a silver bromide emulsion, showed a break at around 500 mμ in every example except that of silver bromide prepared in the absence of gelatin or other protective colloid. Most of their emulsions were sensitive out to about 700 mμ, and the sensitivity in the region 500 - 700 mμ differed according to the method of preparation (e.g., neutral-type or ammonia-type emulsion) and the kind of colloid. These results are consistent with the hypothesis that sensitivity in the region beyond 500 mμ depends upon impurities in the silver bromide grain. Silver sulfide and probably silver itself produce induced sensitization of this type, but it is quite weak and of little practical importance.

Optical Sensitization by Dyes

A marked extension of spectral sensitivity can be obtained by the use of certain dyes. Many such sensitizing dyes are known, and by a suitable choice of dyes the spectral sensitivity of silver bromide emulsions can be extended throughout the visible region and into the infrared to about 1300 mμ. It is doubtful, however, whether the sensitization can be extended much beyond this point. The changes needed in the dye structure to extend the sensitization to much longer wavelengths would probably decrease the stability of the dye by a prohibitive amount.

The extent of spectral sensitivity can be measured conveniently by means of the wedge spectrograph which was described on page 231. Some spectrograms obtained with this instrument are illustrated in Fig. 14·2. The scale indicates the extent of the measured sensitivity, each division representing 10 mμ. (Thus, the 50 marker signifies 500 mμ.) The three spectrograms at the left of the figure represent the inherent sensitivities of the silver halide emulsions. The top is for silver chloride, the middle for silver bromide, and the bottom for silver iodobromide. The second (center) set of spectrograms represents the corresponding emulsions sensitized by erythrosin. Each spectrogram still shows the initial inherent sensitivity of the emulsion, but an additional sensitive region appears in each. This is the region sensitized by the dye. The third (right-hand) set of spectrograms shows the much more extended region of sensitization obtained with a thiacarbocyanine dye.

Figure 14·3 shows wedge spectrograms of a representative group of sensitizing dyes. With the aid of these dyes, the entire visible spectrum and infrared spectrum up to 1100 mμ can be covered.

The Sensitizing Dyes

The discovery of dye sensitization resulted from the systematic investigation of an accidental observation. Vogel, in 1873, noticed

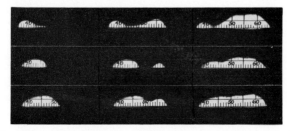

Fig. 14·2 Wedge spectrograms of unsensitized and optically sensitized silver chloride, silver bromide, and silver iodobromide emulsions.

3,3′-Diethyl-4,5,4′,5′-dibenzothiacyanine chloride

3,3′-Diethyl-4,5,4′,5′-dibenzothiacarbocyanine bromide

3,3′-Diethylthiacarbocyanine iodide

1,1′-Diethyl-6,6′-dimethyl-2,4′-cyanine bromide (orthochrome T)

1,1′-Diethyl-2,2′-carbocyanine iodide (pinacyanol)

3,3′-Diethylthiatricarbocyanine iodide

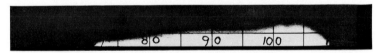

12-Acetoxy-3,3′-diethylthiapentacarbocyanine perchlorate

Fig. 14·3   Wedge spectrograms of a chlorobromide emulsion sensitized with various dyes.

that some collodion dry plates which he was using showed definite sensitivity in the green, and he traced this unusual sensitivity to the presence of a dye which had been added to prevent halation. In the years that followed, dyes of practically all the known classes were tested as sensitizers. Many were found to be effective to varying extents, but sensitization to longer wavelengths was often accompanied by such a sharp decrease in sensitivity to white light (desensitization) that the dyes were of little practical value.

The great majority of dyes contain a conjugated chain of carbon atoms, that is, a chain linked by alternate single and double bonds. Moreover, this chain contains an *uneven* number of carbon atoms and is terminated by atoms which allow the sequence of linkage in the chain to be readily reversible:

$$-\overset{|}{C}=\overset{|}{C}-\overset{|}{C}=\overset{|}{C}-\overset{|}{C}= \quad \leftrightarrow \quad =\overset{|}{C}-\overset{|}{C}=\overset{|}{C}-\overset{|}{C}=\overset{|}{C}- \quad (14\cdot1)$$

This reversible transition can occur easily if the terminal atoms, X and Y, can readily change their covalent linkage to the carbon from one to two, and *vice versa*. The general transition can be represented by

$$X-\overset{|}{C}=(\overset{|}{C}-\overset{|}{C})_n=Y \quad \leftrightarrow \quad X=\overset{|}{C}-(\overset{|}{C}=\overset{|}{C})_n-Y \quad (14\cdot2)$$
$$(a) \qquad\qquad\qquad (b)$$

where n is an integer. If the dye is to show an intense color, the two forms (a) and (b) must be of comparable stability.

Very few atoms are capable of fulfilling the requirements for X and Y, the most important being oxygen and nitrogen. When X and Y are both oxygen, the two forms can be represented by

$$\overset{-}{O}-C=(C-C)_n=O \quad \leftrightarrow \quad O=C-(C=C)_n-\overset{-}{O} \quad (14\cdot3)$$

This system carries a single negative charge and represents an anion in which the charge is shared between two oxygen atoms in the same way as in the carboxyl ion. When X and Y are nitrogen atoms, the two forms can be represented by

$$=N-C=(C-C)_n=\overset{+}{N}= \quad \leftrightarrow \quad =\overset{+}{N}=C-(C=C)_n-N= \quad (14\cdot4)$$

where the system is a cation with a positive charge shared between the terminal nitrogens. When X is oxygen and Y is nitrogen, the system can be represented by

$$O{=}C{-}(C{=}C)_n{-}N{=} \;\leftrightarrow\; \overset{-}{O}{-}C{=}(C{-}C)_n{=}\overset{+}{N}{=} \qquad (14 \cdot 5)$$

The molecule here is not ionized.

In each of the preceding cases, the two forms listed are to be considered extremes in a series of fictitious structures which include intermediates with a positive charge on the carbon atoms. This is not an occurrence of tautomerism. The real dye consists of a single form, a sort of hybrid which lies between the two extremes in structure and possesses a lower potential energy than either. Such a hybrid is termed a resonance hybrid and is represented by the two extreme forms connected by a double-headed arrow ($\leftrightarrow$). The resonance hybrid absorbs the light and is raised to an excited state.

The large majority of the sensitizing dyes belongs to the classes represented by formulas $14 \cdot 3$, $14 \cdot 4$, and $14 \cdot 5$. Representative members of each class will be considered in turn.

Dyes Containing the Carboxyl Ion System (14 · 3)

The phthaleins constitute the most important group of sensitizing dyes containing the carboxyl-ion system represented by formula $14 \cdot 3$. They include the well-known photographic sensitizer erythrosin:

$$(14 \cdot 6)$$

Formula $14 \cdot 6$ represents only one of the fictitious extreme structures, but the formula of the second is clear from the preceding discussion and need not be represented here. The conjugated chain is indicated by heavy lines. The region of sensitization of this dye has already been indicated (Fig. $14 \cdot 2$).

Dyes Containing the Amidinium Ion System (14 · 4)

The amidinium ion system occurs in several classes of dyes. These include the cyanines (the most important group of sensitizers), the hemicyanines and styryls (most of which are sensitizers), and other groups such as the triphenyl methanes (most of which are desensitizers or only weak sensitizers).

In the cyanine dyes, both nitrogen atoms are members of heterocyclic ring systems. The conjugated chain joining these nitrogen atoms passes through a part of each heterocyclic ring. (The latter condition excludes from the cyanine class some dyes which meet the initial requirement.) The simple cyanines contain the single carbon linkage, $=C-$ between the heterocyclic nuclei, as in the formula

$$(14 \cdot 7)$$

1, 1'-Diethyl-4, 4'-cyanine halide

Dyes containing the three-carbon linkage $=C-(C=C)-$ are termed *carbocyanines;* those containing the five-carbon linkage are termed *dicarbocyanines;* those with the seven-carbon linkage, *tricarbocyanines,* and so on.

The position of attachment of the nuclei to the chain is indicated by the appropriate numbers. Each position in a given nucleus is numbered, starting with the key atom (nitrogen for the dyes thus far considered) of the ring as one. Positions in the second nucleus are indicated by primed numbers. Reference to the following formula will clarify the system:

$$(14 \cdot 8)$$

1, 1'-Diethyl-2, 4'-cyanine halide
(Ethyl Red)

This dye is a 2,4'-cyanine as distinguished from formula 14·7, which represents a 4,4'-cyanine. The position of any substituent in the ring is likewise indicated by the appropriate number. If the chain is longer than the simple —C⚌, the appropriate prefix is added in naming the compound: for example, 2,2'-*carbo*cyanine; 4,4'-*dicarbo*cyanine.

The first cyanines used as sensitizers contained only quinoline nuclei, and the terms cyanine, carbocyanine, and the like are still used both for these classes of dyes in general and for the quinoline cyanines in particular. Other heterocyclic nuclei can form cyanines, and some of them are as important as quinoline in practice. Examples are benzothiazole (yielding *thia*cyanine dyes), benzoxazole (*oxa*cyanines), thiazole (*thiazolo*cyanines), thiazoline (*thiazolino*cyanines), benzoselenazole (*selena*cyanines), α-naphthothiazole, and β-napthothiazole.

The positions of any substitutions made in the carbon chain are indicated by number, just as are substitutions made in the nuclei. The numbering of the carbon atoms continues from the last assigned position in the ring. Thus, the dye represented by the formula

$$(14·9)$$

is 3,3'-dimethyl-9-ethylthiacarbocyanine bromide.

The absorption spectrum of a cyanine dye depends upon both the length of the connecting chain and the nature of the nuclei. An increase in the length of the chain results in a shift in absorption toward longer wavelengths. This is well illustrated by a series of thiacyanine dyes having the general formula

$$(14·10)$$

The first member of the series ($n = 0$) is pale yellow and will sensitize a chloride emulsion to the blue. The second member, the

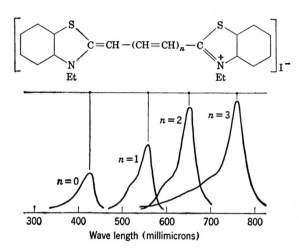

Fig. 14·4 Absorption spectra in methanol solution of thiacarbocyanine dyes of varying chain lengths. (Brooker.)

thiacarbocyanine, is magenta and will sensitize to the green and red. The thiadicarbocyanine is blue and will sensitize to the deep red, and the thiatricarbocyanine is greenish blue and will sensitize to the infrared. The absorption spectra of the dyes in methanol solution[2] are given in Fig. 14·4. The shift in wave length between the maxima amounts to roughly 100 mμ for each added vinylene group. Similar shifts occur in the spectral sensitization. Comparable changes in the absorption maxima have been observed with cyanine dyes containing nuclei other than benzothiazole.

The cyanine dyes considered thus far have all been symmetrical and both ends of the chain have been terminated by the same kind of nucleus. Many dyes are known, however, in which the two nuclei are different in structure. For example, one end of the chain might be attached to a benzothiazole nucleus and the other to a quinoline nucleus. Obviously, the number of possible combinations is very large.

Substitution of other atoms or of radicals for hydrogen atoms, either in the nuclei or in the chain, also can modify the character of a dye. An alkyl group in the central position of a carbocyanine usually produces a slight shift to the shorter wavelengths in the absorption of the dye in solution, but it may cause much larger changes in the location of the sensitization maxima. No general rule can be given for this, or for substitution in the nuclei, although positive groups in the nuclei, such as alkoxy or dialkylamino, normally shift the sensitzation to longer wavelengths.

The Hemicyanines

The hemicyanines form a group of dyes in which only one of the two terminal nitrogen atoms is situated in a heterocyclic ring with the conjugated chain passing through a portion of the ring. An example of a dye of this type is given by the formula

$$\left[\begin{array}{c} \text{(structure)} \end{array} \right]_{} \text{I}^- \qquad (14\cdot11)$$

The styryl dyes, of which pinaflavol is an example, are closely related:

$$\text{(structure)} \qquad (14\cdot12)$$

Pinaflavol

The Merocyanines (14 · 5)

The number of known sensitizers has been considerably augmented in recent years by the discovery[3] of a large new group which can be considered to be derived from formula 14·5. The members of this group are part cyanine (Greek *meros* = part) since the terminal nitrogen atom forms part of a heterocyclic ring and the conjugated chain passes through part of that ring. These dyes can be represented by the following two general formulas:

$$\underset{\substack{\diagup \\ \diagdown}}{\overset{\displaystyle \overset{\textstyle O}{\underset{\displaystyle C}{\|}}}{}} C=(\overset{|}{C}-\overset{|}{C})_n=C \underset{\underset{\displaystyle R}{\displaystyle |}}{\overset{\displaystyle Y}{\diagup}} \Big| \quad \text{and}$$

$$\underset{\substack{\diagup \\ \diagdown}}{\overset{\displaystyle \overset{\textstyle O}{\underset{\displaystyle C}{\|}}}{}} C=(\overset{|}{C}-\overset{|}{C})_n=C \overset{\displaystyle CH=CH}{\underset{\diagdown \diagup}{\diagup \diagdown}} N-R \quad (14 \cdot 13)$$

in which Y represents O, S, Se, Me_2C, or $-CH=CH-$, and R is an alkyl group. The molecule as a whole is neutral, but resonance can occur between the N atom and the oxygen of the carbonyl group.

Certain other sensitizing dyes are known which contain the same amide grouping as the merocyanines, but in which the nitrogen atom is not part of a heterocyclic nucleus.

Mechanism of Dye Sensitizing

Two conditions must be fulfilled to obtain sensitization in a given spectral region: The dye must be adsorbed by the silver halide, and the dye in its adsorbed state must also absorb light in the region to be sensitized. These are necessary, but not sufficient, conditions for optical sensitization.

The adsorption of many sensitizing dyes follows the Langmuir isotherm, but the isotherms of some sensitizing dyes deviate markedly. Some dyes are only slightly adsorbed at low concentrations, then suddenly at some particular concentration the dye begins to attach itself avidly to the grain. From this point on, adsorption proceeds readily until a unimolecular layer is formed. Davey[4] has suggested that the molecules are held flat to the surface in the initial stage of adsorption, and that the discontinuity represents the start of edge-on adsorption. The adsorption of some dyes does not stop when a monolayer is formed, but continues to increase with increasing amount of added dye. The heat of adsorption varies from dye to dye within the range of 5 to 12 kcal/mole, and the heat of adsorption of a particular dye may vary somewhat with the fraction of the available surface covered.[5] The presence of gelatin on the silver halide surface retards adsorption of the sensitizing dyes, but does not prevent it. Displacement of some gelatin from the silver halide surface by adsorbed dyes has been demonstrated experimentally.

The excess halide ion plays an important part in the adsorption of the basic cyanine dyes. These dyes are more strongly adsorbed in the presence of excess halide ion than in its absence, and on the other hand excess silver ion tends to displace the dyes from the surface.[6] This behavior is consistent with an ionic adsorption binding of the positively charged dye ions by the negatively charged halide ions of the silver halide surface. However, quantitative considerations suggest that van der Waals forces are also of importance in the adsorption of the cyanine dyes. The van der Waals forces are even more important in the adsorption of the merocyanine dyes, which have no net charge. A bonding action of silver ions for specific groups in the dye molecule, such as the $C=S$ group in the rhodanine and thiohydantoin dyes, appears to play an important role in the adsorption of these dyes also.

Attempts to correlate sensitizing efficiency with the type of adsorption or the heat of adsorption of the dyes have been unsuccessful. Although adsorption is necessary, apparently no particular orientation of the dye on the silver halide surface is necessary for good sensitization. However, the structure of the adsorbed layer of dye molecules can influence the spectral distribution of sensitization by influencing the absorption spectrum. Certain structural factors in the dye molecule are also important. In general, non-planar dyes do not sensitize even when they are adsorbed.

As stated at the beginning of the chapter, the region of the spectrum to which a dye can sensitize the photographic emulsion is dependent upon the absorption spectrum of the dye in the adsorbed state. Although the absorption spectrum of the adsorbed dye is not identical with that of the dye in solution, characteristic features of the two spectra can be correlated with each other. In addition to the molecular absorption band, like the one illustrated in Fig. 14·4 for methanol solution, many sensitizing dyes in concentrated aqueous solutions show a broad band in the shorter-wave region and often a narrow band in the longer-wave region. The short-wave band is termed the H-band and is attributed to absorption of light by dye in its polymerized form. H-bands appear in both cyanine and merocyanine dyes. The long-wave band is termed the J-band. It results from the interaction of large numbers of molecules aggregated in an orderly array, like a row of books of equal size on a shelf. J-band formation is rare except in the cyanines, which often show it, although a few merocyanine dyes also show it. Both the H-band and the J-band can appear in the absorption spectrum of a layer of dye molecules adsorbed by a silver halide surface. The formation of these aggregated states on the grain surface is favored by an increase in surface concentration, by digestion of the emulsion with the dye, and by the presence of supersensitizers, as described subsequently. Dyes having J-bands are of great practical important since, by the narrowness of the bands, they provide the selective sensitizations needed in color photography.

The correspondence between sensitization and the absorption of light by the sensitized emulsion is illustrated in Fig. $14 \cdot 5$. The sensitivity curve (broken) follows the absorption curve (solid) closely, and the differences between the sensitivity and the absorption maxima in the red are within the limits of experimental error. A good correspondence between absorption and sensitivity is noted also in the region of inherent sensitivity of the silver halide (wavelengths shorter than 500 mμ).

The amount of sensitization increases with increasing amounts of adsorbed dye until an optimum value is reached, beyond which the sensitivity decreases. The observed decrease in sensitization beyond the optimum is not limited to the spectral region of sensitizing, but applies to the blue region as well. The dye is thus acting as a general desensitizer. The optimum sensitization usually occurs when the coverage of the silver halide surface is less than that which corresponds to a monolayer of dye molecules.

The sensitizing efficiency can differ markedly for different dyes, and several factors can decrease the efficiency of sensitization. Instead of using the absorbed energy to form latent image, the excited dye molecule may re-emit it as fluorescence, lose it by internal radiationless transition and subsequent thermal dissipation,[7] or lose it by transfer to some compound other than the silver halide. In none of these eventualities will the energy be available for latent image formation. The intrinsic sensitizing power of a dye can be defined in terms of the energy absorbed and the amount of latent image formed. The quantum efficiency in the sensitized region is difficult to determine in absolute terms,

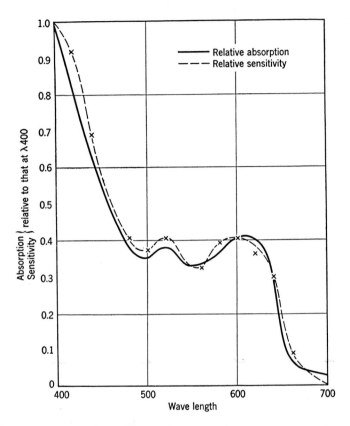

Fig. 14·5 Correspondence between absorption and sensitivity in a panchromatic
photographic emulsion. (Leermakers.)

but a relative value can be obtained by comparing the number
of quanta required to obtain a specified density D in the sensitized region and in the region of inherent sensitivity of the
silver bromide, i.e.,

$$\phi \, (\text{rel}) = \frac{\text{Absorbed quanta to produce } D \text{ at } 400 \text{ m}\mu}{\text{Absorbed quanta to produce } D \text{ at } \lambda \text{ m}\mu}$$

The light absorbed by the best sensitizers is photographically
as efficient as that absorbed by the halide itself, and the relative
efficiency ϕ is then approximately unity.[5] This quantity never
exceeds unity, and it may be very low for poor sensitizers.

Dye sensitization can be influenced by the surroundings or environment of the dye in its adsorbed state.[7] If two or more dyes are used together, the sensitization by each is often affected by the presence of the other. The most common result is mutual interference. Sometimes, however, the dyes actually reinforce each other, and the sensitization is greater than the sum of the separate sensitizations. Such action is termed supersensitizing. It is of considerable practical importance.

Many 2'-cyanines are supersensitized by certain other types of dyes, including oxathiazolocarbocyanines, styryls, and styryl bases. In these combinations, the spectral absorption of the 2'-cyanine is practically unchanged, although that of the other dye is added to it. The supersensitization takes the form of an increase in efficiency of energy transfer from the dye to the grain; the increase can amount to as much as tenfold. Supersensitization can also involve a change in spectral absorption. The 9-alkyl thia- and selenacarbocyanines are supersensitized by some 2'-cyanines with a change of distribution of sensitivity in the red. This is more clearly evident in the supersensitization of dyes of the same type by certain colorless materials, such as certain aromatic ketones; these compounds favor the formation of a new maximum of sensitivity at longer wavelength, which appears to be associated with the formation of an aggregate. In general, dyes which show a J-band have a high susceptibility to supersensitization.

The parallel trends in the spectral distribution of photoconductivity in silver halide crystals and photographic sensitivity of emulsions which had not been optically sensitized was mentioned in Chapter 3. This parallel extends into the sensitized region. Comparisons using actual photographic emulsions for the measurements have been made[8] of the spectral distribution of photoconduction and photographic sensitivity of optically sensitized emulsions. The dyes used included members of the cyanine, carbocyanine, dicarbocyanine, and merocyanine classes. Invariably a parallel between the two phenomena was observed. Moreover, when certain supersensitizers were added the manner in which photoconductance was increased was analogous to that in which the sensitivity was increased.

No general agreement has been reached regarding the mechanism by which the energy absorbed by the sensitizing dye is transferred to the silver halide for the purpose of latent image formation. It is known that some dyes, at least, are not destroyed in the act of sensitizing, and that in such a dye one ion or molecule can sensitize the formation of many silver atoms. Moreover, the distribution of the latent image formed in a dye-sensitized emulsion by light absorbed by the dye does not appear to differ significantly from that formed by light absorbed in the region of intrinsic sensitivity of the silver halide itself, e.g., 400 mμ. Whatever the detailed mechanism may be, a light quantum absorbed by the dye layer evidently introduces a mobile electron and a positive hole into the crystal.

Two types of mechanism for the transfer of the electron to the conductance band of the crystal have been proposed: (1) direct electron transfer from the dye molecule, with the temporary formation of a free radical which subsequently recovers an electron from a halide ion, and (2) transfer of energy from the excited dye molecule to the crystal, where it subsequently causes the ejection of an electron from a halide ion into the conductance band. No direct, decisive experimental distinction between these processes has yet been presented.

More than one mechanism may be involved in supersensitization. Increase in absorption or adsorption can be a contributing cause, as can a decrease in desensitization. The most important cause of supersensitization, however, is an increase in the efficiency of energy transfer which, under favorable circumstances, can amount to an order of magnitude. Carroll and West[8,9] have suggested the following explanation: Optical sensitization can be caused, often with high efficiency, by individual dye molecules adsorbed at random over the grain. At higher concentrations of sensitizer, oriented layers of interacting dye molecules are formed. The resulting periodic field favors the migration of excitons (the excitation energy from the initial absorption of a light quantum) from molecule to molecule, with a corresponding decrease in the probability of transfer to the silver halide. The oriented dye layers thus sensitize with lower efficiency than the isolated molecule. The efficiency can be raised to about that of the isolated molecule by incorporation within the layer of a suitable supersensitizer which provides a singularity in the cooperative layer and, because of the slowing down of the rate of propagation of the energy, increases the probability of energy transfer to the silver halide.

Desensitizing

It is sometimes desirable in practice to carry out photographic development under brighter illumination than can be ordinarily used in the darkroom. Lüppo-Cramer[10] in 1920 showed that this could be done if the exposed plate or film were bathed in a dilute solution of phenosafranine prior to development, or even if the dye were added to the developer itself. Phenosafranine desensitizes the silver halide to the normal action of light.

Numerous desensitizers are now known. An ideal desensitizer should destroy the sensitivity of an emulsion without attacking the latent image. Furthermore, it should be stable in solution, should not cause complications in processing, and should be non-staining. Although no substance that completely fulfills these requirements is known, several have properties near enough to the ideal to be of practical use. Most desensitizers are dyes, but the absorption spectra of the dyes are not connected with the ability to desensitize. Desensitization usually covers the entire spectral range of sensitivity of the silver halide, including the blue. When selective desensitization of an optically sensitized region of the emulsion occurs, an effect on the sensitizing dye itself is involved.

The mechanism of general desensitization is still obscure. Experiments with an azacyanine desensitizer which was almost sufficiently powerful to eliminate normal photographic sensitivity have shown that photoconductance was little impaired by the presence of the dye.[8] Thus, the desensitizer apparently does not inhibit the liberation of photoelectrons; its action is exerted later. The desensitizer may act as alternative traps for photoelectrons and thus reduce the effectiveness of the normal sensitivity centers, or it may attack the latent image after the latter has begun to form. Oxygen plays some rôle in the overall process of desensitization, as normally carried out, since exclusion of oxygen results in a decrease in desensitizing action.[11] The nature of the rôle of oxygen is still a matter for speculation, however.

The activity of many desensitizers appears to be associated with a nitrogen atom which participates in a conjugated chain, but which cannot act as a terminal for that chain. This is brought out in a comparison of two isomeric dyes, one of which is a good sensitizer, the other a desensitizer devoid of sensitizing properties. For example, the dye

$$(14 \cdot 14)$$

is a sensitizer belonging to the azacyanine group.* Its isomer,

$$(14 \cdot 15)$$

in which the central nitrogen is separated from the terminal nitrogens by two carbon atoms on each side, is not only devoid of sensitizing properties but is also a strong desensitizer. A significant distinction between the two dyes is that the chain nitrogen of the former can function as a terminal nitrogen and share a positive charge with the nitrogen atoms of the heterocyclic rings, whereas in the latter dye the nitrogen remains invariably trivalent.

Permanently trivalent nitrogen atoms appear in some of the commonly used desensitizers, such as phenosafranine and pinakryptol green. The latter dye is one of the most useful of all known desensitizers, being superior to phenosafranine chiefly because of a smaller tendency to stain. However, desensitizers are known which do not contain a permanently trivalent nitrogen. For example, some of the triphenylmethane dyes are powerful desensitizers. Likewise, several compounds which have been sold under the name of pinakryptol yellow are good desensitizers. One of these compounds is represented by the formula

---

*These dyes are like the cyanines in structure, except that a CH group of the connecting chain has been replaced by nitrogen.

$$\left[\text{EtO} \underset{\underset{\text{Me}}{\overset{|}{N^+}}}{\bigcirc\bigcirc} -\text{CH}=\text{CH}- \bigcirc \text{NO}_2 \right] \text{Cl}^- \qquad (14\cdot16)$$

The others have similar structures.

If desensitizers are applied to color-sensitized emulsions, the optically sensitized region is often preferentially attacked. This can be ascribed to a partial displacement of the sensitizer from the silver halide surface in some instances and to an antisensitizing action (e.g. a dissipation of migrating excitons as heat) in others. The claim is made in the patent literature that some desensitizers derived from anthraquinone owe their desensitizing properties to their ability to form very insoluble salts with the basic cyanine dyes, thus removing the sensitizer from the silver halide surface. These desensitizers show a definite selective desensitization in the sensitized regions; they are ineffective toward the blue sensitivity and toward sensitization by erythrosin.

REFERENCES

General

Mees, *The Theory of the Photographic Process*, revised edition, Macmillan, New York, 1954 Chapters 10, 11, 12.

Brooker, "Spectra of Dye Molecules. Absorption and Resonance in Dyes," *Rev. Modern Phys.*, 14, 275-293 (1942); "Resonance in Organic Chemistry," *Frontiers in Chemistry*, Interscience Publishers, Inc., New York, 1945, Vol. III, pp. 63–136.

Wheland, *The Theory of Resonance and Its Application to Organic Chemistry*, Wiley, New York, 1944.

Specific

1. Eggert and Kleinschrod, Z. *wiss. Phot.*, 39, 155, 165 (1940).
2. Brooker, *Rev. Modern Phys.*, 14, 275 (1942).
3. Kendall, Brit. Pat. 428,222 and 428,360; Brooker, U.S. Pat. 2,089,729.
4. Davey, *Trans. Faraday Soc.*, 36, 323 (1940).
5. Carroll and West, in Mitchell, *Fundamental Mechanisms of Photographic Sensitivity*, Academic Press, New York, 1951, pp. 162-82.
6. James and Vanselow, *J. Phys. Chem.*, 58, 894 (1954).
7. West and Carroll, *J. Chem. Phys.*, 19, 417 (1951).
8. *Ibid*, 15, 539 (1947).
9. *Ibid., J. Phys. Chem.*, 57, 797 (1953).
10. Lüppo-Cramer, *Phot. Korr.*, 38, 421 (1901); 75, 311 (1920); Z. *angew. Chem.*, 40, 1225 (1927).
11. Blau and Wambacher, *Nature*, 134, 538 (1934).

Appendix

Optical Terminology

The optical terminology employed in this book is that recommended by the Colorimetry Committee of the Optical Society of America.[1] The names, such as transmission and reflection, have been reserved as a description of the process, and the terms, such as transmittance and reflectance, are used to indicate the property of an object. These terms are given in Table I.

TABLE I

PROCESS NAME	PROPERTY
Transmission	Transmittance
Reflection	Reflectance
Illumination	Illuminance*
Absorption	Absorptance

*The term "illumination" is often used for this concept to avoid confusion in sound with "luminance," and is so used regularly by the Illuminating Engineering Society.[2]

The theory of tone reproduction, the measurement of ASA speed, the measurement of graininess, and many other aspects of photographic theory are based on psychophysical measurements. Psychophysics is the science which deals with problems lying between or common to the fields of psychology and physics. The reader who is not familiar with the theory of psychophysical processes is referred to the general references at the end of this Appendix.

Psychophysical quantities are neither physical nor psychological, but a combination of both. In psychophysical theory three categories of quantities must be considered: physical, psychophysical, and psychological. The terms given in Table II are listed under these three headings.

TABLE II

PHYSICAL	PSYCHOPHYSICAL	PSYCHOLOGICAL
Radiance	Luminance	Brightness
Reflectance	Luminous reflectance	Lightness

It should be noted that the term luminance is now employed in the sense in which brightness has commonly been used, and that brightness now refers to the quantity which has previously been referred to as brilliance.

Although luminance is the chief determinant of brightness, the correlation is not simple, because the color of the object and the color and luminance of its surroundings also produce an effect that can be considerable.

Exposure Value System

TABLE III

Constants for Computing Exposure Values

Value	Time T Sec.	Aperture A f-No.	Film Speed S ASEI	Luminance B ft-L	Exposure A^2/T
0	1	1	3	1	1
1	1/2	1.4	6	2	2
2	1/4	2	12	4	4
3	1/8	2.8	25	8	8
4	1/15	4	50	16	16
5	1/30	5.6	100	30	32
6	1/60	8	200	60	64
7	1/125	11	400	125	128
8	1/250	16	800	250	256
9	1/500	22	1600	500	512
10	1/1000	32	3200	1000	1024
11				2000	2048
12				4000	4096
13				8000	8192
14					16384
15					32768
16					65536
17					131072
18					262144

Examples: Am. Std. Exp. Ind., 12 ; $Sv = 2$
 Scene luminance, 2000 ft-L; $Bv = 11$
∴ Exposure value $(2 + 11)$; $Ev = 13$
(a) Shutter Speed, 1/60 sec. ; $Tv = 6$
∴ Aperture $(13 - 6)$; $Av = 7$ or $f/11$
(b) Aperture, $f/5.6$; $Av = 5$
∴ Shutter speed $(13 - 5)$; $Tv = 8$ or 1/250 sec.

REFERENCES

General

L. A. Jones, *J. Optical Soc. Am.*, 34, 66 (1944).

L. T. Troland, *The Principles of Psychophysiology*, Van Nostrand, New York, 1929.

Colorimetry Committee, Optical Society of America, *J. Optical Soc. Am.*, 34, 245 (1944).

Specific

1. Colorimetry Committee, Optical Society of America, *J. Optical Soc. Am.*, 33, 544 (1943); *The Science of Color*, Crowell, New York, 1953, Glossary-Index.

2. American Standards Association, *Illuminating Engineering Nomenclature and Photometric Standards*, Z7.1-1942, Illuminating Engineering Society, New York, 1942.

Index